DIVINE PROPORTIONS

DIVINE PROPORTIONS

RATIONAL TRIGONOMETRY TO UNIVERSAL GEOMETRY

N J WILDBERGER

wild egg

Assoc/Prof N J Wildberger
School of Mathematics
UNSW
Sydney 2052
Australia

email: n.wildberger@unsw.edu.au

webpages: http://web.maths.unsw.edu.au/~norman/

Typeset in Latex
Cover design by Alex Snellgrove
Printed on 100% acid-free paper by BPA Print Group
Printed in Australia

National Library of Australia Cataloguing-in-Publication Data

Wildberger, Norman John,
Divine proportions : rational trigonometry to universal
geometry

Bibliography.
Includes Index.
ISBN 0 9757492 0 X.
1. Trigonometry. 2. Geometry. I. Title.

516.2

Mathematics Subject Classification: 51XX, 14XX

Published in Australia by Wild Egg Pty Ltd

http://wildegg.com

To my parents, John and Trudy Wildberger

Preface

Divine Proportions: Rational Trigonometry to Universal Geometry introduces a remarkable new approach to trigonometry and Euclidean geometry, with dramatic implications for mathematics teaching, industrial applications and the direction of mathematical research in geometry.

The key insight is that *geometry is a quadratic subject.* So *rational trigonometry* replaces the quasi-linear notions of distance and angle with the related, but more elementary, quadratic concepts of *quadrance* and *spread*, thus allowing the development of Euclidean geometry over any field. This text covers the key definitions and results of this new theory in a systematic way, along with many applications including Platonic solids, projectile motion, Snell's law, the problems of Snellius-Pothenot and Hansen, and three-dimensional volumes and surface areas.

The message of this book is controversial, but it will be hard to deny the power of its content. Teachers and students will benefit from a simpler and cleaner theory, which takes less than half of the usual time to learn. Engineers, surveyors and scientists now have a fascinating new set of tools that increase accuracy and reduce computation time for geometric problems. Mathematicians finally have a logically coherent framework for metrical geometry, which opens up exciting areas for investigation in algebraic geometry, number theory, combinatorics and special functions.

Even though the content is in some sense elementary, this text is intended for a mathematically mature audience. The novelty will provide some challenge even for professional mathematicians.

With *Divine Proportions* it should become clearer why so many students are turned off mathematics by trigonometry. The current curriculum attempts to arm them with machine guns to hunt rabbits. Most students sense intuitively that this is not what they need, but until now there has been no reasonable alternative to focus the minds of educators. This book finally addresses the failure of modern geometry to win the minds of young people, and provides the mathematical foundation for a dynamic and elegant new approach to teaching trigonometry and geometry.

N J Wildberger
Sydney, 2005

Acknowledgements

It is a pleasure to warmly thank Walter Bloom, Michael Duffy, Kimmo Eriksson, Shuxiang Goh, Jack Hall, Chris Halse-Rogers, Vinh Le and John Wildberger for careful readings of portions of the manuscript and for suggesting valuable improvements.

Helen Armstrong, Peter Brown, Daniel Chan, Peter Donovan, Hendrik Grundling, Bruce Harvey, Rick Hill, Michael Hirschhorn, Krista Ruffolo, George Szekeres and Martin Wildberger contributed useful comments and discussions. Dolores Knox, Thai Son Huang, Ming Huo, Alex Ma and Ross Moore helped with layout, diagrams and computer programming. Alex Snellgrove created the cover design. Many thanks to them all for making this a more sensible, readable and attractive book.

This work owes a debt to the efforts of many expositors and researchers of geometry. Some of the texts which have been particularly helpful to me have been *Introduction to geometry* [Coxeter], *Geometry Revisited* [Coxeter-Greitzer], *The Elements* [Euclid], the *Concise Encyclopedia of Mathematics* [Weisstein], *Surveying Problems and Solutions* [Shepherd], *Metric Affine Geometry* [Snapper-Troyer], *Trigonometric Delights* [Maor], and last but not least, my favourite 20th century mathematics text, *100 Great Problems of Elementary Mathematics* [Dorrie].

Without wonderful developments in computer software, this project could not have been completed in the given time frame. I would like to thank Donald Knuth for his invention of TeX, the many developers of LaTeX, MacKichan Software for Scientific Workplace, the makers of CorelDraw and Geometric SketchPad, and the people at Microsoft for a dependable operating system.

Thanks go to the Australian Research Council for financial support. The School of Mathematics at UNSW provided a supportive and friendly work environment, and I thank all my colleagues who offered encouragement despite the heretical nature of the project. Finally I would like to thank Kim and Ali, for moral support during the writing of this book.

Contents

III   Universal Geometry   119

Introduction

This book revolutionizes trigonometry, re-evaluates and expands Euclidean geometry, and gives a simpler and more natural approach to many practical geometric problems. This new theory unites the three core areas of mathematics—geometry, number theory and algebra—and expels analysis and infinite processes from the foundations of the subject. Learning trigonometry and geometry should be easier than it currently is, and *Divine Proportions* attempts to develop a complete and precise alternative framework from which educators can draw.

The concise format is suitable for mathematicians, as well as mathematically inclined surveyors, engineers and physical scientists. Mathematics teachers, undergraduate mathematics majors, gifted high school students and dedicated amateurs with a strong interest in geometry and good skills at algebraic manipulation should also be able to follow the development. Others should wait for the author's next book on the subject.

Advanced mathematical knowledge, such as linear algebra, number theory and group theory, is generally not needed. Indeed the geometry in this book often provides motivation for these subjects. Some familiarity with elementary aspects of fields is useful. The chapters on physics and rational spherical coordinates require calculus.

Rational trigonometry

The new form of trigonometry developed here is called *rational trigonometry*, to distinguish it from *classical trigonometry*, the latter involving $\cos\theta$, $\sin\theta$ and the many trigonometric relations currently taught to students. An essential point of rational trigonometry is that *quadrance* and *spread*, not distance and angle, are the right concepts for metrical geometry (i.e. a geometry in which measurement is involved).

Quadrance and spread are quadratic quantities, while distance and angle are almost, but not quite, linear ones. The quadratic view is more general and powerful. At some level, this is known by many mathematicians. When this insight is put firmly into practice, as it is here, a new foundation for mathematics and mathematics education arises which simplifies Euclidean and non-Euclidean geometries, changes our understanding of algebraic geometry, and often simplifies difficult practical problems.

Quadrance measures the separation of points, and spread measures the separation of lines. It turns out that

$$
\begin{aligned}
\text{quadrance} &= (\text{distance})^2 \\
\text{spread} &= (\sin(\text{angle}))^2
\end{aligned}
$$

although the actual definitions used in this text are independent of distance, angle and the trigonometric functions. They are ultimately very simple, based on finite arithmetic and algebra as taught in schools.

New laws now replace the Cosine law, the Sine law, and the dozens of other trigonometric formulas that often cause students difficulty. The most important new laws are the *Triple quad formula*, the *Spread law*, the *Cross law* and the *Triple spread formula*. *Pythagoras' theorem*, restated in terms of quadrances, also plays a key role. The derivation of these rules from first principles is straightforward, involving some moderate skill with basic algebra. The usual trigonometric functions, such as $\cos\theta$ and $\sin\theta$, play no role at all.

Rational trigonometry deals with many practical problems in an easier and more elegant fashion than classical trigonometry, and often ends up with answers that are demonstrably more accurate. In fact rational trigonometry is so elementary that almost all calculations may be done by hand. Tables or calculators are not necessary, although the latter certainly speed up computations. It is a shame that this theory was not discovered earlier, since accurate tables were for many centuries not widely available.

Universal geometry

Because rational trigonometry uses only arithmetic and algebra, it allows the development of Euclidean geometry in a consistent and general way in an arbitrary field. This is *universal geometry*.

Historically metrical geometry has been difficult to develop outside the decimal numbers, due largely to the transcendental nature of angle. Once liberated from a dependence on analysis, the scope is much wider, and the opportunities to effectively harness the power of modern mathematical software, such as MAPLE, MAGMA, MUPAD, MATHEMATICA, MATLAB and others, increase dramatically.

Many classical geometrical subjects are here reformulated into this more general framework, such as Heron's, or Archimedes' formula, similar triangles, parallelograms, Pons Asinorum, centroids, orthocenters, theorems of Menelaus and Ceva, Stewart's theorem, circumcircles, Brahmagupta's formula for cyclic quadrilaterals, regular polygons, the Euler line, the nine point circle and reflection properties of conics.

Some topics, such as vertex bisectors and triangle incenters, become dependent on number theoretic considerations. Many more areas await the attention of researchers.

Universal geometry deals only with geometrical concepts and results which are common to all fields. The usual notions of *convexity* and *betweenness*, for example, hold only in the rational and decimal number fields and some closely related ones, so they are not as fundamental as say *perpendicularity*, which applies to all fields. Over finite fields a host of new geometrical configurations can now be studied, with many number theoretic and combinatorial implications.

Universal geometry does not require a prior understanding of classical geometry. It is a complete, independent system that stands logically separate from the existing treatment of Euclid. It neither contains classical geometry nor is contained by it, although there are many close connections. One of the main features of this new theory is its logical precision and clarity—at least in principle!

A subtle obstacle to beginning a serious study of geometry is the fact that many of the main concepts are already familiar from ordinary life. The temptation arises to dismiss the need for precise definitions, because everyone surely already knows what a point, line and triangle are. But without very clear and careful statements of the key concepts, mathematics generally ends up relying on doubtful arguments.

There are three rocks on which most attempts at developing Euclidean geometry founder. These are

- the ambiguity of defining the 'continuum', or the 'real number line'

- the problem of stating precisely what an 'angle' is

- the difficulty in making the jump from two to three dimensions.

The 'real number line' involves philosophizing about infinite sets, and confusion with issues of computability. Angles require hand-waving about 'rotations', or 'lengths of circular arcs'. 'Three dimensional geometry' usually involves pictures and physically plausible arguments without proper mathematical basis.

All three are serious obstacles. The first two are overcome in this book, the third is not. To avoid the logical deficiencies with 'real numbers', universal geometry works over an arbitrary field. Furthermore the presentation given here avoids any mention of 'infinite sets'. To avoid angles, rational trigonometry deals with spreads.

As for the step from two to three dimensions, in principle this can be done, but it requires considerably more work. With universal geometry, one begins to appreciate the large gulf between these dimensions, both number theoretically and in terms of concepts and proofs required.

All theorems in this book will be presented only in the planar two dimensional case. The applications part of the book however does use three dimensions, so is in parts guilty of the usual logical obscurity.

Universal geometry naturally leads to a rebirth of the traditional idea of algebraic geometry as a study of the *metrical aspects of curves and varieties*, in the spirit of the classical investigations of the ancient Greeks, as well as the work of Fermat, Newton, Euler and their contemporaries. This is a more rigid subject than modern algebraic geometry, and possibly just as rich.

For example, many of the most important and beautiful properties of conics, going back to Apollonius and Archimedes, occur in a metrical setting. In universal geometry there are many unanswered questions even about conics. For more general curves and varieties, this way of thinking opens up a large potential area for investigation, and unifies aspects of algebraic and differential geometry. Tangent conics and higher degree generalizations can be used to classify points on curves and for more accurate approximations in practical problems.

This view of algebraic geometry does not elevate algebraically closed fields to a position of dominance, and also reaffirms the ordinary intuition that curves and varieties are often most natural in an affine rather than a projective setting. In fact the metrical approach extends also to projective varieties.

The foundations of Euclidean geometry established here can be generalized to non-Euclidean geometries as well, including spherical (or elliptic) geometry, and hyperbolic geometry too. Universal geometry leads to a yet much broader vista, in which Euclidean and non-Euclidean geometries merge in a spectacular way to form *chromogeometry*. These topics are more advanced, and will be developed elsewhere.

As well as providing new directions for mathematics, universal geometry offers the possibility for new insights into physics. One reason is that physics is also largely a quadratic subject. Another is that Einstein's special theory of relativity fits naturally into this framework.

Organization of the book

Part I gives first of all an overview of rational trigonometry and how it differs from classical trigonometry. A brief statement of the main definitions and basic laws will allow the reader to get an initial feeling for the subject. (This material is developed carefully in Part II). A preliminary section clarifies terminology and reviews those aspects of basic mathematics that will be needed.

Cartesian planar geometry is introduced in a systematic manner. Fundamental concepts are clearly laid out, and the basic results of planar coordinate geometry are established over a general field. This material is mostly classical, but the definitions are often novel. Another chapter develops the theory of rotations in points and reflections in lines, along with the associated lineations, and includes important formulas that are often absent from geometry courses.

Part II is the heart of the book, and develops rational trigonometry over a general field, with characteristic two, and sometimes three, excluded for technical reasons.

The notions of quadrance, spread and *quadrea* are introduced, as well as the concepts of *cross* and *twist* between lines. The Triple quad formula, Pythagoras' theorem, Spread law, Cross law and Triple spread formula are derived, as well as more complicated extensions involving four quadrances and spreads. The important *spread polynomials* naturally appear and have many interesting properties, valid over a general field.

Another chapter introduces *oriented triangles* and the concept of *turn* between two lines, closely related to the twist. The oriented version allows a notion of *signed areas* of triangles and *n*-gons. This completes the basic material on rational trigonometry.

Part III uses rational trigonometry to develop the fundamentals of universal geometry. Isosceles, equilateral and right triangles are studied, along with the procedures for solving general triangles. Then the laws of proportion for triangles and quadrilaterals are derived, along with Stewart's theorem, Menelaus' theorem and Ceva's theorem. Special lines and centers of triangles are discussed, such as medians, altitudes and vertex bisectors, along with circumcenters, orthocenters and incenters.

An introduction to general conics includes some surprises, as the usual definitions do not always generalize well to universal geometry. Circles and parabolas appear, as well as less familiar conics called *ribbons, quadrolas* and *grammolas*. The geometry of circles is studied. Some basic facts about quadrilaterals, especially cyclic ones, are included, as well as the Four point relation going back to Euler. The notions of a tangent line and a tangent conic are introduced, and illustrated with the folium of Descartes and the lemniscate of Bernoulli.

Every theorem in this book holds over an arbitrary field, with characteristic two excluded. Although sometimes parallel to existing theorems, and given the same names, the results are considerably more general. Note that no familiarity with classical trigonometry or geometry is assumed. The reader need not know what a circle or an ellipse is, what similar triangles are, or even what a line is. Indeed the reader should put aside fixed preconceptions in these directions.

Part IV shows how to apply the theory to a wide variety of practical problems using the decimal numbers, which in practice often means the rational numbers. There are applications to physics, surveying, including the problems of Snellius-Pothenot and Hansen, two and three-dimensional situations, and Platonic solids.

The final chapter requires some knowledge of basic calculus, and derives the new *rational polar* and *spherical coordinates,* with applications to the Beta function, volumes and surface areas of spheres, hyperboloids and other related situations. Some brief discussion shows how to extend this framework to four dimensional space and beyond. One Appendix contains a list of rational polar equations of some classical curves in the plane, and another briefly introduces the beautiful *ellipson.*

In this book, an equation of equality between previously defined objects generally uses the equal sign $=$, while an equation of assignment of a name or a value to a previously defined object generally uses the assignment sign $\equiv$. This follows E. Bishop's famous dictum that "Meaningful distinctions deserve to be maintained." Occasionally both $=$ and $\equiv$ are used in the same equation, hopefully without undue confusion.

All definitions are highlighted in bold. Italics are usually reserved for emphasis. Theorems are given descriptive names, and begin with capitals. Especially important material, such as a major Definition, Theorem or Problem, is enclosed in a gray box. To further structure the content, the ends of Proofs and Solutions are marked by the symbol ■ while the ends of Examples and Exercises are marked by the symbol ◇.

In universal geometry formulas are particularly significant, and proofs by calculation necessarily play an increasingly important role as you delve further into the subject. A computer with a modern algebra package, such as those mentioned earlier, becomes an indispensable tool into higher investigations, as in the approach of [Zeilberger] (see also D. Zeilberger's website for the computer package RENE).

While much effort has been made to avoid ambiguities and to give careful proofs, there are undoubtedly places in this text where this goal has not been reached. I hope nevertheless that the framework is sufficiently solid for others to take the subject further with confidence.

To the reader

Mathematics is a conservative discipline, and it is not easy to acknowledge that traditional thinking might involve elements of misunderstanding.

In this context, the following analogy may be useful. In the Roman period, which saw the beginnings of classical trigonometry, arithmetic used Roman numerals (such as the page numbers in this introduction). Cities were built, students were taught, and an empire was administered, with an arithmetic that was cumbersome and hard to learn, at least when compared to the one we now use built from the Arabic-Hindu numerical system. Today we understand that the difficulty with arithmetic in Roman times was largely due to the awkward conceptual framework.

Much the same holds, in my opinion, for classical trigonometry—it has been such a hurdle to generations of students not because of the essential intractability of the subject, but rather because the basic notions used to study it for the last two thousand years are *not the right ones*.

By the time you have finished this book, you should be comfortable with the fact that *geometry is a quadratic subject, requiring quadratic mathematics*. Using more or less linear ideas, such as distance and angle, may be initially appealing but is ultimately inappropriate. With the natural approach of rational trigonometry, many more people should be able to appreciate the rich patterns of geometry and perhaps even experience the joy of mathematical discovery.

This book asks something from you, the reader—an openness to fresh ideas, attention to detail, and a willingness to explore. In return, it promises to transform your understanding of mathematics, to empower you with knowledge previously hidden, and to shed a new light on the beauty and unity of the world around us.

Part I

Preliminaries

Overview

1.1 Introducing quadrance and spread

Trigonometry is the *measurement of triangles*. In classical trigonometry, measurement uses *distance* and *angle*, while in rational trigonometry measurement uses *quadrance* and *spread*. To appreciate the difference, let's first consider a specific triangle in the decimal number plane from both points of view.

Classical measurements

The triangle with side lengths

$$d_1 \equiv 4 \qquad d_2 \equiv 7 \qquad d_3 \equiv 5$$

has respective angles (approximately)

$$\theta_1 \approx 33.92° \qquad \theta_2 \approx 102.44° \qquad \theta_3 \approx 43.64°.$$

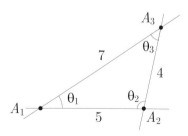

There are numerous classical relations between these six quantities, such as the Sums of angles law

$$\theta_1 + \theta_2 + \theta_3 = 180°,$$

along with the Cosine law, the Sine law, and others. Typically these laws involve the trigonometric functions $\cos\theta, \sin\theta$ and $\tan\theta$, and implicitly their inverse functions $\arccos x$, $\arcsin x$ and $\arctan x$, all of which are difficult to define precisely without calculus.

Rational measurements

In rational trigonometry the most important measurements associated with the same triangle are the *quadrances* of the sides,

$$Q_1 = 16 \qquad Q_2 = 49 \qquad Q_3 = 25$$

and the *spreads* at the vertices

$$s_1 = 384/1225 \qquad s_2 = 24/25 \qquad s_3 = 24/49.$$

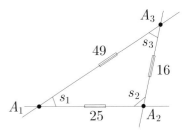

Let's informally explain the meaning of these terms, and show how these numbers were obtained.

Quadrance

Quadrance measures the separation of two points. An easy definition is that *quadrance is distance squared.* Of course this assumes that you already know what distance is. A point in the decimal number plane can be specified by its x and y coordinates with respect to a fixed pair of rectangular axes, and the usual definition of the distance $|A_1, A_2|$ between the points $A_1 \equiv [x_1, y_1]$ and $A_2 \equiv [x_2, y_2]$ is

$$|A_1, A_2| \equiv \sqrt{(x_2 - x_1)^2 + (y_2 - y_1)^2}.$$

So the **quadrance** $Q(A_1, A_2)$ between the points is

$$Q(A_1, A_2) \equiv (x_2 - x_1)^2 + (y_2 - y_1)^2.$$

From this point of view, quadrance is the more fundamental quantity, since it does not involve the square root function. The relationship between the two notions is perhaps more accurately described by the statement that *distance is the square root of quadrance.*

In diagrams, small rectangles along the sides of a triangle indicate that quadrance, not distance, is being measured, a convention maintained throughout the book. Occasionally when this is inconvenient, a quadrance is enclosed in a rectangular box.

Spread

Spread measures the separation of two lines. This turns out to be a much more subtle issue than the separation of two points. Given two intersecting lines such as l_1 and l_2 in Figure 1.1, we would like to define a number that quantifies how 'far apart' the lines are spread. Historically there are a number of solutions to this problem.

The most familiar is the notion of *angle*, which roughly speaking can be described as follows. Draw a circle of radius one with center the intersection A of l_1 and l_2. Let this circle intersect the lines l_1 and l_2 respectively at points B_1 and B_2. Then 'define' the angle θ between the lines to be the length of the circular arc between B_1 and B_2, as in the first diagram in Figure 1.1.

If the lines are close to being parallel, the angle is close to zero, while if the lines are perpendicular, the angle turns out to be, after a highly non-trivial calculation going back to Archimedes, a number with the approximate value $1.570\,796\,326\ldots$.

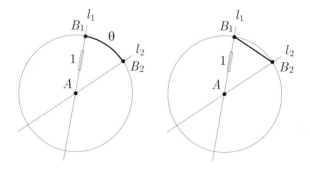

Figure 1.1: Separation of two lines: two dubious approaches

Immediately one observes some difficulties with this 'definition'. First of all there are two possible choices for B_1, and also two possible choices for B_2. There are then four possible pairs $[B_1, B_2]$ to consider. Each such pair divides the circle into *two* circular arcs. In general there are eight possible circular arcs to measure, and four possible results of those measurements. Furthermore, defining the length of a circular arc is not at all straightforward, a point that will be returned to later.

There are other approaches to the question of how to measure the separation of two lines. For example, with the circle of radius one as above, and the same choice of points B_1 and B_2, you could consider the length $|B_1, B_2|$ as the main object of interest, as in the second diagram in Figure 1.1. When the lines are close to parallel, with the right choices of B_1 and B_2, $|B_1, B_2|$ is close to zero, and when the lines are perpendicular $|B_1, B_2|$ is $\sqrt{2}$, independent of the choices.

However in general there are still two different values that can be obtained. This is less than optimal, but it is already an improvement on the first method. An even better choice is the quadrance $Q(B_1, B_2)$, but the two-fold ambiguity in values remains.

A completely different tack would be to give up on the separation between lines, and measure only the separation between *rays*. But a line is a more elementary, fundamental and general notion than a ray, so this would be a form of capitulation.

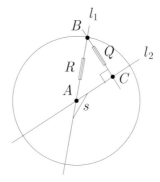

Figure 1.2: Separation of two lines: the right approach

The right idea is remarkably simple, and is shown in Figure 1.2. Take any point $B \neq A$ on one of the lines, and then let C be the foot of the altitude, or perpendicular, from B to the other line. Then let's temporarily define the **spread** $s(l_1, l_2)$ between the two lines l_1 and l_2 to be the ratio of quadrances

$$s(l_1, l_2) \equiv \frac{Q(B,C)}{Q(A,B)} = \frac{Q}{R}. \tag{1.1}$$

This number $s \equiv s(l_1, l_2)$ is independent of the choice of first line, or the choice of the point B on it. It is a unique number, somewhere between 0 and 1, which measures the separation of two lines unambiguously. Note that the circle, which played an important role in the previous constructions, is now essentially irrelevant.

In diagrams, spreads are placed adjacent to small straight line segments joining the relevant lines, instead of the usual circular arcs used to denote angles. There are four possible places to put this spread, each equivalent, as in Figure 1.3.

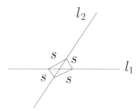

Figure 1.3: Four possible labellings

Why do we not consider the spread to be the ratio of lengths $|B,C| / |A,B|$? This becomes clearer when the spread is expressed in terms of the coordinates of the lines.

Spread in terms of coordinates

A line in the plane can be specified by an equation in the form $y = mx + b$, or the more general form $ax + by + c = 0$. The latter is preferred in this text, for a variety of good reasons, among them being that it includes vertical lines, generalizes well to projective geometry, and is better suited for the jump to linear algebra and higher dimensions.

The equation $ax + by + c = 0$ of a line l is not unique, as you can multiply by an arbitrary non-zero number. This means that it is actually the *proportion* $a : b : c$ that specifies the line, and later on we *define* the line in terms of this proportion.

Two lines l_1 and l_2 with respective equations $a_1 x + b_1 y + c_1 = 0$ and $a_2 x + b_2 y + c_2 = 0$ are **parallel** precisely when

$$a_1 b_2 - a_2 b_1 = 0$$

and **perpendicular** precisely when

$$a_1 a_2 + b_1 b_2 = 0.$$

The spread between them is unchanged if the lines are moved while remaining parallel, so you may assume that the lines have equations $a_1 x + b_1 y = 0$ and $a_2 x + b_2 y = 0$ with intersection the origin $A \equiv [0, 0]$. Let's calculate the spread between these two lines.

A point B on l_1 is $B \equiv [-b_1, a_1]$. An arbitrary point on l_2 is of the form $C \equiv [-\lambda b_2, \lambda a_2]$. The quadrances of the triangle $\overline{ABC}$ are then

$$
\begin{aligned}
Q(A, B) &= b_1^2 + a_1^2 & (1.2)\\
Q(A, C) &= \lambda^2 \left(b_2^2 + a_2^2 \right) & (1.3)\\
Q(B, C) &= (b_1 - \lambda b_2)^2 + (\lambda a_2 - a_1)^2 . & (1.4)
\end{aligned}
$$

Pythagoras' theorem asserts that the triangle $\overline{ABC}$ has a right vertex at C precisely when

$$Q(A, C) + Q(B, C) = Q(A, B).$$

This is the equation

$$\lambda^2 \left(b_2^2 + a_2^2 \right) + (b_1 - \lambda b_2)^2 + (\lambda a_2 - a_1)^2 = b_1^2 + a_1^2.$$

After expansion and simplification you get

$$2\lambda \left(a_1 a_2 + b_1 b_2 - \lambda \left(a_2^2 + b_2^2 \right) \right) = 0.$$

Thus $\lambda = 0$ or

$$\lambda = \frac{a_1 a_2 + b_1 b_2}{a_2^2 + b_2^2}. \qquad (1.5)$$

But $\lambda = 0$ precisely when the lines are perpendicular, in which case (1.5) still holds. So substitute (1.5) back into (1.4) and use some algebraic manipulation to show that

$$Q(B, C) = \frac{(a_1 b_2 - a_2 b_1)^2}{a_2^2 + b_2^2}.$$

Thus

$$s\left(l_1, l_2\right) = \frac{Q\left(B, C\right)}{Q\left(A, B\right)} = \frac{\left(a_1 b_2 - a_2 b_1\right)^2}{\left(a_1^2 + b_1^2\right)\left(a_2^2 + b_2^2\right)}.$$

Now it should be clearer why the idea of a spread as a ratio of quadrances is a good one—the final answer is a *rational expression in the coordinates of the two lines*. If we had chosen to define the spread as a ratio of lengths, then square roots would appear at this point. Square roots are to be avoided whenever possible.

Calculating a spread

To calculate the spread s_1 in the triangle $\overline{A_1 A_2 A_3}$ with side lengths $|A_2, A_3| \equiv 4$, $|A_1, A_3| \equiv 7$ and $|A_1, A_2| \equiv 5$, let B be the foot of the altitude from A_2 to the line $A_1 A_3$, and let $a \equiv |A_1, B|$ and $b \equiv |A_2, B|$ as in Figure 1.4.

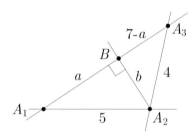

Figure 1.4: Calculating a spread

In the right triangles $\overline{A_1 A_2 B}$ and $\overline{A_3 A_2 B}$, Pythagoras' theorem gives

$$a^2 + b^2 = 25 \qquad \text{and} \qquad (7 - a)^2 + b^2 = 16.$$

Take the difference between these equations to get

$$14a - 49 = 9$$

so that

$$a = 58/14 = 29/7.$$

Then

$$b^2 = 25 - a^2 = 25 - (29/7)^2 = 384/49$$

and so

$$s_1 = \frac{Q\left(A_2, B\right)}{Q\left(A_1, A_2\right)} = \frac{384/49}{25} = \frac{384}{1225}.$$

Exercise 1.1 Verify also that $s_2 = 24/25$ and $s_3 = 24/49$. ◇

1.2 Laws of rational trigonometry

This section introduces the main concepts and basic laws of rational trigonometry. So far the discussion has been in the decimal number plane. The algebraic nature of quadrance and spread have the important consequence that the basic definitions and laws may be formulated to hold with coefficients from an arbitrary field. That involves rethinking the above discussion so that no mention is made of distance or angle.

The laws given below are polynomial, and can be derived rigorously using only algebra and arithmetic, in a way that high school students can follow. This is shown in Part II of the book. If you work with geometrical configurations whose points belong to a particular field, then the solutions to these equations also belong to this field.

So these laws are valid in great generality, and it is now possible to investigate Euclidean geometry over general fields. This is the beginning of *universal geometry*. The following definitions thus hold in a general field.

A **point** A is an ordered pair $[x, y]$ of numbers. The **quadrance** $Q(A_1, A_2)$ between points $A_1 \equiv [x_1, y_1]$ and $A_2 \equiv [x_2, y_2]$ is the number

$$Q(A_1, A_2) \equiv (x_2 - x_1)^2 + (y_2 - y_1)^2 .$$

A **line** l is an ordered proportion $\langle a : b : c \rangle$, representing the equation $ax + by + c = 0$. The **spread** $s(l_1, l_2)$ between lines $l_1 \equiv \langle a_1 : b_1 : c_1 \rangle$ and $l_2 \equiv \langle a_2 : b_2 : c_2 \rangle$ is the number

$$s(l_1, l_2) \equiv \frac{(a_1 b_2 - a_2 b_1)^2}{(a_1^2 + b_1^2)(a_2^2 + b_2^2)} .$$

For distinct points A_1 and A_2 the unique line passing through them both is denoted $A_1 A_2$. Given three distinct points A_1, A_2 and A_3, define the quadrances

$$\begin{aligned}
Q_1 &\equiv Q(A_2, A_3) \\
Q_2 &\equiv Q(A_1, A_3) \\
Q_3 &\equiv Q(A_1, A_2)
\end{aligned}$$

and the spreads

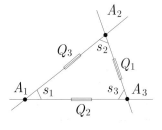

$$\begin{aligned}
s_1 &\equiv s(A_1 A_2, A_1 A_3) \\
s_2 &\equiv s(A_2 A_1, A_2 A_3) \\
s_3 &\equiv s(A_3 A_1, A_3 A_2) .
\end{aligned}$$

Here are the five main laws of rational trigonometry.

Triple quad formula The three points A_1, A_2 and A_3 are collinear (meaning they all lie on a single line) precisely when

$$\left(Q_1 + Q_2 + Q_3\right)^2 = 2\left(Q_1^2 + Q_2^2 + Q_3^2\right).$$

Pythagoras' theorem The lines A_1A_3 and A_2A_3 are perpendicular precisely when

$$Q_1 + Q_2 = Q_3.$$

Spread law For any triangle $\overline{A_1A_2A_3}$ with non-zero quadrances

$$\frac{s_1}{Q_1} = \frac{s_2}{Q_2} = \frac{s_3}{Q_3}.$$

Cross law For any triangle $\overline{A_1A_2A_3}$ define the **cross** $c_3 \equiv 1 - s_3$. Then

$$\left(Q_1 + Q_2 - Q_3\right)^2 = 4Q_1Q_2c_3.$$

Triple spread formula For any triangle $\overline{A_1A_2A_3}$

$$\left(s_1 + s_2 + s_3\right)^2 = 2\left(s_1^2 + s_2^2 + s_3^2\right) + 4s_1s_2s_3.$$

These formulas are related in interesting ways, and deriving them is reasonably straightforward. There are also numerous alternative formulations of these laws, as well as generalizations to four quadrances and spreads, which become important in the study of quadrilaterals. The difference between the two sides of the Triple quad formula is used to define the *quadrea* $\mathcal{A}$ of a triangle, which is the single most important number associated to a triangle. There is also an *oriented* version of the theory, with *signed areas* of triangles and *turns* and *coturns* of oriented vertices.

You also need to understand the *spread polynomials*. If l_1, l_2 and l_3 are lines making spreads $s\left(l_1, l_2\right) = s\left(l_2, l_3\right) \equiv s$, then the Triple spread formula shows that the spread $r \equiv s\left(l_1, l_3\right)$ is either 0, in which case l_1 and l_3 are parallel, or $4s\left(1 - s\right)$.

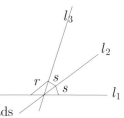

The polynomial function $S_2\left(s\right) \equiv 4s\left(1 - s\right)$ figures prominently in chaos theory, where it is called the *logistic map*.

Generalizing this, $S_n\left(s\right)$ is the spread made by n successive spreads of s, which can be formulated in terms of repeated reflections of lines in lines. It turns out that the *spread polynomial* $S_n\left(s\right)$ is of degree n in s, and in the decimal number field is closely related to the classical Chebyshev polynomial $T_n\left(x\right)$.

The remarkable properties of these polynomials extend to general fields, suggesting new directions for the theory of special functions. There are also analogous *cross polynomials*. These are the basic ingredients for rational trigonometry.

1.3 Why classical trigonometry is hard

For centuries students have struggled to master angles, trigonometric functions and their many intricate relations. Those who learn how to apply the formulas correctly often don't know *why* they are true. Such difficulties are to an extent the natural reflection of an underlying ambiguity at the heart of classical trigonometry. This manifests itself in a number of ways, but can be boiled down to the single critical question:

What precisely is an angle??

The problem is that defining an angle correctly *requires calculus*. This is a point implicit in Archimedes' derivation of the length of the circumference of a circle, using an infinite sequence of successively refined approximations with regular polygons. It is also supported by the fact that *The Elements* [Euclid] does not try to measure angles, with the exception of right angles and some related special cases. Further evidence can be found in the universal reluctance of traditional texts to spell out a clear definition of this supposedly 'basic' concept.

Exercise 1.2 Open up a few elementary and advanced geometry books and see if this claim holds. ◇

Let's clarify the point with a simple example. The rectangle $\overline{ABCD}$ in Figure 1.5 has side lengths $|A, B| = 2$ and $|B, C| = 1$. What is the angle θ between the lines AB and AC in degrees to four decimal places? (Such accuracy is sometimes needed in surveying.)

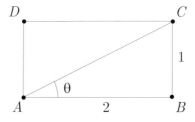

Figure 1.5: A simple problem?

Without tables, a calculator or calculus, a student has difficulty in answering this question, because the usual definition of an angle (page 5) is not precise enough to show how to calculate it. But how can one claim understanding of a mathematical concept without being able to compute it in simple situations? If the notion of an angle θ cannot be made completely clear from the beginning, it cannot be fundamental.

Of course there is one feature about angles that is useful—they transform the essentially nonlinear aspect of a circle into something linear, so that for example the sum of adjacent angles can be computed using only addition, at least if the angles are small. However the price to be paid for this convenience is high.

One difficulty concerns units. Most scientists and engineers work with degrees, the ancient Babylonian scale ranging from $0°$ to $360°$ around a full circle, although in Europe the grad is also used—from 0 to 400. Mathematicians officially prefer radian measure, in which the full circle gets the angle of $6.283\,185\ldots$, also known as 2π. The radian system is theoretically convenient, but practically a nuisance. Whatever scale is chosen, there is then the ambiguity of adding 'multiples of a circle' to any given angle, and of deciding whether angles are to have signs, or to be always positive.

Angles in the range from $90°$ to $180°$ are awkward and students invariably have difficulty with them. For example the angle $156°$ is closely related to the angle $24°$, and a question involving the former can be easily converted into a related question about the latter. There is an unnecessary duplication of information in having separate measurements for an angle and its supplement. For angles in the range from $180°$ to $360°$ similar remarks apply. Indeed, such angles are rarely necessary in elementary geometry.

Another consequence of relying on angles is a surprisingly limited range of configurations that can be analysed in classical trigonometry using elementary techniques. Students are constantly given examples that deal essentially with $90°/60°/30°$ or $90°/45°/45°$ triangles, since these are largely the only ones for which they can make unassisted calculations.

Small wonder that the trigonometric functions $\cos\theta$, $\sin\theta$ and $\tan\theta$ and their inverse functions cause students such difficulties. Although pictures of unit circles and ratios of lengths are used to 'define' these in elementary courses, it is difficult to understand them correctly without calculus. For example, the function $\tan\theta$ is given, for θ in a suitable range, by the infinite series

$$\tan\theta \approx \theta + \frac{1}{3}\theta^3 + \frac{2}{15}\theta^5 + \frac{17}{315}\theta^7 + \frac{62}{2835}\theta^9 + \cdots$$

while the inverse function $\arccos x$ is given by

$$\arccos x \approx \frac{1}{2}\pi - x - \frac{1}{6}x^3 - \frac{3}{40}x^5 - \frac{5}{112}x^7 - \frac{35}{1152}x^9 + \cdots$$

and in the case of $\tan\theta$ the coefficients defy a simple closed-form expression. This kind of subtlety is largely hidden from beginning students with the reliance on the power of calculators.

If the foundations of a building are askew, the entire structure is compromised. The underlying ambiguities in classical trigonometry revolving around the concept of angle are an impediment to learning mathematics, weaken its logical integrity, and introduce an unnecessary element of approximation and inaccuracy into practical applications of the subject.

1.4 Why rational trigonometry is easier

The key concepts of rational trigonometry are simpler, and mathematically more natural, than those of classical trigonometry. *Quadrance* is easier to work with than *distance* (as most mathematicians already know) and a *spread* is more elementary than an *angle*. The spread between two lines is a dimensionless quantity, and in the rational or decimal number fields takes on values between 0 and 1, with 0 occurring when lines are parallel and 1 occurring when lines are perpendicular. Forty-five degrees becomes a spread of $1/2$, while thirty and sixty degrees become respectively spreads of $1/4$ and $3/4$. What could be simpler than that?

Another advantage with spreads is that the measurement is taken between lines, not rays. As a consequence, the two range of angles from $0°$ to $90°$ and from $90°$ to $180°$ are treated symmetrically. For example, the spreads associated to $24°$ and $156°$ are identical (namely $s \approx 0.165\,434\ldots$). If one wishes to distinguish between these two situations in the context of rays, a single binary bit of additional information is required, namely the choice between *acute* (ac) and *obtuse* (ob). The *Triangle spread rules* described in the applications part of the book deal with this additional information.

There are many triangles that can be analysed completely by elementary means using rational trigonometry, giving students exposure to a wider range of examples.

The straightforwardness of rational trigonometry is also evident from the polynomial form of the basic laws, which do not involve any transcendental functions, rely only on arithmetical operations, and are generally quadratic in any one variable. As a consequence, tables of values of trigonometric functions, or modern calculators, are not necessary to do trigonometric calculations. Computations for simple problems can be done by hand, more complicated problems can use computers more efficiently.

With the introduction of rational polar and spherical coordinates in calculus, this simplicity can be put to work in solving a wide variety of sophisticated problems. Computations of volumes, centroids of mass, moments of inertia and surface areas of spheres, paraboloids and hyperboloids become in many cases more elementary. This simplicity extends to higher dimensional spaces, where the basic algebraic relations reduce the traditional reliance on pictures and argument by analogy with lower dimensions.

Rational trigonometry works over any field. So the difficulties inherent in the decimal and 'real number' fields can be avoided. It is not necessary to have a prior model of the continuum before one begins geometry. Furthermore many calculations become much simpler over finite fields, which can be a significant advantage.

Even when extended to *spherical trigonometry* and *hyperbolic geometry*, the theory's basic formulas are polynomial, as will be shown in a future volume. The concepts of rational trigonometry also have advantages when working statistically, but this point will not be developed here.

1.5 Comparison example

Here is an illustration of how rational trigonometry allows you to solve explicit practical problems, and why this method is superior to the classical approach. There is nothing particularly special about this example or the numbers appearing in it.

Problem 1 The triangle $\overline{A_1 A_2 A_3}$ has side lengths $|A_1, A_2| \equiv 5$, $|A_2, A_3| \equiv 4$ and $|A_3, A_1| \equiv 6$. The point B is on the line $A_1 A_3$ with the angle between $A_1 A_2$ and $A_2 B$ equal to $45°$. What is the length $d \equiv |A_2, B|$?

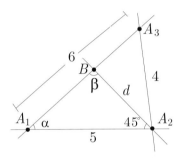

Figure 1.6: Classical version

Classical solution

Let the angles at A_1 and B be α and β respectively, as shown in Figure 1.6. The Cosine law in the triangle $\overline{A_1 A_2 A_3}$ gives

$$4^2 = 5^2 + 6^2 - 2 \times 5 \times 6 \times \cos \alpha$$

so that using a calculator

$$\alpha = \arccos \frac{3}{4} \approx 41.4096°.$$

Since the sum of the angles in $\overline{A_1 A_2 B}$ is $180°$,

$$\beta \approx 180° - 45° - 41.4096° \approx 93.5904°.$$

Now the Sine law in $\overline{A_1 A_2 B}$ states that

$$\frac{\sin \alpha}{d} = \frac{\sin \beta}{5}$$

so that again using the calculator

$$d \approx \frac{5 \sin 41.4096°}{\sin 93.5904°} \approx 3.3137.$$

Rational solution

To apply rational trigonometry, first convert the initial information about lengths and angles into quadrances and spreads. The three quadrances of the triangle are the squares of the side lengths, so that $Q_1 = 16$, $Q_2 = 36$ and $Q_3 = 25$.

The spread corresponding to the angle $45°$ is $1/2$, as can be easily seen from Figure 1.7.

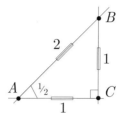

Figure 1.7: Spread of $1/2$

Let s be the spread between the lines $A_1 A_2$ and $A_1 A_3$, and let r be the spread between the lines BA_1 and BA_2. Let $Q \equiv Q(A_2, B)$. This yields Figure 1.8 involving only quantities from rational trigonometry.

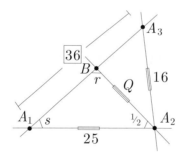

Figure 1.8: Rational version

Let's follow the use of the basic laws to first find s, then r, and then Q. Use the Cross law in $\overline{A_1 A_2 A_3}$ to get

$$(25 + 36 - 16)^2 = 4 \times 25 \times 36 \times (1 - s)$$

so that $s = 7/16$.

Use the Triple spread formula in $\overline{A_1 A_2 B}$ to obtain for r the quadratic equation

$$\left(\frac{7}{16} + \frac{1}{2} + r \right)^2 = 2 \left(\frac{49}{256} + \frac{1}{4} + r^2 \right) + 4 \times \frac{7}{16} \times \frac{1}{2} \times r.$$

This simplifies to

$$r^2 - r + \frac{1}{256} = 0$$

so that

$$r = \frac{1}{2} \pm \frac{3}{16}\sqrt{7}.$$

For each of these values of r, use the Spread law in $\overline{A_1 A_2 B}$

$$\frac{r}{25} = \frac{s}{Q}$$

and solve for Q, giving values

$$Q_1 = 1400 - 525\sqrt{7}$$

$$Q_2 = 1400 + 525\sqrt{7}.$$

To convert these answers back into distances, take square roots

$$d_1 = \sqrt{Q_1} \approx 3.3137\ldots$$

$$d_2 = \sqrt{Q_2} \approx 264.056\ldots.$$

Clearly the answer is d_1. Where does d_2 come from? The initial information (apart from the picture) describes two different possibilities. The second one is that the line $A_2 B$ makes a spread of $1/2$ with $A_1 A_2$ as shown in Figure 1.9, with the intersection B off the page in the direction shown, since $s = 7/16$ is less than $1/2$.

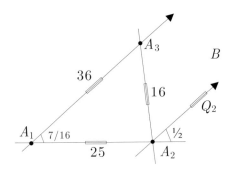

Figure 1.9: Alternate possibility

Comparison

Clearly the solution using rational trigonometry is more accurate, and reveals that the irrational number $\sqrt{7}$ is intimately bound up in this problem, which is certainly not obvious from the initial data, nor apparent from the classical solution.

Perhaps it appears that the classical solution is however shorter. That is because the main computations of $\arccos 3/4$, $\sin\alpha$ and $\sin\beta$ were done by the calculator.

The rational solution can be found entirely by hand. To be fair, it should be added that classical trigonometry *is* capable of getting the exact answers obtained by the rational method, but a more sophisticated approach is needed. One can simulate rational trigonometry from within classical trigonometry—by never calculating angles!

The rational method has solved two problems at the same time. This phenomenon is closely related to the fact that spreads, unlike angles, do not distinguish between the concepts of *acute* and *obtuse*, although in the Applications part of the book these concepts do appear in the context of the *Triangle spread rules*.

Since rational trigonometry is so much simpler than the existing theory, why was it not discovered a long time ago? In fact bits and pieces of rational trigonometry have surfaced throughout the history of mathematics, and have also been used by physicists.

It is well known, for example, that many trigonometric identities and integrals can be easily verified and solved by appropriate rational substitutions and/or use of the complex exponential function. The ubiquitous role of squared quantities in Euclidean geometry is also familiar, as is the insight of linear algebra to avoid angles as much as possible by using dot products and cross products. Modern geometry is very aware of the central importance of quadratic forms. In Einstein's theory of relativity the quadratic 'interval' plays a crucial role.

Perhaps these different clues have not been put together formerly because of the strength of established tradition, and in particular the reverence for Greek geometry.

1.6 Ancient Greek triumphs and difficulties

The serious study of geometry began with the ancient Greeks, whose mathematical heritage is one of the most remarkable and sublime achievements of humanity. Nevertheless, they encountered some difficulties, some of which persist today and interfere with our understanding of geometry.

A Pythagorean dilemma

The Pythagoreans believed that the workings of the universe could ultimately be described by *proportions between whole numbers*, such as $4 : 5$. This was not necessarily a mistake—the future may reveal the utility of such an idea. After early successes in applying this principle to music and geometry, however, they discovered a now famous dilemma. The length of the diagonal to the length of the side of a square, namely $\sqrt{2} : 1$, could not be realized as a proportion between two whole numbers.

Unfortunately, this difficulty was something of a red herring. Had they stuck with their original beliefs in the workings of the Divine Mind, and boldly concluded that the *squares* of the lengths ought to be more important than the lengths themselves, then the history of mathematics would look quite different.

Circles and trigonometric functions

Points, lines and circles are the most important objects in Euclidean geometry. The ancient Greeks were much enamoured with the elegance of the circle, and chose to give the compass equal importance to the straightedge in their geometry. Following their lead, mathematics courses still rely heavily on the circle and its properties to introduce the basic concepts of classical trigonometry. Most high school students will be familiar with the unit circle used to define both angles, as on page 5, as well as the trigonometric ratios $\cos\theta$, $\sin\theta$ and $\tan\theta$.

This thinking is unfortunate. A circle is a more complicated object than a line. In Cartesian coordinates it is described by a second degree equation, while a line is described by a first degree equation. Defining arc lengths of curves other than line segments is quite sophisticated, even for arcs of circles. So it does not make mathematical sense to treat circles on a par with lines, or to attempt to use circles to define the basic measurement between lines.

In rational trigonometry *points and lines are more fundamental than circles.* The essential formulas involve only points and lines, while circles appear later as particular kinds of conics in universal geometry, where they can be studied purely in the rational context without the use of trigonometric functions. Even rotations can be investigated solely within universal geometry.

The essential roles of $\cos\theta$, $\sin\theta$ and $\tan\theta$ arise rather when considering *uniform motion* around a circle, which has more to do with mechanics than geometry. Trigonometric functions also occur in harmonic analysis and complex analysis, where they are however secondary to the complex exponential function, whose theory is simpler and more fundamental.

And what about all those engineering problems with spherical or cylindrical symmetry? Rational trigonometry solves many of these problems in a more direct fashion, as shown by the last chapter in this book. The reality is that *the trigonometric functions are overrated*, and their intensive study in high schools is for many students an unnecessary complication.

Euclid's ambiguities

To develop a general and powerful geometry, it is critical to ensure that the basic definitions are completely unambiguous, and that circular reasoning plays no role.

Unfortunately, it is too easy to loosely convey a geometric idea with a picture. Students can seemingly learn concepts—such as parallel and perpendicular lines, triangles, quadrilaterals, tangent lines to a circle, angles and many others—by being shown a sufficient number of illustrative examples. However, when they want to use these ideas in proofs or precise calculations, the lack of clear definitions becomes a burden, not a convenience.

One of the appeals of mathematics is that one can understand completely the basic concepts and then logically derive the entire theory, step by step, using only valid logical arguments. When students meet mathematics in which the logical structure is not clearly evident, their confidence and understanding suffers. This applies to all students, even—perhaps *especially*—to weaker ones.

The extraordinary work of Euclid, *The Elements*, which set the tone of mathematics for two thousand years, is guilty of ambiguity in its initial definitions, despite the otherwise generally high standard of logic and precision throughout. The historical dominance of Euclid's work, with its supposedly axiomatic framework, has coloured mathematical thinking to this day, not altogether in a positive way.

According to Euclid, a *point* is that which 'has no parts or magnitude', a *line* is 'length without breadth', and *perpendicularity* of lines is defined as 'lying evenly between each other'. For someone who already has an intuitive idea of what a point, line and perpendicular mean, perhaps by having been shown many relevant pictures from an early age, these definitions may seem reasonable, but to someone without prior experience of geometry they are surely quite unintelligible.

For many centuries it appeared that there was no alternative to the geometry of Euclid. But in the seventeenth century the work of Fermat, Descartes and others opened up a dramatic new possibility. The Cartesian idea of defining a point as an ordered pair of numbers, and then analysing curves by algebraic manipulations of their defining equations is very powerful. It reduces the foundations of geometry to that of arithmetic and algebra, and allows the formulation of many geometrical questions over general fields.

Rational trigonometry adopts the logical and precise Cartesian approach of Descartes, but it adds a metrical aspect with the notions of quadrance and spread, still in the purely algebraic setting. This allows Euclidean geometry to be put on a firm and proper foundation.

1.7 Modern ambiguities

In the nineteenth century some of the difficulties and limitations with Euclid's geometry became more recognized, and for this reason and others, the twentieth century saw a slow but steady decline in the importance of Euclid as the basis of education in geometry. Unfortunately, there was no successful attempt to put into place an alternative framework.

One of those who realized the importance of the task was D. Hilbert, whose *Foundations of Geometry* [Hilbert] was an attempt to shore up the logical deficiencies of Euclid. This approach was not universally accepted, and the thought arose that perhaps the task was intrinsically impossible, and that a certain amount of ambiguity could not be removed from the subject.

Twentieth century mathematics largely resigned itself to an acceptance of vagueness in the foundations of mathematics. It became accepted wisdom that any treatment of Euclidean geometry had to incorporate the philosophical aspects of the 'construction of the continuum' and Cantor's theory of 'infinite sets'. Distance, angle and the trigonometric functions required the usual framework of modern analysis, along with its logical deficiencies.

A common feeling was that the best strategy was to adopt an *axiomatic system*, involving formal manipulations of underlying concepts that are not given meaning. It was often supposed that this is what Euclid had in mind.

But this is *not* what Euclid had in mind. When he stated his 'axioms', Euclid wanted only to clarify which facts he was going to regard as obvious, before deriving all other facts using deduction. The meaning of these basic facts was never in question. Euclid's work in this sense is quite different from formalist systems which came to be modelled on it.

When we begin a study of universal geometry, these preconceived twentieth century notions must be put aside. It *is* possible to start from the beginning, and to aspire to give a complete and precise account of geometry, without any missing gaps. The logical framework should be clearly visible at all times. The basic concepts should be easy to state to someone beginning the subject. Pulling in theorems from the outside is not allowed. The 'continuum' need not be understood. 'Infinite set theory' and its attendant logical difficulties—deliberately swept under the carpet by modern mathematics—should be avoided.

With such an approach the logical coherence and beauty of mathematics become easier to verify and appreciate directly, without appeals to authority and convention. To build up mathematics properly, axioms are not necessary. You do not have to engage in philosophy to do geometry, nor require sophisticated modern logic to understand foundations. Clear thinking, careful definitions and an interest in applications should suffice.

So let's begin the story, starting with an informal review of the basic assumed knowledge from algebra and arithmetic. Then let's build up trigonometry and geometry, one step at a time.

2

Background

2.1 Fields

A *field* is a number system involving the operations of addition and multiplication obeying particular laws. It is possible to read this book without any knowledge of the theory of fields by working only with **rational numbers**—expressions of the form a/b where a and b are integers with b non-zero, with the convention that $a_1/b_1 = a_2/b_2$ precisely when $a_1 b_2 - a_2 b_1 = 0$, and with the usual arithmetical operations.

In this book, the term field refers not to a set, but rather to the specification of a *type of number*. Thus for example we do not need the 'infinite set' of 'all' rational numbers in order to specify what a rational number is, and to define addition and multiplication between two of them. This understanding fits naturally with common usage outside of pure mathematical circles, and avoids metaphysical speculations.

A field F contains numbers $0, 1$ and -1. By defining $2 \equiv 1 + 1$, $-2 \equiv (-1) + (-1)$, $3 \equiv 1 + 1 + 1$ and so on, the integer a is associated to an element in F. Thus also any rational number expression a/b has a meaning in F, provided that $b \neq 0$. This convention allows polynomials with integer coefficients to be defined over any field.

The **characteristic** of a field F is the least natural number $n \geq 1$ such that $n = 0$ in F, if it exists. This book adopts the convention that *characteristic two fields are excluded*, since many formulas have denominators involving 2 or 4. Characteristic three fields are occasionally problematic.

For simplicity the main fields used as examples in this book are the field of rational numbers, the field of integers modulo an odd prime p, denoted $\mathbb{F}_p$, the field of decimal numbers, and the field of complex numbers. Of course other fields may be used too.

There are unfortunately serious logical difficulties with the decimal number system, and even more remarkable confusions with the field of so-called 'real numbers'.

The reader is warned that the views expressed on the following two pages represent the author's position, which is currently a minority view.

The field of decimal numbers

When the term *decimal number* is used in this book, it refers to a number such as

$$\pi^2/16 \approx 0.616\,850\,275 \ldots$$

with a decimal expansion that is specified by an algorithm, computer program or function. All the constants of mathematics, such as $\sqrt{2}, \pi, e, \gamma$ and so on, are decimal numbers in this sense, as are any arithmetical expressions formed by them, even those using infinite sequences and series, provided of course that these sequences and series are specified in a finite way.

Arithmetic with decimal numbers is thus intimately connected with the theory of computation. Unfortunately it is difficult in practice, and perhaps impossible in theory, to consistently determine when two algorithms *generate the same decimal number*.

This is a very serious deficiency, and implies that there is no effective notion of equality in the theory. So there is no general procedure to tell whether a given arithmetical statement involving decimal numbers is correct. Consider for example the formula

$$\left(\frac{1}{1} - \frac{1}{2} + \frac{1}{3} - \frac{1}{4} + \cdots\right)^2 = \frac{3}{8}\left(\frac{1}{1^2} + \frac{1}{2^2} + \frac{1}{3^2} + \cdots\right)$$

which is essentially a statement of equality between two algorithms. How could one check the validity of this equation without recognizing that the decimal number represented by both sides is $\pi^2/16$?

The topic of decimal numbers is a source of considerable confusion and ambiguity in mathematics. A proper development of the subject, which might have been a major agenda item for twentieth century mathematics, has yet to be taken sufficiently seriously. It is too difficult to be attempted here.

As an illustration of the problems that arise, it is generally accepted lore that the decimal numbers are *countable* and *not complete*. However with a careful examination of the definitions involved, it turns out that the reverse is true—the field of decimal numbers is both *complete* and *not countable*!

Despite such confusions, it is convenient to refer to numbers such as $\sqrt{2}, \pi, e$ and so on, temporarily putting aside the conceptual difficulties. So the *decimal number field* will be flagged as an 'informal' field, awaiting a proper treatment.

A *complex number* will here be of the form $a + bi$, with a and b decimal numbers, and the usual operations based on $i^2 = -1$. Algebraic numbers have decimal expansions given by algorithms (such as Newton's method), so they fit into this framework. The fundamental theorem of algebra holds in the field of complex numbers, meaning that any polynomial with complex coefficients has a zero.

The field of 'real numbers'

Even more logically unsound than the field of decimal numbers is the field of so-called 'real numbers'. Believers in 'real numbers', which currently includes the majority of mathematicians, assert that the decimal numbers of the previous section should be called *computable decimal numbers*, to be distinguished from '*non-computable decimal numbers*'. These latter 'numbers', which play the role of Leprechauns in modern mathematics, supposedly have infinite decimal expansions which are *not* determined by an algorithm, formula or computer program. In other words, these are decimal expansions which by definition cannot be described explicitly by finite beings such as ourselves, or our computers.

There are consequently no known examples of 'non-computable decimal numbers'. Actual mathematical or scientific computations never involve 'non-computable decimal numbers'. Defining addition and multiplication of 'non-computable decimal numbers' is necessarily even more ambiguous than for computable decimal numbers (see [Wildberger]), and not surprisingly standard texts uniformly ignore the issue.

Nonetheless, according to the adherents, the 'real number field'—comprising both the computable decimal numbers together with the 'non-computable decimal numbers'—provides the correct model of the continuum, and forms the basis of geometry, as well as much of mathematics. This is a curious position, to put it mildly!

In this book, 'non-computable decimals' play no role. Readers who are adamant about their existence may replace, in their minds, any reference to the field of decimal numbers with the field of 'real numbers'. No computational outcomes are in the least affected.

The field $\mathbb{F}_p$

For p an odd prime, the field $\mathbb{F}_p$ will be considered to consist of expressions of the form a/b, where a and b are integers with b not divisible by p, with the convention of equality

$$a_1/b_1 = a_2/b_2$$

precisely when $a_1 b_2 - a_2 b_1$ is divisible by p. In practice that means that a/b is unchanged if a multiple of p is added or subtracted from either a or b. It is then a standard fact that any such number is equal to one of the form $a/1 \equiv a$, for a one of the p numbers $0, 1, 2, \cdots, p-1$. Arithmetic now follows the usual rules for ordinary fractions, and so the usual congruence notation becomes unnecessary.

Example 2.1 Here are some illustrations of arithmetic in $\mathbb{F}_7$.

$$3 + 5 = 8 = 1$$
$$3 \times 6 = 18 = 4$$
$$\frac{34}{53} + \frac{19}{17} = \frac{6}{4} + \frac{5}{3} = \frac{38}{12} = \frac{3}{5} = 2. \quad \diamond$$

Square and spread numbers

Fix a field F. The term **number** refers to an element of F.

A number a in F is a **square number** (or just a **square**) precisely when it is of the form $a = r^2$ for some number r in F. Clearly 0 and 1 are square numbers in any field. Whether or not -1 is a square number is an interesting question which strongly influences the behavior of arithmetic in a field, and has consequences for geometry too.

Example 2.2 In the field $\mathbb{F}_p$ with p elements, there are exactly $(p+1)/2$ distinct square numbers. Here is a list for small values of p.

p	Squares in $\mathbb{F}_p$
3	$0, 1$
5	$0, 1, 4$
7	$0, 1, 2, 4$
11	$0, 1, 3, 4, 5, 9$
13	$0, 1, 3, 4, 9, 10, 12$
17	$0, 1, 2, 4, 8, 9, 13, 15, 16$
19	$0, 1, 4, 5, 6, 7, 9, 11, 16, 17$

Note that in $\mathbb{F}_{11}$, the number $-1 = 10$ is not a square, while in $\mathbb{F}_{13}$, the number $-1 = 12$ is a square. ◇

In the field $\mathbb{F}_p$, if p is a prime of the form $p = 4l + 1$ then -1 is a square, while if $p = 4l + 3$ then the number -1 is not a square.

Definition A number s in a field F is a **spread number** precisely when $s(1-s)$ is a square. Clearly 0 and 1 are spread numbers in any field.

Example 2.3 In the decimal number field the square numbers are precisely the positive numbers, and the spread numbers are precisely those s satisfying $0 \le s \le 1$. ◇

Example 2.4 In the field $\mathbb{F}_p$ there are either $(p+1)/2$ or $(p+3)/2$ spread numbers, depending on whether p is of the form $4l + 1$ or $4l + 3$ respectively. Here is a list for small values of p.

p	Spread numbers in $\mathbb{F}_p$
3	$0, 1, 2$
5	$0, 1, 3$
7	$0, 1, 3, 4, 5$
11	$0, 1, 2, 3, 6, 9, 10$
13	$0, 1, 4, 6, 7, 8, 10$
17	$0, 1, 2, 6, 7, 9, 11, 12, 16$
19	$0, 1, 2, 4, 8, 9, 10, 11, 12, 16, 18$ ◇

Exercise 2.1 Show that for any number u with $u^2 \neq -1$, the number $s \equiv u^2 / \left(1 + u^2\right)$ is a spread number, and that every spread number $s \neq 1$ is of this form. ◇

Exercise 2.2 Show that for any numbers x and y satisfying $x^2 \neq -1$ and $y^2 \neq -1$, the number

$$s \equiv \frac{(x - y)^2}{\left(1 + x^2\right)\left(1 + y^2\right)}$$

is a spread number. If $xy \neq -1$ then find a number u so that $s = u^2 / \left(1 + u^2\right)$. ◇

Definition A number s in a field F is a **square-spread number** precisely when it is both a square number and a spread number.

Example 2.5 Here is a list of square-spread numbers in $\mathbb{F}_p$ for small values of p.

p	Square-spread numbers in $\mathbb{F}_p$
3	$0, 1$
5	$0, 1, 4$
7	$0, 1, 4$
11	$0, 1, 3, 9$
13	$0, 1, 4, 10$
17	$0, 1, 2, 9, 16$
19	$0, 1, 4, 9, 11, 16$ ◇

Exercise 2.3 (Harder) How many square-spread numbers are there in $\mathbb{F}_p$? ◇

2.2 Proportions

The ancient Greeks believed that the relative sizes of two objects was a more fundamental notion than the absolute size of either of them. This idea has largely gone out of fashion in mathematical circles, but there is something to be said for it, as appreciated by modern physicists.

Definition A 2-**proportion** is an expression of the form $a : b$ where a and b are numbers, not both zero, with the convention that

$$a : b = \lambda a : \lambda b$$

for any non-zero number λ. If the context is clear, a 2-proportion will be called simply a **proportion**.

The convention for equality may be restated as

$$a_1 : b_1 = a_2 : b_2 \Leftrightarrow a_1 b_2 - a_2 b_1 = 0.$$

Example 2.6 In the rational number field

$$3 : 7 = \frac{12}{7} : 4$$

since

$$3 \times 4 - \frac{12}{7} \times 7 = 0. \quad \diamond$$

One difference between fractions and proportions is rather important for geometry. The fraction a/b makes sense only if b is non-zero, while the proportion $a : b$ is valid as long as one of a or b is non-zero.

Another difference between fractions and proportions is that the concept of proportion can be extended to three or more numbers. This is quite natural when dealing with the relative sizes of more than two objects.

Definition A 3-**proportion** is an expression of the form $a : b : c$ where a, b and c are numbers, not all zero, with the convention that

$$a : b : c = \lambda a : \lambda b : \lambda c$$

for any non-zero number λ. If the context is clear, a 3-proportion will be called simply a **proportion**.

The convention of equality may be restated as

$$a_1 : b_1 : c_1 = a_2 : b_2 : c_2$$

precisely when

$$a_1 b_2 - a_2 b_1 = 0 \qquad b_1 c_2 - b_2 c_1 = 0 \qquad c_1 a_2 - c_2 a_1 = 0.$$

Exercise 2.4 Show that in general one has to check all three conditions to ensure that two 3-proportions are equal. $\diamond$

Definition For a natural number n, an n-**proportion** is an expression of the form

$$a_1 : a_2 : \cdots : a_n$$

where $a_1, a_2, \cdots, a_n$ are not all zero, with the convention that

$$a_1 : a_2 : \cdots : a_n = \lambda a_1 : \lambda a_2 : \cdots : \lambda a_n$$

for any non-zero number λ.

Note that there are $(n-1)\,n/2$ corresponding conditions for equality between two n-proportions.

2.3 Identities and determinants

The rational approach to geometry inevitably involves polynomial and rational identities, some of which become rather involved.

Example 2.7 The familiar **Binomial theorem** gives the expansion of $(x_1 + x_2)^n$ for n a natural number and x_1, x_2 elements of a field, using the integers

$$\binom{n}{k} \equiv \frac{n\,(n-1)\cdots(n-k+1)}{k\,(k-1)\cdots 1}.$$

The statement is

$$(x_1 + x_2)^n = x_1^n + \binom{n}{1}x_1^{n-1}x_2 + \cdots + \binom{n}{n-1}x_1 x_2^{n-1} + x_2^n. \quad \diamond$$

Example 2.8 Another useful identity is the following special case of the extended Binomial theorem for three variables

$$(x_1 + x_2 + x_3)^2 = x_1^2 + x_2^2 + x_3^2 + 2\,(x_1 x_2 + x_1 x_3 + x_2 x_3).$$

Both sides are **symmetric** functions of the variables x_1, x_2 and x_3, meaning that if any two of the indices are interchanged, the expression remains the same. $\diamond$

Example 2.9 The most important identity in geometry, and also possibly in number theory, is **Fibonacci's identity**

$$(x_1 y_2 - x_2 y_1)^2 + (x_1 x_2 + y_1 y_2)^2 = (x_1^2 + y_1^2)(x_2^2 + y_2^2).$$

It was probably known to Diophantus, but the first recorded proof is in Fibonacci's *Liber quadratorum* of 1225. $\diamond$

Example 2.10 An extension of Fibonacci's identity is **Cauchy's identity**

$$(x_1 y_2 - x_2 y_1)^2 + (y_1 z_2 - y_2 z_1)^2 + (z_1 x_2 - z_2 x_1)^2 + (x_1 x_2 + y_1 y_2 + z_1 z_2)^2$$
$$= (x_1^2 + y_1^2 + z_1^2)(x_2^2 + y_2^2 + z_2^2)$$

which plays a major role in projective trigonometry. $\diamond$

Exercise 2.5 Check the Fibonacci and Cauchy identities, as well as the following variant of Fibonacci's identity

$$(x_1 y_2 + x_2 y_1)^2 + (x_1 x_2 - y_1 y_2)^2 = (x_1^2 + y_1^2)(x_2^2 + y_2^2). \quad \diamond$$

Exercise 2.6 Check the following identity, which occurs in the proof of the Spread ratio theorem (page 77)

$$(y_1 - y_2)(x_3 - x_1) - (y_1 - y_3)(x_2 - x_1) = (y_1 - y_3)(x_3 - x_2) - (y_2 - y_3)(x_3 - x_1). \quad \diamond$$

Zero denominator convention

In this book the following *Zero denominator convention* is used.

A statement involving a rational identity will be assumed to be empty when a choice of variables creates a denominator of zero.

For example the rational identity

$$\frac{(x_1y_2 - x_2y_1)^2}{(x_1^2 + y_1^2)(x_2^2 + y_2^2)} + \frac{(x_1x_2 + y_1y_2)^2}{(x_1^2 + y_1^2)(x_2^2 + y_2^2)} = 1$$

which follows from Fibonacci's identity in the previous section will be considered a true statement for *any* values of the variables, even those that create a situation where one of the factors $x_1^2 + y_1^2$ or $x_2^2 + y_2^2$ is zero, since in this case the identity is considered to be an empty statement, so still true. This removes the need to prohibit special cases, but means that the reader must be particularly careful, when faced with a rational expression, to ask

When is the denominator zero?

In addition, some care is needed when such identities form part of an extended logical argument—one must remember the conditions that resulted in zero denominators, even after the denominators may have disappeared.

Determinants and anti-symmetric polynomials

Determinants are particularly useful polynomial expressions which occur frequently in geometry. This section introduces convenient notation which extends the idea of a determinant to create more general anti-symmetric polynomials.

Example 2.11 A common determinant is

$$\begin{vmatrix} x_1 & y_1 & z_1 \\ x_2 & y_2 & z_2 \\ x_3 & y_3 & z_3 \end{vmatrix} = x_1y_2z_3 - x_1y_3z_2 + x_2y_3z_1 - x_3y_2z_1 + x_3y_1z_2 - x_2y_1z_3.$$

The six terms in this expression are obtained from the first by performing all six permutations of the indices $i = 1, 2$ and 3, and multiplying by the sign of the permutation. Note the convention that the position of the variables in the terms do not move, only the indices do. The above determinant will also be written as $[x_1y_2z_3]_3^-$. ◇

Example 2.12 A special case of the previous is

$$\begin{vmatrix} x_1 & y_1 & 1 \\ x_2 & y_2 & 1 \\ x_3 & y_3 & 1 \end{vmatrix} = x_1y_2 - x_1y_3 + x_2y_3 - x_3y_2 + x_3y_1 - x_2y_1.$$

This expression will also be written as $[x_1y_2]_3^-$. ◇

More generally, for any natural numbers m_1, m_2 and m_3 define the anti-symmetric polynomial

$$[x_1^{m_1} y_2^{m_2}\ z_3^{m_3}]_3^- \equiv \begin{vmatrix} x_1^{m_1} & y_1^{m_2} & z_1^{m_3} \\ x_2^{m_1} & y_2^{m_2} & z_2^{m_3} \\ x_3^{m_1} & y_3^{m_2} & z_3^{m_3} \end{vmatrix}.$$

Then

$$\begin{aligned} [x_1^{m_1} y_2^{m_2}\ z_3^{m_3}]_3^- &= x_1^{m_1} y_2^{m_2} z_3^{m_3} - x_1^{m_1} y_3^{m_2} z_2^{m_3} + x_2^{m_1} y_3^{m_2} z_1^{m_3} \\ &\quad - x_3^{m_1} y_2^{m_2} z_1^{m_3} + x_3^{m_1} y_1^{m_2} z_2^{m_3} - x_2^{m_1} y_1^{m_2} z_3^{m_3} \end{aligned}$$

is obtained by taking the alternating sum of monomials, starting with $x_1^{m_1} y_2^{m_2}\ z_3^{m_3}$, and successively performing interchanges on the (sub)indices $1, 2$ and 3, in the order

$$2 \longleftrightarrow 3 \quad 1 \longleftrightarrow 2 \quad 2 \longleftrightarrow 3 \quad 1 \longleftrightarrow 2 \quad 2 \longleftrightarrow 3.$$

More generally, for any sequence of variables

$$x_1, x_2, x_3, y_1, y_2, y_3, z_1, z_2, z_3, w_1, w_2, w_3, \cdots$$

with (sub)indices in the range $\{1, 2, 3\}$, and any polynomial p in these variables, define $[p]_3^-$ to be the alternating sum of the six terms obtained from p by applying these same interchanges to the indices, in this same order.

Example 2.13

$$[x_1 x_2^5 y_2]_3^- = x_1 x_2^5 y_2 - x_1 x_3^5 y_3 + x_2 x_3^5 y_3 - x_3 x_2^5 y_2 + x_3 x_1^5 y_1 - x_2 x_1^5 y_1. ◇$$

Example 2.14

$$[x_1]_3^- = x_1 - x_1 + x_2 - x_3 + x_3 - x_2 = 0. ◇$$

Exercise 2.7 Prove the identity

$$[x_1^2 y_2]_3^- + [x_1 x_2 y_2]_3^- = (x_1 + x_2 + x_3)[x_1 y_2]_3^-. ◇$$

This notational device can be extended to larger index sets. For example, for a polynomial p involving terms with indices in $\{1, 2, 3, 4\}$, define $[p]_4^-$ to be the alternating sum of the 24 terms obtained from p by applying all possible permutations of the four indices, with each term multiplied by the sign of the corresponding permutation.

Example 2.15

$$\begin{aligned}
\left[x_1^2 x_2 y_3\right]_4^- &= x_1^2 x_2 y_3 - x_1^2 x_2 y_4 + x_1^2 x_3 y_4 - x_1^2 x_4 y_3 + x_1^2 x_4 y_2 - x_1^2 x_3 y_2 \\
&\quad + x_2^2 x_3 y_1 - x_2^2 x_4 y_1 + x_3^2 x_4 y_1 - x_3^2 x_4 y_2 + x_2^2 x_4 y_3 - x_2^2 x_3 y_4 \\
&\quad + x_3^2 x_2 y_4 - x_4^2 x_2 y_3 + x_4^2 x_3 y_2 - x_4^2 x_3 y_1 + x_4^2 x_2 y_1 - x_3^2 x_2 y_1 \\
&\quad + x_3^2 x_1 y_2 - x_4^2 x_1 y_2 + x_4^2 x_1 y_3 - x_3^2 x_1 y_4 + x_2^2 x_1 y_4 - x_2^2 x_1 y_3. \quad \diamond
\end{aligned}$$

2.4　Linear equations

The following facts should be familiar over the rational or decimal numbers, and indeed they hold in any field. Consider two linear equations in variables x and y of the form

$$a_1 x + b_1 y + c_1 = 0$$
$$a_2 x + b_2 y + c_2 = 0$$

where a_1 and b_1 are not both zero, and also a_2 and b_2 are not both zero. A unique solution $[x, y]$ exists precisely when

$$a_1 b_2 - a_2 b_1 = \begin{vmatrix} a_1 & b_1 \\ a_2 & b_2 \end{vmatrix} \neq 0.$$

In this case

$$x = \frac{b_1 c_2 - b_2 c_1}{a_1 b_2 - a_2 b_1} = - \begin{vmatrix} c_1 & b_1 \\ c_2 & b_2 \end{vmatrix} \Big/ \begin{vmatrix} a_1 & b_1 \\ a_2 & b_2 \end{vmatrix}$$

$$y = \frac{c_1 a_2 - c_2 a_1}{a_1 b_2 - a_2 b_1} = - \begin{vmatrix} a_1 & c_1 \\ a_2 & c_2 \end{vmatrix} \Big/ \begin{vmatrix} a_1 & b_1 \\ a_2 & b_2 \end{vmatrix}.$$

On the other hand suppose that $a_1 b_2 - a_2 b_1 = 0$, so that $a_1 : b_1 = a_2 : b_2$. If

$$a_1 : b_1 : c_1 = a_2 : b_2 : c_2$$

then there is more than one solution, while if

$$a_1 : b_1 : c_1 \neq a_2 : b_2 : c_2$$

then there is no solution.

Another common situation is the case of three homogeneous equations in variables x, y and z

$$a_1 x + b_1 y + c_1 z = 0$$
$$a_2 x + b_2 y + c_2 z = 0$$
$$a_3 x + b_3 y + c_3 z = 0.$$

There is always the solution $[x, y, z] = [0, 0, 0]$. Another solution exists precisely when

$$\begin{vmatrix} a_1 & b_1 & c_1 \\ a_2 & b_2 & c_2 \\ a_3 & b_3 & c_3 \end{vmatrix} = 0.$$

2.5   Polynomial functions and zeroes

Polynomial functions with integer coefficients have a meaning in any field. Such a polynomial $p(x)$ has a **zero** at the number x_0 precisely when $p(x_0) = 0$. For example the spread polynomial

$$S_5(x) \equiv x\left(16x^2 - 20x + 5\right)^2 \tag{2.1}$$

turns out to control five-fold symmetry in any field, and its zeroes relate to the existence of regular pentagons.

Example 2.16 Over the decimal numbers the function $S_5(s)$ may be (partially) visualized in the usual way by plotting some of the values $[x, S_5(x)]$ as in Figure 2.1.

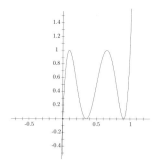

Figure 2.1: Spread polynomial $S_5(x) \equiv x\left(16x^2 - 20x + 5\right)^2$ ◇

In a finite field a polynomial may be conveniently represented by a table of values.

Example 2.17 In $\mathbb{F}_{19}$ the polynomial $S_5(x) \equiv x\left(16x^2 - 20x + 5\right)^2$ has values

x	0	1	2	3	4	5	6	7	8	9
$S_5(x)$	0	1	10	13	1	5	17	6	10	0

x	10	11	12	13	14	15	16	17	18
$S_5(x)$	10	1	10	14	3	15	0	7	10

◇

Recall the important **Factor theorem**, which asserts that if a polynomial function $p(x)$ has a zero at x_0, then there is a natural number k less than or equal to the degree of p such that

$$p(x) = (x - x_0)^k q(x)$$

for some polynomial $q(x)$ with $q(x_0) \neq 0$. The number k is the **multiplicity** of the zero x_0.

Example 2.18 In $\mathbb{F}_{19}$ the polynomial $S_5(x)$ has zeroes 0, 9 and 16, the former with multiplicity one and the latter two with multiplicity two. In fact

$$S_5(x) = 9x(x - 9)^2(x - 16)^2. \quad ◇$$

2.6 Quadratic equations

Geometry is a quadratic subject, and so is intimately connected with the subject of quadratic equations. This section reviews the familiar procedure for solving a quadratic equation, along with an important result on pairs of quadratic equations. Recall that we are working in a given field F, not of characteristic two.

Completing the square

A **quadratic equation** in x is a polynomial equation of degree two in x of the form

$$ax^2 + bx + c = 0$$

where a and b are numbers with $a \neq 0$. The **normal form** of a quadratic equation is

$$(x - p)^2 = q$$

for some numbers p and q. The quadratic equation $ax^2 + bx + c = 0$ can always be rewritten in normal form by the process of *completing the square*, as follows.

Step 1. Take c to the other side, and divide both sides by the non-zero number a

$$x^2 + \frac{b}{a}x = -\frac{c}{a}.$$

Step 2. Add the square of one half the coefficient of x to both sides

$$x^2 + \frac{b}{a}x + \frac{b^2}{4a^2} = \frac{b^2}{4a^2} - \frac{c}{a}.$$

Step 3. Factor the left side and simplify the right to obtain

$$\left(x + \frac{b}{2a}\right)^2 = \frac{b^2 - 4ac}{4a^2}.$$

This has a solution in x precisely when $b^2 - 4ac$ is a square, say r^2, in which case

$$x = \frac{-b \pm r}{2a}.$$

Note that the usual 'quadratic formula' is subsumed by this derivation. Over a general field square roots do not always exist, and if they do they are generally not unique. The usual situation with the decimal numbers exploits the existence of a distinguished (positive) square root of a positive number, and is a good example of 'symmetry breaking' in mathematics.

Pairs of quadratic equations

Definition Two quadratic equations

$$(x - p_1)^2 = q_1 \qquad (x - p_2)^2 = q_2$$

in x are **compatible** precisely when they have a common solution.

Here is our first theorem, and although entirely algebraic, it anticipates aspects of rational trigonometry and universal geometry.

Theorem 1 (Quadratic compatability) The quadratic equations

$$(x - p_1)^2 = q_1 \qquad (x - p_2)^2 = q_2$$

are compatible precisely when

$$\left((p_1 - p_2)^2 - (q_1 + q_2) \right)^2 = 4q_1 q_2.$$

In this case, if $p_1 \neq p_2$ then there is a unique common solution

$$x = \frac{p_1 + p_2}{2} - \frac{(q_1 - q_2)}{2(p_1 - p_2)}.$$

Proof. If $p_1 = p_2$ then the two equations

$$(x - p_1)^2 = q_1 \qquad (x - p_2)^2 = q_2$$

are compatible precisely when $q_1 = q_2$, which is equivalent to the condition that

$$(q_1 + q_2)^2 = 4q_1 q_2.$$

Suppose otherwise that $p_1 \neq p_2$. If the two equations are compatible with common solution x, then take the difference between the equations to obtain

$$2(p_1 - p_2)x = p_1^2 - p_2^2 - q_1 + q_2$$

so that

$$x = \frac{p_1 + p_2}{2} - \frac{(q_1 - q_2)}{2(p_1 - p_2)}. \tag{2.2}$$

Since this x satisfies the second equation,

$$\left(\frac{p_1 + p_2}{2} - \frac{(q_1 - q_2)}{2(p_1 - p_2)} - p_2 \right)^2 = q_2.$$

Now deduce the following equivalent equations

$$\left((p_1 - p_2)^2 - (q_1 - q_2)\right)^2 = 4(p_1 - p_2)^2 q_1$$
$$(p_1 - p_2)^4 - 2(p_1 - p_2)^2(q_1 - q_2) + (q_1 - q_2)^2 = 4(p_1 - p_2)^2 q_1$$
$$(p_1 - p_2)^4 + 2(p_1 - p_2)^2(q_1 + q_2) + (q_1 - q_2)^2 = 0$$
$$\left((p_1 - p_2)^2 - (q_1 + q_2)\right)^2 = 4q_1 q_2.$$

Conversely if

$$\left((p_1 - p_2)^2 - (q_1 + q_2)\right)^2 = 4q_1 q_2.$$

then retrace the steps and use the symmetry between the two original equations to show that (2.2) is a common solution. ∎

Note that if $p_1 = p_2$ in the theorem, then the two quadratic equations are compatible precisely when they are identical, and so in this case there are two common solutions.

Example 2.19 In the rational number field the quadratic equations

$$(x - 4)^2 = 9 \qquad (x - 6)^2 = 1$$

are compatible since

$$\left((4 - 6)^2 - (9 + 1)\right)^2 = 36 = 4 \times 9 \times 1.$$

As $4 \neq 6$, the unique common solution is

$$x = \frac{4 + 6}{2} - \frac{(9 - 1)}{2(4 - 6)} = 7. \quad \diamond$$

Exercise 2.8 Show that the quadratic equations

$$a_1 x^2 + b_1 x + c_1 = 0$$
$$a_2 x^2 + b_2 x + c_2 = 0$$

are compatible precisely when

$$\begin{vmatrix} a_1 & c_1 \\ a_2 & c_2 \end{vmatrix}^2 = \begin{vmatrix} a_1 & b_1 \\ a_2 & b_2 \end{vmatrix} \begin{vmatrix} b_1 & c_1 \\ b_2 & c_2 \end{vmatrix}$$

in which case

$$x = \frac{a_2 c_1 - a_1 c_2}{a_1 b_2 - a_2 b_1}. \quad \diamond$$

Exercise 2.9 Show that the equations

$$(x - p_1)^2 = q \qquad (x - p_2)^2 = q$$

are compatible precisely when either $p_1 = p_2$ or $p_1 - p_2 = \pm 2q$. In the latter case show that the unique common solution is

$$x = \frac{p_1 + p_2}{2}. \quad \diamond$$

Cartesian coordinate geometry

This foundational chapter introduces careful and novel definitions of the basic building blocks of planar Cartesian geometry, and establishes fundamental facts that will be used repeatedly throughout the rest of the book. This includes notions of points, lines, triangles, quadrilaterals, parallel, perpendicular, affine combinations and reflections. Throughout we work in, or over, a fixed field F, not of characteristic two, whose elements are called numbers. Diagrams generally illustrate the situation in the rational and decimal number fields, or occasionally in a finite field.

3.1 Points and lines

Definition A **point** $A \equiv [x, y]$ is an ordered pair of numbers. The numbers x and y are the **coordinates** of A.

Example 3.1 Figure 3.1 shows the points $[2, 3]$ and $[5, 2]$ in the rational or decimal number fields.

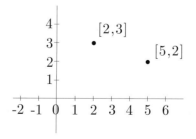

Figure 3.1: Two points over the rational or decimal fields ⋄

Over the field $\mathbb{F}_p$, a point may be represented by a box in a square array of boxes, with horizontal and vertical positions numbered from 0 to $p-1$. Alternative labellings will also be used; for example over $\mathbb{F}_{11}$ the horizontal and vertical positions could be labelled with the numbers $-5, -4, \cdots, 4, 5$. Sometimes such a diagram will be repeated periodically in both directions to illustrate a larger view.

Example 3.2 Figure 3.2 shows the points $[3,7]$ and $[6,1]$ in the field $\mathbb{F}_{11}$.

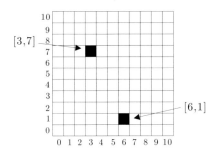

Figure 3.2: Two points over $\mathbb{F}_{11}$ ◇

Definition A **line** $l \equiv \langle a : b : c \rangle$ is a 3-proportion, enclosed in pointed brackets, with the property that a and b are not both zero.

The alternative notation

$$l \equiv \left\langle \begin{array}{ccc} a & : & b \\ & c & \end{array} \right\rangle$$

is also useful, as it clarifies the distinguished role played by c, while $\langle a : b : c \rangle$ anticipates the development of projective rational trigonometry, where all three coefficients are treated equally.

Definition The line $l \equiv \langle a : b : c \rangle$ is a **null line** precisely when

$$a^2 + b^2 = 0.$$

Otherwise l is a **non-null** line.

If the line $l \equiv \langle a : b : c \rangle$ is a null line then a and b must both be non-zero and $(b/a)^2 = -1$, so that -1 is a square.

Conversely if -1 is a square, say $-1 = i^2$ for some number i, then there are only two solutions to the equation $x^2 = -1$, namely i and $-i$. Thus either $b = ia$ or $b = -ia$, and since a is non-zero the coefficients a, b and c of l can be divided by a to obtain $l = \langle 1 : i : d \rangle$ or $l = \langle 1 : -i : d \rangle$ for some d.

Definition The point $A \equiv [x, y]$ **lies on** the line $l \equiv \langle a : b : c \rangle$, or equivalently the line l **passes through** the point A, precisely when

$$ax + by + c = 0.$$

Note carefully that a line is *not* a set of points. This allows us to circumvent the logical difficulties with 'infinite set theory'. In diagrams a line is illustrated by exhibiting the points, or some of the points, which lie on it.

A line $l \equiv \langle a : b : c \rangle$ is **central** or **standard** precisely when it passes through the **origin** $O \equiv [0, 0]$. This is equivalent to the condition that $c = 0$.

Example 3.3 In the rational or decimal number fields, Figure 3.3 shows the line $\langle 1 : 3 : -11 \rangle$, which passes through the points $[2, 3]$ and $[5, 2]$.

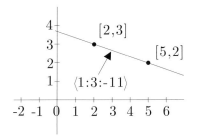

Figure 3.3: The line $\langle 1 : 3 : -11 \rangle$ ◇

Example 3.4 In the field $\mathbb{F}_{11}$, Figure 3.4 shows the line $\langle 10 : 5 : 1 \rangle$, which passes through the points $[3, 7]$ and $[6, 1]$.

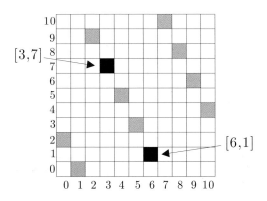

Figure 3.4: The line $\langle 10 : 5 : 1 \rangle$ in $\mathbb{F}_{11}$ ◇

3.2 Collinear points and concurrent lines

Theorem 2 (Line through two points) For any two distinct points A_1 and A_2, there is a unique line $l \equiv A_1 A_2$ passing through them both. If $A_1 \equiv [x_1, y_1]$ and $A_2 \equiv [x_2, y_2]$ then

$$l = A_1 A_2 = \langle y_1 - y_2 : x_2 - x_1 : x_1 y_2 - x_2 y_1 \rangle.$$

Proof. If $A_1 \equiv [x_1, y_1]$ and $A_2 \equiv [x_2, y_2]$ are distinct points, then

$$l \equiv \langle y_1 - y_2 : x_2 - x_1 : x_1 y_2 - x_2 y_1 \rangle$$

passes through them both, since

$$(y_1 - y_2) x_1 + (x_2 - x_1) y_1 + x_1 y_2 - x_2 y_1 = 0$$
$$(y_1 - y_2) x_2 + (x_2 - x_1) y_2 + x_1 y_2 - x_2 y_1 = 0.$$

On the other hand if $m \equiv \langle a : b : c \rangle$ is a line passing through both A_1 and A_2 then

$$ax_1 + by_1 + c = 0$$
$$ax_2 + by_2 + c = 0.$$

Take the difference of these two equations to get

$$a(x_2 - x_1) + b(y_2 - y_1) = 0$$

so that

$$a : b = y_1 - y_2 : x_2 - x_1.$$

Thus

$$m = \langle y_1 - y_2 : x_2 - x_1 : d \rangle$$

for some number d, and since A_1 lies on m,

$$(y_1 - y_2) x_1 + (x_2 - x_1) y_1 + d = 0.$$

Conclude that

$$d = x_1 y_2 - x_2 y_1$$

so that

$$m = \langle y_1 - y_2 : x_2 - x_1 : x_1 y_2 - x_2 y_1 \rangle. \blacksquare$$

Definition Three or more points which lie on a common line are **collinear**. Three or more lines which pass through a common point are **concurrent**.

Theorem 3 (Collinear points) The points $[x_1, y_1]$, $[x_2, y_2]$ and $[x_3, y_3]$ are collinear precisely when

$$x_1 y_2 - x_1 y_3 + x_2 y_3 - x_3 y_2 + x_3 y_1 - x_2 y_1 = 0.$$

Proof. If all three points are identical then the identity is automatic. Otherwise assume by symmetry that $[x_1, y_1] \neq [x_2, y_2]$. From the previous theorem, $[x_3, y_3]$ lies on the unique line passing through $[x_1, y_1]$ and $[x_2, y_2]$ precisely when

$$(y_1 - y_2) x_3 + (x_2 - x_1) y_3 + x_1 y_2 - x_2 y_1 = 0.$$

This is the required condition. ∎

Recall that

$$x_1 y_2 - x_1 y_3 + x_2 y_3 - x_3 y_2 + x_3 y_1 - x_2 y_1 = \begin{vmatrix} x_1 & y_1 & 1 \\ x_2 & y_2 & 1 \\ x_3 & y_3 & 1 \end{vmatrix} = [x_1 y_2]_3^- .$$

Theorem 4 (Concurrent lines) If the lines $\langle a_1 : b_1 : c_1 \rangle$, $\langle a_2 : b_2 : c_2 \rangle$ and $\langle a_3 : b_3 : c_3 \rangle$ are concurrent then

$$a_1 b_2 c_3 - a_1 b_3 c_2 + a_2 b_3 c_1 - a_3 b_2 c_1 + a_3 b_1 c_2 - a_2 b_1 c_3 = 0.$$

Proof. If the three lines pass through the point $[x, y]$ then $[x, y, 1]$ is a non-zero solution to the homogeneous linear system

$$a_1 x + b_1 y + c_1 z = 0$$
$$a_2 x + b_2 y + c_2 z = 0$$
$$a_3 x + b_3 y + c_3 z = 0$$

so that by Section 2.4,

$$\begin{vmatrix} a_1 & b_1 & c_1 \\ a_2 & b_2 & c_2 \\ a_3 & b_3 & c_3 \end{vmatrix} = a_1 b_2 c_3 - a_1 b_3 c_2 + a_2 b_3 c_1 - a_3 b_2 c_1 + a_3 b_1 c_2 - a_2 b_1 c_3 = 0. \; \blacksquare$$

Exercise 3.1 Show that the converse does not hold. ◇

Exercise 3.2 Show that in the field $\mathbb{F}_p$ there are exactly $p + 1$ lines passing through every point, and that every line passes through exactly p points. ◇

Exercise 3.3 Show that if there are null lines, then there are exactly two null lines passing through any given point. ◇

3.3 Parallel and perpendicular lines

Definition The lines $l_1 \equiv \langle a_1 : b_1 : c_1 \rangle$ and $l_2 \equiv \langle a_2 : b_2 : c_2 \rangle$ are **parallel** precisely when

$$a_1 b_2 - a_2 b_1 = 0$$

or equivalently when $a_1 : b_1 = a_2 : b_2$.

Theorem 5 (Point on two lines) If the lines l_1 and l_2 are not parallel, then there is a unique point $A \equiv l_1 l_2$ which lies on them both. If $l_1 \equiv \langle a_1 : b_1 : c_1 \rangle$ and $l_2 \equiv \langle a_2 : b_2 : c_2 \rangle$ then

$$A \equiv l_1 l_2 = \left[\frac{b_1 c_2 - b_2 c_1}{a_1 b_2 - a_2 b_1}, \frac{c_1 a_2 - c_2 a_1}{a_1 b_2 - a_2 b_1} \right].$$

Proof. The point $[x, y]$ lies on $l_1 \equiv \langle a_1 : b_1 : c_1 \rangle$ and $l_2 \equiv \langle a_2 : b_2 : c_2 \rangle$ precisely when

$$a_1 x + b_1 y + c_1 = 0$$
$$a_2 x + b_2 y + c_2 = 0.$$

Since l_1 and l_2 are not parallel, $a_1 b_2 - a_2 b_1 \neq 0$, so as in Section 2.4 the unique solution to this system of equations is

$$x = \frac{b_1 c_2 - b_2 c_1}{a_1 b_2 - a_2 b_1}$$
$$y = \frac{c_1 a_2 - c_2 a_1}{a_1 b_2 - a_2 b_1}. \quad \blacksquare$$

The point $A \equiv l_1 l_2 = l_2 l_1$ is the **intersection** of the two lines l_1 and l_2. Alternatively, the lines l_1 and l_2 **intersect** at $A \equiv l_1 l_2$.

Now comes the *single most important definition in all of geometry*. It *colours* the entire subject. In a subsequent volume, the geometry presented here in this book, based on this definition, will be called *blue geometry*, and other colours also appear.

Definition The lines $l_1 \equiv \langle a_1 : b_1 : c_1 \rangle$ and $l_2 \equiv \langle a_2 : b_2 : c_2 \rangle$ are **perpendicular** precisely when

$$a_1 a_2 + b_1 b_2 = 0$$

or equivalently when $a_1 : b_1 = -b_2 : a_2$.

Exercise 3.4 Show that if the lines l_1 and l_2 are parallel, with the line l_3 parallel (respectively perpendicular) to l_1, then l_3 is parallel (respectively perpendicular) to l_2.
◇

Exercise 3.5 Show that if the lines l_1 and l_2 are perpendicular, and the lines l_2 and l_3 are perpendicular, then l_1 and l_3 are parallel. ⋄

Exercise 3.6 Show that if $-1 = i^2$ then any two null lines of the form $\langle 1 : i : d \rangle$ and $\langle 1 : i : e \rangle$ are both parallel and perpendicular, as are any two null lines of the form $\langle 1 : -i : d \rangle$ and $\langle 1 : -i : e \rangle$. ⋄

Exercise 3.7 Show that if two lines l_1 and l_2 are both parallel and perpendicular, then they are both null lines. ⋄

3.4 Parallels and altitudes

Theorem 6 (Parallel to a line) For any point $A \equiv [x, y]$ and any line $l \equiv \langle a : b : c \rangle$ there is a unique line k, called the **parallel through A to l,** which passes through A and is parallel to l, namely

$$k = \langle a : b : -ax - by \rangle.$$

Proof. If $l \equiv \langle a : b : c \rangle$ then any line k parallel to l must have the form $k \equiv \langle a : b : d \rangle$ for some number d, passing through $A \equiv [x, y]$ precisely when

$$ax + by + d = 0.$$

Thus such a line k is uniquely determined, and has the form

$$k = \langle a : b : -ax - by \rangle. \quad \blacksquare$$

Theorem 7 (Altitude to a line) For any point $A \equiv [x, y]$ and any line $l \equiv \langle a : b : c \rangle$ there is a unique line n, called the **altitude from A to l,** which passes through A and is perpendicular to l, namely

$$n = \langle -b : a : bx - ay \rangle.$$

Proof. If $l \equiv \langle a : b : c \rangle$ then any line n perpendicular to l must have the form $n \equiv \langle -b : a : d \rangle$ for some number d, passing through $A \equiv [x, y]$ precisely when

$$-bx + ay + d = 0$$

Thus such a line n is uniquely determined, and has the form

$$n = \langle -b : a : bx - ay \rangle. \quad \blacksquare$$

Exercise 3.8 Show that for any points $A \equiv [x, y]$, $A_1 \equiv [x_1, y_1]$ and $A_2 \equiv [x_2, y_2]$ with A_1 and A_2 distinct, the parallel through A to $A_1 A_2$ is the line

$$k \equiv \langle y_1 - y_2 : x_2 - x_1 : (y_2 - y_1)\, x + (x_1 - x_2)\, y \rangle. \quad \diamond$$

Exercise 3.9 Show that for any points $A \equiv [x, y]$, $A_1 \equiv [x_1, y_1]$ and $A_2 \equiv [x_2, y_2]$ with A_1 and A_2 distinct, the altitude from A to $A_1 A_2$ is the line

$$n \equiv \langle x_1 - x_2 : y_1 - y_2 : (x_2 - x_1)\, x + (y_2 - y_1)\, y \rangle. \quad \diamond$$

Theorem 8 (Foot of an altitude) For any point $A \equiv [x, y]$ and any non-null line $l \equiv \langle a : b : c \rangle$, the altitude n from A to l intersects l at the point

$$F \equiv \left[\frac{b^2 x - aby - ac}{a^2 + b^2}, \frac{abx + a^2 y - bc}{a^2 + b^2} \right].$$

Proof. By the Altitude to a line theorem, the altitude from $A \equiv [x, y]$ to $l \equiv \langle a : b : c \rangle$ is $n \equiv \langle -b : a : bx - ay \rangle$. These two lines are not parallel since by assumption $a^2 + b^2 \neq 0$. By the Point on two lines theorem (page 40)

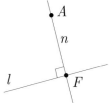

$$F \equiv nl = \left[\frac{b^2 x - aby - ac}{a^2 + b^2}, \frac{-abx + a^2 y - bc}{a^2 + b^2} \right]. \quad \blacksquare$$

The intersection F of the altitude n from A to l with the line l is the **foot** of the altitude. Note that if l is a null line then the altitude n from a point A to l is parallel to l, so there is no foot of the altitude.

Example 3.5 In the field $\mathbb{F}_{11}$, the altitude from $A \equiv [7, 6]$ to the line $l \equiv \langle 10 : 5 : 1 \rangle$ (gray boxes) is $n \equiv \langle 9 : 4 : 1 \rangle$ (black circles) and the foot of the altitude is $F \equiv [2, 9]$, as shown in Figure 3.5.

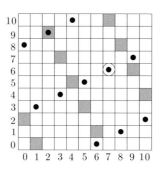

Figure 3.5: Altitude to a line in $\mathbb{F}_{11}$ $\diamond$

Example 3.6 In the field $\mathbb{F}_{13}$, the altitude from $A \equiv [5,2]$ to the null line $l \equiv \langle 3:2:1 \rangle$ (gray boxes) is the null line $n \equiv \langle 6:4:1 \rangle$ (black circles), as shown in Figure 3.6. These two lines are both perpendicular and parallel.

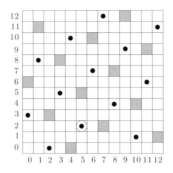

Figure 3.6: Altitude to a null line in $\mathbb{F}_{13}$ ◇

Exercise 3.10 Show that the foot $F \equiv [x_0, y_0]$ of the altitude from $A \equiv [x, y]$ to the non-null line passing through $[x_1, y_1]$ and $[x_2, y_2]$ has coordinates

$$x_0 \equiv \frac{(x_2 - x_1)^2 x - (y_1 - y_2)(x_2 - x_1) y - (y_1 - y_2)(x_1 y_2 - x_2 y_1)}{(x_2 - x_1)^2 + (y_1 - y_2)^2}$$

$$y_0 \equiv \frac{(y_1 - y_2)^2 y - (y_1 - y_2)(x_2 - x_1) x - (x_2 - x_1)(x_1 y_2 - x_2 y_1)}{(x_2 - x_1)^2 + (y_1 - y_2)^2}. \quad ◇$$

3.5 Sides, vertices and triangles

The following definitions are more precise than usual.

Definition A **side** $\overline{A_1 A_2} \equiv \{A_1, A_2\}$ is a set with A_1 and A_2 points. The **line** of the side $\overline{A_1 A_2}$ is the line $A_1 A_2$. The side $\overline{A_1 A_2}$ is a **null side** precisely when $A_1 A_2$ is a null line.

Note that A_1 and A_2 are automatically distinct by the convention that repetitions are not allowed in a set.

Two sides $\overline{A_1 A_2}$ and $\overline{A_3 A_4}$ are **parallel** (respectively **perpendicular**) precisely when $A_1 A_2$ is parallel (respectively perpendicular) to $A_3 A_4$.

Definition A **vertex** $\overline{l_1 l_2} \equiv \{l_1, l_2\}$ is a set with l_1 and l_2 intersecting lines. The **point** of the vertex $\overline{l_1 l_2}$ is the point $l_1 l_2$. The vertex $\overline{l_1 l_2}$ is a **null vertex** precisely when l_1 or l_2 is a null line, and is a **right vertex** precisely when l_1 and l_2 are perpendicular.

Definition A **triangle** $\overline{A_1A_2A_3} \equiv \{A_1, A_2, A_3\}$ is a set with A_1, A_2 and A_3 non-collinear points.

The points A_1, A_2 and A_3 are the **points** of the triangle $\overline{A_1A_2A_3}$, and the lines $l_1 \equiv A_2A_3$, $l_2 \equiv A_1A_3$ and $l_3 \equiv A_1A_2$ are the **lines** of the triangle. The sides $\overline{A_1A_2}$, $\overline{A_2A_3}$ and $\overline{A_1A_3}$ are the **sides** of the triangle, and the vertices $\overline{l_1l_2}$, $\overline{l_2l_3}$ and $\overline{l_1l_3}$ are the **vertices** of the triangle.

The point A_1 is **opposite** the side $\overline{A_2A_3}$, and so on, and the line l_1 is **opposite** the vertex $\overline{l_2l_3}$, and so on. With this terminology a triangle has *exactly three points*, necessarily non-collinear, and *exactly three lines*, necessarily non-concurrent. A triangle also has exactly three sides, and exactly three vertices.

Definition A triangle $\overline{A_1A_2A_3}$ is a **right triangle** precisely when it has a right vertex. A triangle $\overline{A_1A_2A_3}$ is a **null triangle** precisely when one or more of its lines is a null line.

In the rational or decimal number fields, there are no null triangles, since there are no null lines.

Example 3.7 In the field $\mathbb{F}_{13}$ the points $A_1 \equiv [2, 8]$, $A_2 \equiv [9, 9]$ and $A_3 \equiv [10, 0]$ form a triangle $\overline{A_1A_2A_3}$ with lines $l_1 \equiv A_2A_3 = \langle 9 : 1 : 1 \rangle$ (gray boxes), $l_2 \equiv A_1A_3 = \langle 9 : 9 : 1 \rangle$ (open circles) and $l_3 \equiv A_1A_2 = \langle 7 : 3 : 1 \rangle$ (solid circles) shown in Figure 3.7.

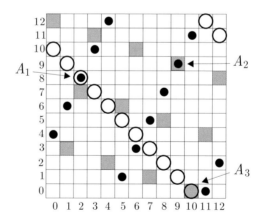

Figure 3.7: A triangle in $\mathbb{F}_{13}$ ◇

Exercise 3.11 Show that a triangle has at most one right vertex. ◇

Exercise 3.12 Show that it is impossible for a triangle to have three null lines. ◇

Exercise 3.13 (Harder) How many triangles are there over $\mathbb{F}_p$? How many of these are null triangles? ◇

3.6 Quadrilaterals

Definition A **quadrilateral** $\overline{A_1 A_2 A_3 A_4}$ is a list $[A_1, A_2, A_3, A_4]$ of four distinct points, no three of which are collinear, with the conventions that

$$\overline{A_1 A_2 A_3 A_4} \equiv \overline{A_2 A_3 A_4 A_1} \qquad \text{and} \qquad \overline{A_1 A_2 A_3 A_4} \equiv \overline{A_4 A_3 A_2 A_1}.$$

The points A_1, A_2, A_3 and A_4 are the **points** of the quadrilateral $\overline{A_1 A_2 A_3 A_4}$, and the lines $l_{12} \equiv A_1 A_2$, $l_{23} \equiv A_2 A_3$, $l_{34} \equiv A_3 A_4$ and $l_{14} \equiv A_1 A_4$ are the **lines** of the quadrilateral. The lines $l_{13} \equiv A_1 A_3$ and $l_{24} \equiv A_2 A_4$ are the **diagonal lines** (or just **diagonals**) of the quadrilateral.

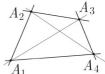

The sides $\overline{A_1 A_2}$, $\overline{A_2 A_3}$, $\overline{A_3 A_4}$ and $\overline{A_1 A_4}$ are the **sides** of the quadrilateral, and the vertices $\overline{l_{12} l_{23}}$, $\overline{l_{23} l_{34}}$, $\overline{l_{34} l_{14}}$ and $\overline{l_{14} l_{12}}$ are the **vertices** of the quadrilateral. The sides $\overline{A_1 A_3}$ and $\overline{A_2 A_4}$ are the **diagonal sides** of the quadrilateral.

Two vertices which contain a common line are **adjacent**, otherwise vertices are **opposite**. Two sides which contain a common point are **adjacent**, otherwise sides are **opposite**.

Note that the notation for quadrilaterals is different than for triangles. These notions generalize in an obvious way to defining n-**gons** $\overline{A_1 A_2 \cdots A_n}$, except that only any three *consecutive* points are required to be non-collinear.

A **parallelogram** is a quadrilateral $\overline{A_1 A_2 A_3 A_4}$ with the property that both pairs of opposite sides are parallel, so that $\overline{A_1 A_2}$ and $\overline{A_3 A_4}$ are parallel, and $\overline{A_2 A_3}$ and $\overline{A_1 A_4}$ are parallel, as in Figure 3.8. A **rectangle** is a quadrilateral with the property that any pair of adjacent sides are perpendicular. Every rectangle is a parallelogram.

A **rhombus** is a parallelogram with the property that the diagonals are perpendicular, as in the second parallelogram of Figure 3.8.

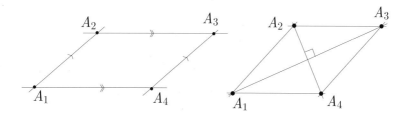

Figure 3.8: Parallelogram and rhombus

Exercise 3.14 Give an example where the diagonals of a quadrilateral are parallel. ◇

3.7   Affine combinations

Definition For any points $A_1 \equiv [x_1, y_1]$ and $A_2 \equiv [x_2, y_2]$ and any two numbers λ_1 and λ_2 satisfying $\lambda_1 + \lambda_2 = 1$, the **affine combination** $\lambda_1 A_1 + \lambda_2 A_2$ is the point

$$\lambda_1 A_1 + \lambda_2 A_2 \equiv [\lambda_1 x_1 + \lambda_2 x_2, \lambda_1 y_1 + \lambda_2 y_2].$$

Theorem 9 (Affine combination) Every point lying on the line $A_1 A_2$ is a unique affine combination $\lambda_1 A_1 + \lambda_2 A_2$ for some numbers λ_1 and λ_2 with $\lambda_1 + \lambda_2 = 1$, and conversely any affine combination of this form lies on $A_1 A_2$.

Proof. Suppose that $A_1 \equiv [x_1, y_1]$ and $A_2 \equiv [x_2, y_2]$ are distinct, and that $A_3 \equiv \lambda_1 A_1 + \lambda_2 A_2$ for some numbers λ_1 and λ_2 satisfying $\lambda_1 + \lambda_2 = 1$. Then the identity

$$(y_1 - y_2)(\lambda_1 x_1 + \lambda_2 x_2) + (x_2 - x_1)(\lambda_1 y_1 + \lambda_2 y_2) + x_1 y_2 - x_2 y_1$$
$$= (\lambda_1 + \lambda_2 - 1)(x_2 y_1 - x_1 y_2)$$

together with the Line through two points theorem (page 38) shows that A_3 lies on $A_1 A_2$.

Conversely suppose that $A \equiv [x, y]$ lies on $A_1 A_2$, so that

$$(y_1 - y_2) x + (x_2 - x_1) y + x_1 y_2 - x_2 y_1 = 0. \qquad (3.1)$$

Since A_1 and A_2 are distinct, one of $(x_2 - x_1)$ and $(y_2 - y_1)$ are non-zero. Suppose without loss of generality that $x_2 - x_1 \neq 0$. Then set

$$\lambda \equiv \frac{x - x_2}{x_1 - x_2}$$

so that

$$x = \lambda x_1 + (1 - \lambda) x_2.$$

Substitute this value of x into (3.1) and factor, to obtain

$$(y - \lambda y_1 - (1 - \lambda) y_2)(x_2 - x_1) = 0.$$

Thus

$$y = \lambda y_1 + (1 - \lambda) y_2$$

and so

$$A = \lambda A_1 + (1 - \lambda) A_2.$$

For the uniqueness, if

$$\lambda A_1 + (1 - \lambda) A_2 = \mu A_1 + (1 - \mu) A_2$$

then the difference between the left and right hand sides yields

$$(\lambda - \mu)(x_1 - x_2) = 0$$
$$(\lambda - \mu)(y_1 - y_2) = 0.$$

Since by assumption $A_1 \neq A_2$, you may conclude that $\lambda = \mu$. ∎

Example 3.8 Figure 3.9 shows the affine combination $(1/3) A_1 + (2/3) A_2$ for two points A_1, A_2 in the rational or decimal number fields.

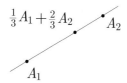

Figure 3.9: An affine combination over the rationals ◇

Definition For distinct points $A_1 \equiv [x_1, y_1]$ and $A_2 \equiv [x_2, y_2]$, the point

$$M \equiv \frac{1}{2} A_1 + \frac{1}{2} A_2 = \left[\frac{x_1 + x_2}{2}, \frac{y_1 + y_2}{2} \right]$$

is the **midpoint** of the side $\overline{A_1 A_2}$.

In the rational or decimal number fields, the midpoint of a side will often be illustrated by small bars (perhaps more than one).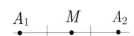

Exercise 3.15 Suppose that the numbers α_1, α_2 and α_3 are each distinct from 1, and satisfy $\alpha_1 + \alpha_2 + \alpha_3 = 1$. Show that for any three points A_1, A_2 and A_3

$$\alpha_1 A_1 + (1 - \alpha_1) \left(\frac{\alpha_2}{1 - \alpha_1} A_2 + \frac{\alpha_3}{1 - \alpha_1} A_3 \right)$$
$$= \alpha_2 A_2 + (1 - \alpha_2) \left(\frac{\alpha_3}{1 - \alpha_2} A_3 + \frac{\alpha_1}{1 - \alpha_2} A_1 \right)$$
$$= \alpha_3 A_3 + (1 - \alpha_3) \left(\frac{\alpha_1}{1 - \alpha_3} A_1 + \frac{\alpha_2}{1 - \alpha_3} A_2 \right)$$

which allows an unambiguous meaning to the expression $\alpha_1 A_1 + \alpha_2 A_2 + \alpha_3 A_3$. ◇

A **median** of a triangle $\overline{A_1 A_2 A_3}$ is a line m passing through a point of the triangle and the midpoint of the opposite side.

Exercise 3.16 Show that if the field has characteristic three, then all the medians are parallel, while otherwise they intersect at a point G, called the **centroid** of the triangle, as in Figure 3.10. Furthermore if $A_1 \equiv [x_1, y_1]$, $A_2 \equiv [x_2, y_2]$ and $A_3 \equiv [x_3, y_3]$ then

$$G = \frac{1}{3}A_1 + \frac{1}{3}A_2 + \frac{1}{3}A_3 = \left[\frac{x_1 + x_2 + x_3}{3}, \frac{y_1 + y_2 + y_3}{3}\right].$$

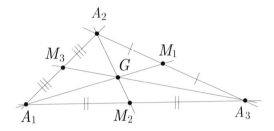

Figure 3.10: Medians and centroid ◇

Theorem 10 (Thales' theorem) Suppose that A_1, A_2 and A_3 are three distinct points. For any number $\lambda \neq 0$ set

$$B_2 \equiv (1 - \lambda) A_1 + \lambda A_2$$
$$B_3 \equiv (1 - \lambda) A_1 + \lambda A_3.$$

Then $B_2 B_3$ is parallel to $A_2 A_3$.

Proof. Since A_2 and A_3 are distinct, so are B_2 and B_3.
If $A_1 \equiv [x_1, y_1]$, $A_2 \equiv [x_2, y_2]$ and $A_3 \equiv [x_3, y_3]$ then

$$B_2 = [(1 - \lambda) x_1 + \lambda x_2, (1 - \lambda) y_1 + \lambda y_2]$$
$$B_3 = [(1 - \lambda) x_1 + \lambda x_3, (1 - \lambda) y_1 + \lambda y_3].$$

Then by the Line through two points theorem (page 38)

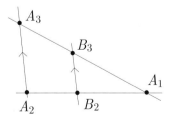

$$A_2 A_3 = \langle y_2 - y_3 : x_3 - x_2 : x_2 y_3 - x_3 y_2 \rangle$$
$$B_2 B_3 = \langle \lambda (y_2 - y_3) : \lambda (x_3 - x_2) : c \rangle$$

for some number c. These two lines are parallel. ∎

- Page 128: In Exercise 10.11 remove the second statement

- Page 134: In Theorem 74 insert the condition that $\overline{A_1A_2A_3}$ is a non-null triangle

- Page 171: First diagram has too many points (some of quadrance 8)

- Page 189: In Example 17.3, insert condition 'cyclic' in front of 'quadrilateral'

- Page 195: 'Since M_3P_3 is a diagonal...' should be 'Since M_3P_3 is a diameter...'

- Page 266: Figure should have point labelled A rather than P

- Page 271: Figure should have points labelled A and A_{12} rather than P and P_{12}

- Page 283 (top): The equation should be

$$\left(s - \frac{Q+A}{4A}\right)^2 = \frac{Q}{4A}.$$

Errata will also be posted at http://wildegg.com.

Errata to Divine Proportions

- Page 3: Line 8 should be

$$\theta_1 \approx 34.05° \qquad \theta_2 \approx 101.54° \qquad \theta_3 \approx 44.42°.$$

- Page 22: $(1 - 1/2 + 1/3 - 1/4 + \cdots)^2$ should be $(1 - 1/3 + 1/5 - 1/7 + \cdots)^2$

- Page 34 (top): The first two equations should end in $4(p_1 - p_2)^2 q_2$ instead of $4(p_1 - p_2)^2 q_1$, and the third equation should have a minus sign instead of a plus sign, to read

$$(p_1 - p_2)^4 - 2(p_1 - p_2)^2 (q_1 + q_2) + (q_1 - q_2)^2 = 0.$$

- Page 34 (bottom): '$p_1 = p_2$ or $p_1 - p_2 = \pm 2q$,' should be '$p_1 = p_2$ or $(p_1 - p_2)^2 = 4q$.'

- Page 46: In line after (3.1) 'are' should be 'is'

- Page 51 (top): 'associate' should be 'associated'

- Page 52: Figure caption should be 'Successive...'

- Page 54: In Exercise 4.4 l_1 might also be equal to l.

- Page 69: In Exercise 5.17, insert condition 'distinct' before 'numbers'

- Page 72: Exercise 7.9 is incorrect

- Page 75 Line 8: 'non-parallel' should be 'non-perpendicular'

- Page 96: Line 11 should read (25/34)/12, (100/221)/8, (25/26)/17, 25/442

Theorem 11 (Parallelogram center) If $\overline{A_1 A_2 A_3 A_4}$ is a parallelogram, then the midpoints of the diagonal sides $\overline{A_1 A_3}$ and $\overline{A_2 A_4}$ coincide.

Proof. Suppose that $A_1 \equiv [x_1, y_1]$, $A_2 \equiv [x_2, y_2]$, $A_3 \equiv [x_3, y_3]$ and $A_4 \equiv [x_4, y_4]$. Then since

$$A_1 A_2 = \langle y_1 - y_2 : x_2 - x_1 : x_1 y_2 - x_2 y_1 \rangle$$
$$A_3 A_4 = \langle y_3 - y_4 : x_4 - x_3 : x_3 y_4 - x_4 y_3 \rangle$$

are parallel, it follows that

$$(y_1 - y_2)(x_4 - x_3) - (y_3 - y_4)(x_2 - x_1) = 0. \tag{3.2}$$

Similarly, since $A_2 A_3$ and $A_1 A_4$ are parallel,

$$(y_2 - y_3)(x_1 - x_4) - (y_4 - y_1)(x_3 - x_2) = 0. \tag{3.3}$$

Write (3.2) and (3.3) as a pair of linear equations in x_4 and y_4

$$(y_1 - y_2)x_4 + (x_2 - x_1)y_4 - (y_1 - y_2)x_3 - (x_2 - x_1)y_3 = 0 \tag{3.4}$$
$$(y_3 - y_2)x_4 + (x_2 - x_3)y_4 + (x_3 - x_2)y_1 + (y_2 - y_3)x_1 = 0. \tag{3.5}$$

The points A_1, A_2 and A_3 are not collinear, so by the Collinear points theorem (page 39)

$$\begin{vmatrix} y_1 - y_2 & x_2 - x_1 \\ y_3 - y_2 & x_2 - x_3 \end{vmatrix} = -(x_1 y_2 - x_1 y_3 + x_2 y_3 - x_3 y_2 + x_3 y_1 - x_2 y_1) \neq 0.$$

Solve the equations (3.4) and (3.5) to get

$$x_4 = x_1 - x_2 + x_3$$
$$y_4 = y_1 - y_2 + y_3$$

so that

$$\frac{1}{2}A_1 + \frac{1}{2}A_3 = \frac{1}{2}A_2 + \frac{1}{2}A_4. \quad \blacksquare$$

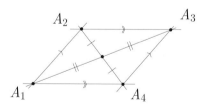

Note in particular that the two diagonals of a parallelogram are not parallel, as they intersect at their common midpoint. This point is the **center** of the parallelogram.

Exercise 3.17 If $\overline{A_1 A_2 A_3 A_4}$ is a parallelogram and M_{12}, M_{23}, M_{34} and M_{14} are the midpoints of the sides $\overline{A_1 A_2}, \overline{A_2 A_3}, \overline{A_3 A_4}$ and $\overline{A_1 A_4}$ respectively, then show that $\overline{M_{12} M_{23} M_{34} M_{14}}$ is a parallelogram, with the same center as $\overline{A_1 A_2 A_3 A_4}$. ◇

3.8 Perpendicular bisectors

Definition The **perpendicular bisector** of the side $\overline{A_1 A_2}$ is the altitude from the midpoint M of $\overline{A_1 A_2}$ to the line $A_1 A_2$.

Theorem 12 (Perpendicular bisector) If $A_1 \equiv [x_1, y_1]$ and $A_2 \equiv [x_2, y_2]$ are distinct points then the side $\overline{A_1 A_2}$ has perpendicular bisector

$$p \equiv \left\langle x_1 - x_2 : y_1 - y_2 : \frac{x_2^2 - x_1^2 + y_2^2 - y_1^2}{2} \right\rangle.$$

Proof. Since

$$A_1 A_2 = \left\langle y_1 - y_2 : x_2 - x_1 : x_1 y_2 - x_2 y_1 \right\rangle$$

any line perpendicular to $A_1 A_2$ has the form

$$p \equiv \left\langle x_1 - x_2 : y_1 - y_2 : c \right\rangle$$

for some number c. Then p passes through the midpoint

$$M \equiv \left[\frac{x_1 + x_2}{2}, \frac{y_1 + y_2}{2} \right]$$

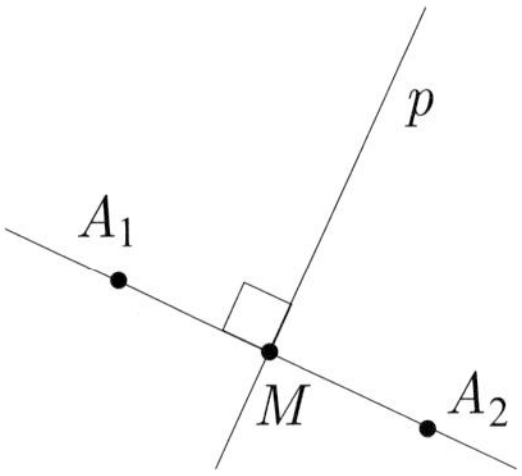

of $\overline{A_1 A_2}$ precisely when

$$\frac{(x_1 - x_2)(x_1 + x_2)}{2} + \frac{(y_1 - y_2)(y_1 + y_2)}{2} + c = 0.$$

Thus

$$c = \frac{x_2^2 - x_1^2 + y_2^2 - y_1^2}{2}$$

and so

$$p = \left\langle x_1 - x_2 : y_1 - y_2 : \frac{x_2^2 - x_1^2 + y_2^2 - y_1^2}{2} \right\rangle. \quad \blacksquare$$

4

Reflections

This chapter introduces affine transformations, and in particular the *reflections in lines* and the associate *lineations,* which reflect lines in lines. These are the most important symmetries in planar geometry. Formulas for reflections and lineations are derived. The results are not all easy, and they are too often taken for granted in courses on geometry. Beginners might skim the proofs of this chapter and return to them later.

4.1 Affine transformations

Definition A **transformation** is a function which inputs and outputs points.

Small Greek letters will generally be used for transformations. The effect of the transformation τ on the point A is denoted $\tau(A)$. The transformation ι defined by $\iota(A) \equiv A$ for any point A is the **identity**. The convention for composition is

$$(\tau_2 \circ \tau_1)(A) \equiv (\tau_2\tau_1)(A) \equiv \tau_2(\tau_1(A)).$$

A transformation τ is **invertible** precisely when there is a transformation υ such that $\tau\upsilon = \upsilon\tau = \iota$. Then $\upsilon \equiv \tau^{-1}$ is the **inverse** of τ. A transformation τ **fixes** a point A precisely when $\tau(A) = A$.

Definition A transformation τ is **affine** precisely when for any points A_1 and A_2, and any two numbers λ_1 and λ_2 satisfying $\lambda_1 + \lambda_2 = 1$,

$$\tau(\lambda_1 A_1 + \lambda_2 A_2) = \lambda_1 \tau(A_1) + \lambda_2 \tau(A_2).$$

Definition For a point A define ρ_A, the **rotation in** A, to be the transformation defined by

$$\rho_A (B) \equiv 2A + (-1) B.$$

Then $\rho_A (B)$ lies on AB by the Affine combination theorem (page 46), and $A = (1/2) B + (1/2) \rho_A (B)$, so that A is the midpoint of $\overline{B \rho_A (B)}$.

Exercise 4.1 Show that for any point A, the rotation ρ_A is an invertible affine transformation, with $\rho_A^{-1} = \rho_A$. $\diamond$

Exercise 4.2 For any two points A_1 and A_2 define the successive rotations $A_3 \equiv \rho_{A_2} (A_1)$, $A_4 \equiv \rho_{A_3} (A_2)$ and so on, as well as $A_0 \equiv \rho_{A_1} (A_2)$, $A_{-1} \equiv \rho_{A_0} (A_1)$ and so on. Show that for any integers k and l, $\rho_{A_k} (A_l) = A_{2k-l}$.

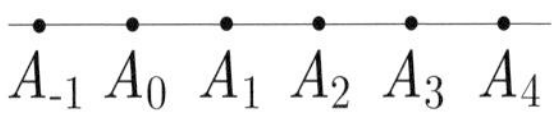

$$A_{-1}\ A_0\ A_1\ A_2\ A_3\ A_4$$

Figure 4.1: Succesive rotations in points $\diamond$

Definition If l is a non-null line and F the foot of the altitude from a point A to l, then the transformation that sends A to $B \equiv \rho_F (A)$ is the **reflection in the line l** and is denoted σ_l.

Theorem 13 (Reflection of a point in a line) If $l \equiv \langle a : b : c \rangle$ is a non-null line and $A \equiv [x, y]$, then

$$\sigma_l (A) = \left[\frac{(b^2 - a^2) x - 2aby - 2ac}{a^2 + b^2}, \frac{-2abx + (a^2 - b^2) y - 2bc}{a^2 + b^2} \right].$$

Proof. The foot F of the altitude from $A \equiv [x, y]$ to $l \equiv \langle a : b : c \rangle$ is, by the Foot of an altitude theorem (page 42),

$$F = \left[\frac{b^2 x - aby - ac}{a^2 + b^2}, \frac{-abx + a^2 y - bc}{a^2 + b^2} \right].$$

By definition $\sigma_l (A) \equiv \sigma_F (A) \equiv 2F + (-1) A$ so that

$$\sigma_l (A) = \left[\frac{(b^2 - a^2) x - 2aby - 2ac}{a^2 + b^2}, \frac{-2abx + (a^2 - b^2) y - 2bc}{a^2 + b^2} \right]. \qquad \blacksquare$$

Exercise 4.3 Show that the reflection σ_l in a non-null line l is an invertible affine transformation, with $\sigma_l^{-1} = \sigma_l$. ◇

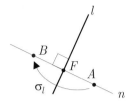

Figure 4.2: Reflection of a point in a line ◇

4.2 Lineations and reflection sequences

Definition A **lineation** is a function which inputs and outputs lines.

If τ is an invertible affine transformation, then define the **associated lineation** Σ by the rule
$$\Sigma(A_1 A_2) \equiv \tau(A_1)\,\tau(A_2).$$
By the Affine combination theorem (page 46), this is well defined.

Theorem 14 (Rotation of a line in a point) For any point $A \equiv [x, y]$, the rotation ρ_A has associated lineation Σ_A given by
$$\Sigma_A(\langle a : b : c\rangle) = \langle a : b : -2xa - 2yb - c\rangle. \quad ◇$$

Proof. Suppose that $A_1 \equiv [x_1, y_1]$ and $A_2 \equiv [x_2, y_2]$ are distinct points, so that by the Line through two points theorem (page 38),
$$A_1 A_2 = \langle y_1 - y_2 : x_2 - x_1 : x_1 y_2 - x_2 y_1\rangle = \langle a : b : c\rangle.$$
By the definition of ρ_A
$$\begin{aligned}
\rho_A(A_1) &= 2A + (-1)A_1 = [2x - x_1, 2y - y_1] \\
\rho_A(A_2) &= 2A + (-1)A_2 = [2x - x_2, 2y - y_2].
\end{aligned}$$
Then again by the Line through two points theorem,
$$\begin{aligned}
\rho_A(A_1)\rho_A(A_2) &= \langle -y_1 + y_2 : -x_2 + x_1 : (2x - x_1)(2y - y_2) - (2x - x_2)(2y - y_1)\rangle \\
&= \langle -y_1 + y_2 : -x_2 + x_1 : 2x(y_1 - y_2) + 2y(x_2 - x_1) + x_1 y_2 - x_2 y_1\rangle \\
&= \langle -a : -b : 2xa + 2yb + c\rangle \\
&= \langle a : b : -2xa - 2yb - c\rangle. \quad ∎
\end{aligned}$$

Theorem 15 (Reflection of a line in a line) For any non-null line $l \equiv \langle a : b : c \rangle$, the reflection σ_l has associated lineation Σ_l given by

$$\Sigma_l\left(\langle a_1 : b_1 : c_1 \rangle\right) = \left\langle \begin{array}{c} \left(a^2 - b^2\right) a_1 + 2abb_1 : 2aba_1 - \left(a^2 - b^2\right) b_1 \\ 2aca_1 + 2bcb_1 - \left(a^2 + b^2\right) c_1 \end{array} \right\rangle .$$

Proof. Suppose $l \equiv \langle a : b : c \rangle$ is non-null, so that $a^2 + b^2 \neq 0$, and that $A_1 \equiv [x_1, y_1]$ and $A_2 \equiv [x_2, y_2]$ are distinct, with

$$A_1 A_2 = \langle y_1 - y_2 : x_2 - x_1 : x_1 y_2 - x_2 y_1 \rangle \equiv \langle a_1 : b_1 : c_1 \rangle .$$

Then by the Reflection of a point in a line theorem

$$\sigma_l\left(A_1\right) = \left[\frac{\left(b^2 - a^2\right) x_1 - 2aby_1 - 2ac}{a^2 + b^2} , \frac{-2abx_1 + \left(a^2 - b^2\right) y_1 - 2bc}{a^2 + b^2} \right]$$

$$\sigma_l\left(A_2\right) = \left[\frac{\left(b^2 - a^2\right) x_2 - 2aby_2 - 2ac}{a^2 + b^2} , \frac{-2abx_2 + \left(a^2 - b^2\right) y_2 - 2bc}{a^2 + b^2} \right] .$$

Use the Line through two points theorem and simplify to see that

$$\begin{aligned}
\Sigma_l\left(\langle a_1 : b_1 : c_1 \rangle\right) &= \sigma_l\left(A_1\right) \sigma_l\left(A_2\right) \\
&= \left\langle \begin{array}{c} \left(a^2 - b^2\right) a_1 + 2abb_1 : 2aba_1 - \left(a^2 - b^2\right) b_1 \\ 2aca_1 + 2bcb_1 - \left(a^2 + b^2\right) c_1 \end{array} \right\rangle . \quad \blacksquare
\end{aligned}$$

The line $l_2 \equiv \Sigma_l\left(l_1\right)$ is the **reflection of** l_1 **in the line** l. The lineation Σ_l is the **reflection lineation** in l.

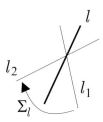

Figure 4.3: Reflection of a line in a line

Exercise 4.4 Show that $\Sigma_l\left(l_1\right) = l_1$ precisely when l_1 is perpendicular to l. ◇

Exercise 4.5 Show that $\Sigma_l^{-1} = \Sigma_l$ for any non-null line l. ◇

Exercise 4.6 Show that the formula for the reflection Σ_l in the previous theorem makes sense even if l is a null line. Show that in this case $\Sigma_l\left(l_1\right) = l$ for any line l_1. ◇

Theorem 16 (Reflection) If l_1 and l_2 are non-null lines, then

$$\sigma_{l_2}\sigma_{l_1} = \sigma_{\Sigma_{l_2}(l_1)}\sigma_{l_2}.$$

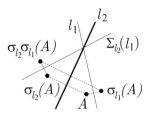

Figure 4.4: Reflection theorem

Proof. Suppose that $l_1 \equiv \langle a_1 : b_1 : c_1 \rangle$ and $l_2 \equiv \langle a_2 : b_2 : c_2 \rangle$ are non-null lines and $A \equiv [x, y]$. Then by the Reflection of a line in a line theorem, $\Sigma_{l_2}(l_1) \equiv l_3$ is

$$\left\langle \left(a_2^2 - b_2^2\right) a_1 + 2a_2b_2b_1 : 2a_2b_2a_1 - \left(a_2^2 - b_2^2\right) b_1 : 2a_2c_2a_1 + 2b_2c_2b_1 - \left(a_2^2 + b_2^2\right) c_1 \right\rangle.$$

Now use the Reflection of a point in a line theorem to show that both

$$\sigma_{l_2}\left(\sigma_{l_1}(A)\right) = \sigma_{l_2}\left(\left[\frac{\left(b_1^2 - a_1^2\right) x - 2a_1b_1y - 2a_1c_1}{a_1^2 + b_1^2}, \frac{-2a_1b_1x + \left(a_1^2 - b_1^2\right) y - 2b_1c_1}{a_1^2 + b_1^2}\right]\right)$$

and

$$\sigma_{l_3}\left(\sigma_{l_2}(A)\right) = \sigma_{l_3}\left(\left[\frac{\left(b_2^2 - a_2^2\right) x - 2a_2b_2y - 2a_2c_2}{a_2^2 + b_2^2}, \frac{-2a_2b_2x + \left(a_2^2 - b_2^2\right) y - 2b_2c_2}{a_2^2 + b_2^2}\right]\right)$$

are equal to the point

$$\left[\frac{p}{\left(a_1^2 + b_1^2\right)\left(a_2^2 + b_2^2\right)}, \frac{q}{\left(a_1^2 + b_1^2\right)\left(a_2^2 + b_2^2\right)}\right]$$

where

$$
\begin{aligned}
p = \ & (a_1a_2 + b_1b_2 + a_2b_1 - a_1b_2)(a_1a_2 + b_1b_2 - a_2b_1 + a_1b_2)\, x \\
& -2\left(a_1b_2 - a_2b_1\right)\left(a_1a_2 + b_1b_2\right) y + 4a_2b_1b_2c_1 + 2a_1\left(a_2^2 - b_2^2\right) c_1 - 2a_2\left(a_1^2 + b_1^2\right) c_2 \\
q = \ & (a_1a_2 + b_1b_2 + a_2b_1 - a_1b_2)(a_1a_2 + b_1b_2 - a_2b_1 + a_1b_2)\, y \\
& +2\left(a_1b_2 - a_2b_1\right)\left(a_1a_2 + b_1b_2\right) x + 4a_1a_2b_2c_1 - 2b_1\left(a_2^2 - b_2^2\right) c_1 - 2b_2\left(a_1^2 + b_1^2\right) c_2.
\end{aligned}
$$

Thus $\sigma_{l_2}\left(\sigma_{l_1}(A)\right) = \sigma_{\Sigma_{l_2}(l_1)}\left(\sigma_{l_2}(A)\right)$. ∎

It is useful to note that the Reflection theorem can be restated in the form

$$\sigma_{\Sigma_{l_2}(l_1)} = \sigma_{l_2}\sigma_{l_1}\sigma_{l_2}^{-1} = \sigma_{l_2}\sigma_{l_1}\sigma_{l_2}.$$

Theorem 17 (Lineation) If l_1 and l_2 are non-null lines, then

$$\Sigma_{l_2}\Sigma_{l_1} = \Sigma_{\Sigma_{l_2}(l_1)}\Sigma_{l_2}.$$

Proof. Since the reflection $\Sigma_l(m)$ of the line m in the line l is determined by the reflections $\sigma_l(A_1)$ and $\sigma_l(A_2)$ of any two distinct points A_1 and A_2 lying on m, this is a direct consequence of the previous theorem. ∎

Definition A two-sided sequence of lines $\cdots, l_{-2}, l_{-1}, l_0, l_1, l_2, \cdots$ is a **reflection sequence** precisely when for any integer k

$$\Sigma_{l_k}(l_{k-1}) = l_{k+1}.$$

Theorem 18 (Cyclic reflection) Suppose that $\cdots, l_{-2}, l_{-1}, l_0, l_1, l_2, \cdots$ is a reflection sequence of lines. Then for any integers k and j

$$\Sigma_{l_k}(l_j) = l_{2k-j}. \quad \diamond$$

Proof. We will prove that
$$\Sigma_{l_k}(l_{k+n}) = l_{k-n}$$
for fixed k by induction on $n = 0, 1, 2, \cdots$. For $n = 0$ and $n = 1$ the statement is clear, since $\Sigma_{l_k}^{-1} = \Sigma_{l_k}$. Assume it is true for all values up to $n \geq 1$. Then since

$$l_{k+n+1} = \Sigma_{l_{k+n}}(l_{k+n-1})$$

the Lineation theorem shows that

$$
\begin{aligned}
\Sigma_{l_k}(l_{k+n+1}) &= \Sigma_{l_k}\left(\Sigma_{l_{k+n}}(l_{k+n-1})\right) \\
&= \Sigma_{\Sigma_{l_k}(l_{k+n})}\left(\Sigma_{l_k}(l_{k+n-1})\right) \\
&= \Sigma_{l_{k-n}}(l_{k-n+1}) \\
&= l_{k-n-1} = l_{k-(n+1)}.
\end{aligned}
$$

So the statement is also true for $n + 1$. So it is true for any positive n, and so true for any integer n, since the following statements are equivalent

$$\Sigma_{l_k}(l_{k+n}) = l_{k-n} \qquad \text{and} \qquad \Sigma_{l_k}(l_{k-n}) = l_{k+n}.$$

Now set $k + n = j$ to get

$$\Sigma_{l_k}(l_j) = l_{2k-j}. \quad \blacksquare$$

Part II

Rational trigonometry

Quadrance

This chapter begins with the concept of the *quadrance* between points, and then examines null lines, midpoints, the Triple quad formula, Pythagoras' theorem, the quadrea of a triangle, and a generalization of the classical Heron's formula called—in this text—Archimedes' formula. Perpendicular bisectors and quadrance from a point to a line are discussed. Archimedes' function and the Quadruple quad formula are defined. All these topics hold in an arbitrary field F not of characteristic two (from now on this will not necessarily be repeated).

5.1 Quadrances of triangles and quadrilaterals

Definition The **quadrance** $Q(A_1, A_2)$ between the points $A_1 \equiv [x_1, y_1]$ and $A_2 \equiv [x_2, y_2]$ is the number

$$Q(A_1, A_2) \equiv (x_2 - x_1)^2 + (y_2 - y_1)^2.$$

Sometimes $Q(A_1, A_2)$ will be called the quadrance **from** A_1 **to** A_2, or the **quadrance of the side** $\overline{A_1 A_2}$. Clearly

$$Q(A_1, A_2) = Q(A_2, A_1).$$

In the rational or decimal number fields $Q(A_1, A_2)$ is always positive, and is zero precisely when $A_1 = A_2$. This is not necessarily the case for other fields.

Example 5.1 In the complex number field with $A_1 \equiv [0, 0]$ and $A_2 \equiv [1, i]$

$$Q(A_1, A_2) = 1^2 + i^2 = 0. \quad \diamond$$

Theorem 19 (Null line) If A_1 and A_2 are distinct points, then A_1A_2 is a null line precisely when $Q(A_1, A_2) = 0$.

Proof. If $A_1 \equiv [x_1, y_1]$ and $A_2 \equiv [x_2, y_2]$ are distinct points, then by the Line through two points theorem (page 38)

$$A_1 A_2 = \langle y_1 - y_2 : x_2 - x_1 : x_1 y_2 - x_2 y_1 \rangle.$$

This is a null line precisely when

$$(y_1 - y_2)^2 + (x_2 - x_1)^2 = 0$$

which is exactly the condition that $Q(A_1, A_2) = 0$. ∎

Theorem 20 (Midpoint) If A_1A_2 is a non-null line, then there is a unique point A lying on A_1A_2 which satisfies

$$Q(A_1, A) = Q(A, A_2).$$

This is the midpoint $M \equiv (1/2) A_1 + (1/2) A_2$ of the side $\overline{A_1 A_2}$. Furthermore

$$Q(A_1, M) = Q(M, A_2) = Q(A_1, A_2)/4.$$

Proof. If $A_1 \equiv [x_1, y_1]$ and $A_2 \equiv [x_2, y_2]$ are distinct points, then by the Affine combination theorem (page 46) any point on the line $A_1 A_2$ has the form

$$A \equiv \lambda A_1 + (1 - \lambda) A_2 = [\lambda x_1 + (1 - \lambda) x_2, \lambda y_1 + (1 - \lambda) y_2]$$

for some number λ. The condition $Q(A_1, A) = Q(A, A_2)$ is then

$$
\begin{aligned}
&((\lambda - 1) x_1 + (1 - \lambda) x_2)^2 + ((\lambda - 1) y_1 + (1 - \lambda) y_2)^2 \\
={}& (\lambda x_1 + (-\lambda) x_2)^2 + (\lambda y_1 + (-\lambda) y_2)^2.
\end{aligned}
$$

Rewrite this as

$$\left((1 - \lambda)^2 - \lambda^2\right)\left((x_2 - x_1)^2 + (y_2 - y_1)^2\right) = 0.$$

By assumption $A_1 A_2$ is a non-null line, so by the previous Null line theorem, $(x_2 - x_1)^2 + (y_2 - y_1)^2 \neq 0$. Thus $\lambda = 1/2$, and A is the midpoint

$$M \equiv (1/2) A_1 + (1/2) A_2 = [(x_1 + x_2)/2, (y_1 + y_2)/2]$$

of the side $\overline{A_1 A_2}$. Then

$$
\begin{aligned}
Q(A_1, M) &= \left(\frac{x_1 - x_2}{2}\right)^2 + \left(\frac{y_1 - y_2}{2}\right)^2 = Q(M, A_2) \\
&= Q(A_1, A_2)/4. \quad \blacksquare
\end{aligned}
$$

Exercise 5.1 (Harder) Show that if $l_1 \equiv \langle a_1 : b_1 : c_1 \rangle$, $l_2 \equiv \langle a_2 : b_2 : c_2 \rangle$ and $l_3 \equiv \langle a_3 : b_3 : c_3 \rangle$ then

$$Q\left(l_1 l_2, l_1 l_3\right) = \frac{\left(a_1^2 + b_1^2\right)\left(a_1 b_2 c_3 - a_1 b_3 c_2 + a_2 b_3 c_1 - a_3 b_2 c_1 + a_3 b_1 c_2 - a_2 b_1 c_3\right)^2}{\left(a_1 b_2 - a_2 b_1\right)^2 \left(a_1 b_3 - a_3 b_1\right)^2}. \quad \diamond$$

Definition For a triangle $\overline{A_1 A_2 A_3}$, the numbers $Q_1 \equiv Q\left(A_2, A_3\right)$, $Q_2 \equiv Q\left(A_1, A_3\right)$ and $Q_3 \equiv Q\left(A_1, A_2\right)$ are the **quadrances** of the triangle, with Q_1 the **quadrance of the side** $\overline{A_2 A_3}$, or the **quadrance opposite the vertex** $\overline{l_2 l_3}$, and similarly for the other quadrances.

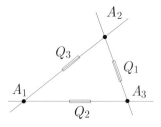

Figure 5.1: Quadrances of a triangle

This convention will generally be followed for A_1, A_2 and A_3 any three points, even if they are collinear.

Definition For a quadrilateral $\overline{A_1 A_2 A_3 A_4}$, the numbers $Q_{12} \equiv Q\left(A_1, A_2\right)$, $Q_{23} \equiv Q\left(A_2, A_3\right)$, $Q_{34} \equiv Q\left(A_3, A_4\right)$ and $Q_{14} \equiv Q\left(A_1, A_4\right)$ are the **quadrances** of the quadrilateral. The numbers $Q_{13} \equiv Q\left(A_1, A_3\right)$ and $Q_{24} \equiv Q\left(A_2, A_4\right)$ are the **diagonal quadrances** of the quadrilateral.

With this notation a quadrilateral has four quadrances and two diagonal quadrances.

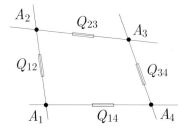

Figure 5.2: Quadrances of a quadrilateral

Exercise 5.2 Show that if the characteristic of the field is not three, then the centroid G of a triangle $\overline{A_1 A_2 A_3}$ with midpoints M_1, M_2 and M_3 of the sides satisfies

$$Q(A_1, G) = \frac{4Q(A_1, M_1)}{9}$$

$$Q(G, M_1) = \frac{Q(A_1, M_1)}{9}$$

$$Q(A_1, G) = 4Q(G, M_1). \quad \diamond$$

Exercise 5.3 Show that in the complex number field, given complex numbers Q_1, Q_2 and Q_3, not all zero, there is always a triangle with these numbers as quadrances. $\diamond$

Theorem 21 (Parallelogram quadrance) In a parallelogram $\overline{A_1 A_2 A_3 A_4}$ the quadrances of opposite sides are equal.

Proof. Suppose that $A_1 \equiv [x_1, y_1]$, $A_2 \equiv [x_2, y_2]$, $A_3 \equiv [x_3, y_3]$ and $A_4 \equiv [x_4, y_4]$. From the Parallelogram center theorem (page 49), the midpoints of $\overline{A_1 A_3}$ and $\overline{A_2 A_4}$ coincide, so that

$$x_1 + x_3 = x_2 + x_4$$
$$y_1 + y_3 = y_2 + y_4.$$

Thus

$$x_1 - x_2 = x_4 - x_3$$
$$y_1 - y_2 = y_4 - y_3.$$

But then

$$\begin{aligned}
Q(A_1, A_2) &= (x_2 - x_1)^2 + (y_2 - y_1)^2 \\
&= (x_4 - x_3)^2 + (y_4 - y_3)^2 \\
&= Q(A_3, A_4). \quad \blacksquare
\end{aligned}$$

Exercise 5.4 Show that the diagonal sides $\overline{A_1 A_3}$ and $\overline{A_2 A_4}$ of a parallelogram $\overline{A_1 A_2 A_3 A_4}$ have equal quadrances precisely when the parallelogram is a rectangle. $\diamond$

Exercise 5.5 Suppose that the parallelogram $\overline{A_1 A_2 A_3 A_4}$ has quadrances $Q \equiv Q(A_1, A_2) = Q(A_3, A_4)$ and $P \equiv Q(A_2, A_3) = Q(A_1, A_4)$ and that $R \equiv Q(A_1, A_3)$ and $T \equiv Q(A_2, A_4)$ are the quadrances of the diagonal sides. Show that

$$R + T = 2(Q + P). \quad \diamond$$

Exercise 5.6 Show that all four quadrances of a parallelogram are equal precisely when the parallelogram is a rhombus. $\diamond$

5.2 Triple quad formula

This key result has ramifications and generalizations throughout the subject.

Theorem 22 (Triple quad formula) Suppose that A_1, A_2 and A_3 are points with $Q_1 \equiv Q(A_2, A_3)$, $Q_2 \equiv Q(A_1, A_3)$ and $Q_3 \equiv Q(A_1, A_2)$. Then

$$(Q_1 + Q_2 + Q_3)^2 = 2\left(Q_1^2 + Q_2^2 + Q_3^2\right)$$

precisely when A_1, A_2 and A_3 are collinear.

Proof. First verify the important polynomial identity

$$(Q_1 + Q_2 + Q_3)^2 - 2\left(Q_1^2 + Q_2^2 + Q_3^2\right) = 4Q_1Q_2 - (Q_1 + Q_2 - Q_3)^2.$$

Assume that $A_1 \equiv [x_1, y_1]$, $A_2 \equiv [x_2, y_2]$ and $A_3 \equiv [x_3, y_3]$. Then

$$Q_1 = (x_3 - x_2)^2 + (y_3 - y_2)^2$$
$$Q_2 = (x_3 - x_1)^2 + (y_3 - y_1)^2$$
$$Q_3 = (x_2 - x_1)^2 + (y_2 - y_1)^2.$$

Rewrite this in the form

$$Q_1 = a_1^2 + b_1^2$$
$$Q_2 = a_2^2 + b_2^2$$
$$Q_3 = (a_2 - a_1)^2 + (b_2 - b_1)^2$$

where $a_1 \equiv x_3 - x_2$, $b_1 \equiv y_3 - y_2$, $a_2 \equiv x_3 - x_1$ and $b_2 \equiv y_3 - y_1$, so that

$$Q_1 + Q_2 - Q_3 = 2(a_1a_2 + b_1b_2).$$

Then

$$4Q_1Q_2 - (Q_1 + Q_2 - Q_3)^2$$
$$= 4\left(\left(a_1^2 + b_1^2\right)\left(a_2^2 + b_2^2\right) - (a_1a_2 + b_1b_2)^2\right)$$
$$= 4(a_1b_2 - a_2b_1)^2$$
$$= 4(x_1y_2 - x_1y_3 + x_2y_3 - x_3y_2 + x_3y_1 - x_2y_1)^2$$

where Fibonacci's identity (page 27) was used to go from the second line to the third. Since $4 \neq 0$, the Collinear points theorem (page 39) shows that this is zero precisely when the three points A_1, A_2 and A_3 are collinear. ∎

Definition Archimedes' function $A(a,b,c)$ for numbers a,b and c is defined by

$$A(a,b,c) \equiv (a+b+c)^2 - 2\left(a^2+b^2+c^2\right).$$

Note that $A(a,b,c)$ is a symmetric function of a,b and c. This motivates and justifies the following definition.

Definition A set $\{a,b,c\}$ of numbers is a **quad triple** precisely when

$$A(a,b,c) = 0.$$

Exercise 5.7 Show that

$$\begin{aligned}
A(a,b,c) &= 4ab - (a+b-c)^2 \\
&= 2(ab+bc+ca) - \left(a^2+b^2+c^2\right) \\
&= 4(ab+bc+ca) - (a+b+c)^2 \\
&= \begin{vmatrix} 2a & a+b-c \\ a+b-c & 2b \end{vmatrix} \\
&= -\begin{vmatrix} 0 & a & b & 1 \\ a & 0 & c & 1 \\ b & c & 0 & 1 \\ 1 & 1 & 1 & 0 \end{vmatrix}. \quad \diamond
\end{aligned}$$

Exercise 5.8 Show that if three quantities a,b and c satisfy one of the relations $a \pm b = \pm c$, then $A \equiv a^2$, $B \equiv b^2$ and $C \equiv c^2$ form a quad triple $\{A,B,C\}$. $\diamond$

Exercise 5.9 Show that in general not every quad triple is of the form

$$\left\{a^2, b^2, (a+b)^2\right\}$$

for some numbers a and b. $\diamond$

Exercise 5.10 Show that as a quadratic equation in Q_3, the Triple quad formula is

$$Q_3^2 - 2(Q_1 + Q_2) Q_3 + (Q_1 - Q_2)^2 = 0. \quad \diamond$$

Exercise 5.11 Show that the two quadratic equations in x

$$\begin{aligned}
(x - p_1)^2 &= q_1 \\
(x - p_2)^2 &= q_2
\end{aligned}$$

are compatible precisely when $\left\{q_1, q_2, (p_1 - p_2)^2\right\}$ is a quad triple. $\diamond$

5.3 Pythagoras' theorem

This most famous of geometrical theorems becomes here more general, extending to an arbitrary field, not of characteristic two.

Theorem 23 (Pythagoras' theorem) Suppose that the triangle $\overline{A_1 A_2 A_3}$ has quadrances $Q_1 \equiv Q(A_2, A_3)$, $Q_2 \equiv Q(A_1, A_3)$ and $Q_3 \equiv Q(A_1, A_2)$. Then

$$Q_1 + Q_2 = Q_3$$

precisely when $A_1 A_3$ and $A_2 A_3$ are perpendicular.

Proof. Suppose the points are $A_1 \equiv [x_1, y_1]$, $A_2 \equiv [x_2, y_2]$ and $A_3 \equiv [x_3, y_3]$. Then by the Line through two points theorem (page 38)

$$A_1 A_3 = \langle y_1 - y_3 : x_3 - x_1 : x_1 y_3 - x_3 y_1 \rangle$$

and

$$A_2 A_3 = \langle y_2 - y_3 : x_3 - x_2 : x_2 y_3 - x_3 y_2 \rangle.$$

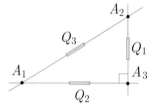

These lines are perpendicular precisely when

$$(y_1 - y_3)(y_2 - y_3) + (x_3 - x_1)(x_3 - x_2) = 0.$$

Now

$$
\begin{aligned}
Q_1 + Q_2 - Q_3 &= (x_2 - x_3)^2 + (y_2 - y_3)^2 + (x_1 - x_3)^2 + (y_1 - y_3)^2 \\
&\quad - (x_2 - x_1)^2 - (y_2 - y_1)^2 \\
&= 2\left(x_3^2 - x_2 x_3 - x_1 x_3 + x_2 x_1 + y_1 y_2 - y_1 y_3 - y_2 y_3 + y_3^2\right) \\
&= 2\left((y_1 - y_3)(y_2 - y_3) + (x_3 - x_1)(x_3 - x_2)\right).
\end{aligned}
$$

Since $2 \neq 0$, $A_1 A_3$ and $A_2 A_3$ are perpendicular precisely when $Q_1 + Q_2 = Q_3$. ∎

Exercise 5.12 Show that if $\overline{A_1 A_2 A_3}$ is a right triangle with right vertex at A_3, then it is impossible for either Q_1 or Q_2 to be zero. Give an example to show that in some fields it is possible for Q_3 to be zero. ◇

Example 5.2 In the field $\mathbb{F}_{11}$ the right triangle $\overline{A_1 A_2 A_3}$ where

$$A_1 \equiv [3, 7] \qquad A_2 \equiv [10, 3] \qquad A_3 \equiv [6, 1]$$

is shown in Figure 5.3, along with its lines.

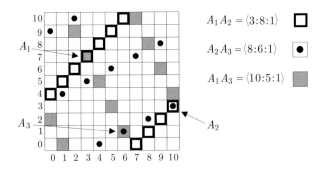

Figure 5.3: A right triangle in $\mathbb{F}_{11}$

You may check that A_1A_3 and A_2A_3 are perpendicular lines. The quadrances of $\overline{A_1A_2A_3}$ are $Q_1 = 9$, $Q_2 = 1$ and $Q_3 = 10$, and indeed $Q_1 + Q_2 = Q_3$.   ◇

5.4   Quadrance to a line

Theorem 24 (Equal quadrance to two points) Suppose that p is the perpendicular bisector of the side $\overline{A_1A_2}$. Then every point A lying on p satisfies

$$Q(A, A_1) = Q(A, A_2)$$

and conversely every point A satisfying this equation lies on p.

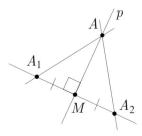

Figure 5.4: Equal quadrance to two points

Proof. Suppose that A lies on p. If $p = A_1A_2$ then A_1A_2 is a null line, so by the Null line theorem $Q(A, A_1) = Q(A, A_2) = 0$. If $p \neq A_1A_2$ then A_1A_2 is a non-null line. In this case if A lies on A_1A_2, then A is the midpoint of $\overline{A_1A_2}$, so by the Midpoint theorem (page 60) $Q(A, A_1) = Q(A, A_2)$. Otherwise A does not lie on $A_1 A_2$. Then $\overline{AMA_1}$ and $\overline{AMA_2}$ both have right vertices at the midpoint M of $\overline{A_1 A_2}$, so from Pythagoras' theorem

$$
\begin{aligned}
Q(A, A_1) &= Q(A, M) + Q(M, A_1) \\
Q(A, A_2) &= Q(A, M) + Q(M, A_2).
\end{aligned}
$$

By the Midpoint theorem $Q(M, A_1) = Q(M, A_2)$, so $Q(A, A_1) = Q(A, A_2)$.

Conversely suppose that A is a point with $Q(A, A_1) = Q(A, A_2) \equiv Q$. If $Q(A_1, A_2) = 0$, then by the Null line theorem (page 60) $A_1 A_2$ is a null line. In that case the quadrances of $\{A, A_1, A_2\}$ are Q, Q and 0, so that they satisfy the Triple quad formula. Thus the three points are collinear, and A lies on $A_1 A_2$, which is itself the perpendicular bisector p of $\overline{A_1 A_2}$.

Otherwise suppose that $Q(A_1, A_2) \neq 0$, so that $A_1 A_2$ is a non-null line. Let F be the foot of the altitude from A to the line $A_1 A_2$. Then by Pythagoras' theorem

$$
Q(F, A_1) = Q - Q(A, F) = Q(F, A_2)
$$

so that by the Midpoint theorem F is indeed the midpoint M of the side $\overline{A_1 A_2}$, and A lies on the perpendicular bisector p of $\overline{A_1 A_2}$. ∎

Theorem 25 (Quadrance to a line) For a point $A \equiv [x, y]$ and a non-null line $l \equiv \langle a : b : c \rangle$, the quadrance from A to the foot F of the altitude from A to l is

$$
Q(A, F) = \frac{(ax + by + c)^2}{a^2 + b^2}.
$$

Proof. From the Foot of an altitude theorem (page 42) the foot of the altitude from A to l is

$$
F \equiv \left[\frac{b^2 x - aby - ac}{a^2 + b^2}, \frac{-abx + a^2 y - bc}{a^2 + b^2} \right].
$$

The required quadrance is then

$$
\begin{aligned}
Q(A, F) &= \left(\frac{b^2 x - aby - ac}{a^2 + b^2} - x \right)^2 + \left(\frac{-abx + a^2 y - bc}{a^2 + b^2} - y \right)^2 \\
&= \frac{a^2 (ax + by + c)^2}{(a^2 + b^2)^2} + \frac{b^2 (ax + by + c)^2}{(a^2 + b^2)^2} \\
&= \frac{(ax + by + c)^2}{a^2 + b^2}. \quad \blacksquare
\end{aligned}
$$

Definition The **quadrance** $Q(A, l)$ **from the point** A **to the non-null line** l is the quadrance from A to the foot F of the altitude from A to l.

5.5   Quadrea

Definition For three points A_1, A_2 and A_3 with quadrances $Q_1 \equiv Q(A_2, A_3)$, $Q_2 \equiv Q(A_1, A_3)$ and $Q_3 \equiv Q(A_1, A_2)$, the **quadrea** $\mathcal{A}$ of the set $\{A_1, A_2, A_3\}$ is the number

$$\mathcal{A} \equiv A(Q_1, Q_2, Q_3) = (Q_1 + Q_2 + Q_3)^2 - 2(Q_1^2 + Q_2^2 + Q_3^2).$$

The quadrea of $\{A_1, A_2, A_3\}$ is also denoted $\mathcal{A}(\{A_1, A_2, A_3\})$ and is a symmetric function of the three points. In Chapter 9 the quadrea $\mathcal{A}$ of a triangle will be shown to be sixteen times the square of the *signed area* of an associated *oriented triangle*.

Theorem 26 (Quadrea) The quadrea $\mathcal{A}$ of $\{A_1, A_2, A_3\}$, for $A_1 \equiv [x_1, y_1]$, $A_2 \equiv [x_2, y_2]$ and $A_3 \equiv [x_3, y_3]$, is

$$\mathcal{A} = 4(x_1 y_2 - x_1 y_3 + x_2 y_3 - x_3 y_2 + x_3 y_1 - x_2 y_1)^2.$$

In particular the quadrea $\mathcal{A}$ is a square, and $\{A_1, A_2, A_3\}$ is a triangle precisely when $\mathcal{A}$ is non-zero.

Proof. The formula for $\mathcal{A}$ was derived in the course of the proof of the Triple quad formula (page 63) and shows that $\mathcal{A}$ is a square. By the Collinear points theorem (page 39)

$$x_1 y_2 - x_1 y_3 + x_2 y_3 - x_3 y_2 + x_3 y_1 - x_2 y_1 \neq 0$$

precisely when A_1, A_2 and A_3 are not collinear, that is when they form a triangle. Since $4 \neq 0$, this condition is equivalent to $\mathcal{A} \neq 0$. ∎

Theorem 27 (Right quadrea) If a right triangle $\overline{A_1 A_2 A_3}$ has quadrances Q_1, Q_2 and Q_3, and right vertex at A_3, then it has quadrea

$$\mathcal{A} = 4Q_1 Q_2.$$

Proof. Use the asymmetric form

$$\mathcal{A} = 4Q_1 Q_2 - (Q_1 + Q_2 - Q_3)^2$$

of the quadrea together with Pythagoras' theorem. ∎

Exercise 5.13 In the rational or decimal number fields, show that a variable triangle $\overline{A_1 A_2 A_3}$ with two fixed quadrances Q_1 and Q_2 has maximum possible quadrea $\mathcal{A}$ precisely when it has a right vertex at A_3. ◇

Exercise 5.14 Show that

$$A\left(Q_1, Q_2, Q_3\right) = Q_1\left(Q_2 + Q_3 - Q_1\right) + Q_2\left(Q_3 + Q_1 - Q_2\right) + Q_3\left(Q_1 + Q_2 - Q_3\right). \quad \diamond$$

Exercise 5.15 Show that

$$
\begin{aligned}
A\left(Q_1, Q_2, Q_3\right) = \ & \left(Q_3 + Q_1 - Q_2\right)\left(Q_1 + Q_2 - Q_3\right) \\
& + \left(Q_1 + Q_2 - Q_3\right)\left(Q_2 + Q_3 - Q_1\right) \\
& + \left(Q_2 + Q_3 - Q_1\right)\left(Q_3 + Q_1 - Q_2\right). \quad \diamond
\end{aligned}
$$

Exercise 5.16 (Harder) Show that if the triangle $\overline{A_1 A_2 A_3}$ has lines $l_1 \equiv \langle a_1 : b_1 : c_1 \rangle$, $l_2 \equiv \langle a_2 : b_2 : c_2 \rangle$ and $l_3 \equiv \langle a_3 : b_3 : c_3 \rangle$ then the quadrea is

$$\mathcal{A} = \frac{4\left(a_1 b_2 c_3 - a_1 b_3 c_2 + a_2 b_3 c_1 - a_3 b_2 c_1 + a_3 b_1 c_2 - a_2 b_1 c_3\right)^4}{\left(a_2 b_3 - a_3 b_2\right)^2 \left(a_3 b_1 - a_1 b_3\right)^2 \left(a_1 b_2 - a_2 b_1\right)^2}. \quad \diamond$$

The next result is due to V. Le.

Theorem 28 (Triangle quadrea) Suppose Q_1, Q_2 and Q_3 are not all zero and are each the sum of two squares. Then a triangle $\overline{A_1 A_2 A_3}$ with these quadrances exists precisely when $\mathcal{A} = A\left(Q_1, Q_2, Q_3\right)$ is a non-zero square.

Proof. If such a triangle exists, then by the Quadrea theorem $A\left(Q_1, Q_2, Q_3\right)$ is a non-zero square. Conversely suppose that there exists $r \neq 0$ such that

$$A\left(Q_1, Q_2, Q_3\right) = 4Q_1 Q_2 - \left(Q_1 + Q_2 - Q_3\right)^2 = r^2.$$

Then choose $A_3 \equiv [0, 0]$ and $A_1 \equiv [a_1, b_1]$ such that $a_1^2 + b_1^2 = Q_2 \neq 0$. Now define

$$R \equiv Q_1 + Q_2 - Q_3$$

and

$$
\begin{aligned}
a_2 &\equiv \frac{a_1 R - b_1 r}{2 Q_2} \\
b_2 &\equiv \frac{b_1 R + a_1 r}{2 Q_2}.
\end{aligned}
$$

Then check that $A_2 \equiv [a_2, b_2]$ satisfies both $Q\left(A_2, A_3\right) = Q_1$ and $Q\left(A_2, A_1\right) = Q_3$. ∎

Exercise 5.17 (V. Le) In $\mathbb{F}_p$ suppose that Q_1, Q_2 and Q_3 are numbers such that $\mathcal{A} \equiv A\left(Q_1, Q_2, Q_3\right)$ is a non-zero square. Show that i) if $p = 4l + 3$ then there are exactly $2p^2\left(p + 1\right)$ triangles with quadrances Q_1, Q_2 and Q_3 and ii) if $p = 4l + 1$ then there are exactly $2p^2\left(p - 1\right)$ triangles with quadrances Q_1, Q_2 and Q_3. $\diamond$

5.6 Archimedes' formula

Heron's formula of Euclidean geometry over the decimal number field is extended to a general field, and now attributed (more properly) to Archimedes.

Theorem 29 (Archimedes' formula) Suppose that a triangle $\overline{A_1 A_2 A_3}$ has square quadrances of the form $Q_1 \equiv d_1^2$, $Q_2 \equiv d_2^2$ and $Q_3 \equiv d_3^2$ for some numbers d_1, d_2 and d_3. Then the quadrea is

$$\mathcal{A} = (d_1 + d_2 + d_3)(d_1 + d_2 - d_3)(d_2 + d_3 - d_1)(d_3 + d_1 - d_2).$$

Proof. Proceed as follows

$$\begin{aligned}
\mathcal{A} &= 4Q_1 Q_2 - (Q_1 + Q_2 - Q_3)^2 = 4d_1^2 d_2^2 - \left(d_1^2 + d_2^2 - d_3^2\right)^2 \\
&= \left(2d_1 d_2 - \left(d_1^2 + d_2^2 - d_3^2\right)\right)\left(2d_1 d_2 + \left(d_1^2 + d_2^2 - d_3^2\right)\right) \\
&= \left(d_3^2 - (d_1 - d_2)^2\right)\left((d_1 + d_2)^2 - d_3^2\right) \\
&= (d_3 - d_1 + d_2)(d_3 + d_1 - d_2)(d_1 + d_2 - d_3)(d_1 + d_2 + d_3).\ \blacksquare
\end{aligned}$$

5.7 Quadruple quad formula

The next two theorems extend the Triple quad formula to four points.

Definition The **Quadruple quad function** $Q(a, b, c, d)$ is defined by

$$Q(a, b, c, d) \equiv \left((a + b + c + d)^2 - 2\left(a^2 + b^2 + c^2 + d^2\right)\right)^2 - 64abcd.$$

Theorem 30 (Two quad triples) Suppose that $\{a, b, x\}$ and $\{c, d, x\}$ are both quad triples. Then

$$Q(a, b, c, d) = 0.$$

If $a + b \neq c + d$ then

$$x = \frac{(a - b)^2 - (c - d)^2}{2(a + b - c - d)}.$$

Proof. If $\{a, b, x\}$ and $\{c, d, x\}$ are quad triples then

$$(x - a - b)^2 = 4ab$$
$$(x - c - d)^2 = 4cd.$$

The Quadratic compatibility theorem (page 33) asserts that then a, b, c and d must satisfy the condition

$$\left((a + b - c - d)^2 - 4\,(ab + cd)\right)^2 = 64abcd$$

which can be rewritten more symmetrically as

$$\left((a + b + c + d)^2 - 2\,(a^2 + b^2 + c^2 + d^2)\right)^2 = 64abcd.$$

The same theorem also asserts that if $a + b \neq c + d$ then

$$x = \frac{(a + b) + (c + d)}{2} - \frac{4ab - 4cd}{2\,(a + b - c - d)}$$
$$= \frac{(a - b)^2 - (c - d)^2}{2\,(a + b - c - d)}. \quad\blacksquare$$

The expression $(a + b + c + d)^2 - 2\,(a^2 + b^2 + c^2 + d^2)$ appears in a theorem of Descartes as well as in F. Soddy's circle theorem. This is discussed in [Coxeter, pages 14, 15], which also has an amusing related verse by Soddy.

Theorem 31 (Quadruple quad formula) Suppose that A_1, A_2, A_3 and A_4 are collinear points and that $Q_{ij} \equiv Q\,(A_i, A_j)$ for all $i, j = 1, 2, 3$ and 4. Then

$$Q\,(Q_{12}, Q_{23}, Q_{34}, Q_{14}) = 0.$$

Furthermore

$$Q_{13} = \frac{(Q_{12} - Q_{23})^2 - (Q_{34} - Q_{14})^2}{2\,(Q_{12} + Q_{23} - Q_{34} - Q_{14})}$$
$$Q_{24} = \frac{(Q_{23} - Q_{34})^2 - (Q_{12} - Q_{14})^2}{2\,(Q_{23} + Q_{34} - Q_{12} - Q_{14})}$$

provided the denominators are not zero.

Proof. If A_1, A_2, A_3 and A_4 are collinear points, then $\{Q_{12}, Q_{23}, Q_{13}\}$ and $\{Q_{14}, Q_{13}, Q_{34}\}$ are both quad triples. Apply the Two quad triples theorem to see that $Q\,(Q_{12}, Q_{23}, Q_{34}, Q_{14}) = 0$, and to obtain the stated formula for Q_{13}. The formula for Q_{24} is analogous. $\blacksquare$

Theorem 32 (Brahmagupta's identity) Suppose that $Q_{12} \equiv d_{12}^2$, $Q_{23} \equiv d_{23}^2$, $Q_{34} \equiv d_{34}^2$ and $Q_{14} \equiv d_{14}^2$ for some numbers d_{12}, d_{23}, d_{34} and d_{14}. Then

$$Q\left(Q_{12}, Q_{23}, Q_{34}, Q_{14}\right)$$
$$= \left(d_{12} - d_{14} + d_{23} + d_{34}\right)\left(d_{12} + d_{14} + d_{23} - d_{34}\right)\left(d_{14} - d_{12} + d_{23} + d_{34}\right)$$
$$\times \left(d_{12} + d_{14} - d_{23} + d_{34}\right)\left(d_{12} + d_{14} + d_{23} + d_{34}\right)\left(d_{12} - d_{14} - d_{23} + d_{34}\right)$$
$$\times \left(d_{12} - d_{14} + d_{23} - d_{34}\right)\left(d_{23} - d_{14} - d_{12} + d_{34}\right).$$

Proof. Make the substitutions $Q_{ij} \equiv d_{ij}^2$ for all i and j to turn the expression

$$\left(\left(Q_{12} + Q_{23} + Q_{34} + Q_{14}\right)^2 - 2\left(Q_{12}^2 + Q_{23}^2 + Q_{34}^2 + Q_{14}^2\right)\right)^2 - 64 Q_{12} Q_{23} Q_{34} Q_{14}$$

into a difference of squares. This is then the product of the expression

$$\left(d_{12}^2 + d_{23}^2 + d_{14}^2 + d_{34}^2\right)^2 - 2\left(d_{12}^4 + d_{23}^4 + d_{14}^4 + d_{34}^4\right) + 8 d_{12} d_{23} d_{34} d_{14}$$
$$= \left(d_{12} - d_{14} + d_{23} + d_{34}\right)\left(d_{12} + d_{14} + d_{23} - d_{34}\right)$$
$$\times \left(d_{14} - d_{12} + d_{23} + d_{34}\right)\left(d_{12} + d_{14} - d_{23} + d_{34}\right)$$

and the expression

$$\left(d_{12}^2 + d_{23}^2 + d_{14}^2 + d_{34}^2\right)^2 - 2\left(d_{12}^4 + d_{23}^4 + d_{14}^4 + d_{34}^4\right) - 8 d_{12} d_{23} d_{34} d_{14}$$
$$= \left(d_{12} + d_{14} + d_{23} + d_{34}\right)\left(d_{12} - d_{14} - d_{23} + d_{34}\right)$$
$$\times \left(d_{12} - d_{14} + d_{23} - d_{34}\right)\left(d_{23} - d_{14} - d_{12} + d_{34}\right). \blacksquare$$

The first of the two expressions involved in the proof of Brahmagupta's identity corresponds in the decimal number system to sixteen times the square of the area of a convex cyclic quadrilateral with side lengths d_{12}, d_{23}, d_{34} and d_{14}. The other corresponds to an analogous result for a non-convex cyclic quadrilateral with these side lengths (see [Robbins]). These connections with cyclic quadrilaterals will become clearer in Chapter 17 with the Cyclic quadrilateral quadrea theorem (page 187).

Exercise 5.18 Show that if $\{a, b, x\}$ and $\{b, c, x\}$ are quad triples and $a \neq c$ then

$$x = \frac{a + c - 2b}{2}. \quad \diamond$$

Exercise 5.19 (Harder) Is there a Quintuple quad formula? Generalize. $\diamond$

Spread

This chapter introduces the spread between non-null lines in terms of the coefficients of the lines, and derives an alternative formulation as the ratio of two quadrances. The related notions of the *cross* and *twist* between two lines are also introduced.

Spread and cross are seen to be essentially equivalent, but spread is here given pride of place. This becomes particularly useful in elliptic and hyperbolic geometries. The Spread law and Cross law are derived, along with some formulas allowing us to calculate spreads from coordinates of points. The subtle issue of bisectors of a vertex is examined.

6.1 Spreads of triangles and quadrilaterals

Definition The **spread** $s(l_1, l_2)$ between the non-null lines $l_1 \equiv \langle a_1 : b_1 : c_1 \rangle$ and $l_2 \equiv \langle a_2 : b_2 : c_2 \rangle$ is the number

$$s(l_1, l_2) \equiv \frac{(a_1 b_2 - a_2 b_1)^2}{(a_1^2 + b_1^2)(a_2^2 + b_2^2)}.$$

If one or both of l_1, l_2 is a null line, then the spread $s(l_1, l_2)$ is an empty expression and any statement involving it is considered an empty statement. The spread is otherwise well-defined, in the sense that if the coefficients of one of the proportions are multiplied by a non-zero number, then the spread remains unchanged.

Also $s(l_1, l_2) = s(l_2, l_1)$, and $s(l_1, l_2) = 0$ precisely when l_1 and l_2 are parallel. The spread $s(l_1, l_2)$ is unchanged if l_1 is replaced with a line parallel to it, or if l_2 is replaced by a line parallel to it.

Definition Given a triangle $\overline{A_1 A_2 A_3}$, the numbers $s_1 \equiv s\,(A_1 A_2, A_1 A_3)$, $s_2 \equiv s\,(A_2 A_1, A_2 A_3)$ and $s_3 \equiv s\,(A_3 A_1, A_3 A_2)$ are the **spreads** of the triangle, with s_1 the **spread of the vertex** $\overline{l_2 l_3}$, or the **spread opposite the side** $\overline{A_2 A_3}$, and similarly for the other spreads.

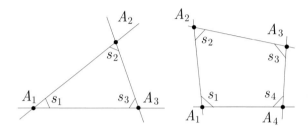

Figure 6.1: Spreads of a triangle and quadrilateral

More generally if l_1, l_2 and l_3 are any three lines, the usual convention is that the three spreads formed by the pairs of lines are denoted $s_1 \equiv s\,(l_2, l_3)$, $s_2 \equiv s\,(l_1, l_3)$ and $s_3 \equiv s\,(l_1, l_2)$.

Definition Given a quadrilateral $\overline{A_1 A_2 A_3 A_4}$, the numbers $s_1 \equiv s\,(A_1 A_2, A_1 A_4)$, $s_2 \equiv s\,(A_2 A_1, A_2 A_3)$, $s_3 \equiv s\,(A_3 A_2, A_3 A_4)$ and $s_4 \equiv s\,(A_4 A_1, A_4 A_3)$ are the **spreads** of the quadrilateral.

6.2 Cross

Definition The **cross** $c\,(l_1, l_2)$ between the non-null lines $l_1 \equiv \langle a_1 : b_1 : c_1 \rangle$ and $l_2 \equiv \langle a_2 : b_2 : c_2 \rangle$ is the number

$$c\,(l_1, l_2) \equiv \frac{(a_1 a_2 + b_1 b_2)^2}{(a_1^2 + b_1^2)\,(a_2^2 + b_2^2)}.$$

A cross involving a null line is an empty concept. Also $c\,(l_1, l_2) = c\,(l_2, l_1)$, and $c\,(l_1, l_2) = 0$ precisely when l_1 and l_2 are perpendicular. The cross is unchanged if either of the lines is replaced by a line parallel to it.

In a triangle, the conventions are similar to the ones for spread, so that c_1 is the **cross at the vertex** $\overline{l_2 l_3}$ and so on. In a diagram in the rational or decimal number fields, the cross between intersecting lines will be written *inside* the small triangle formed by the two lines and a small line segment joining them, as in Figure 6.2.

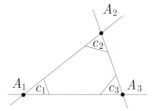

Figure 6.2: Crosses of a triangle

Given three lines l_1, l_2 and l_3, the usual convention is that the three crosses formed by the pairs of lines are denoted $c_1 \equiv c\,(l_2, l_3)$, $c_2 \equiv c\,(l_1, l_3)$ and $c_3 \equiv c\,(l_1, l_2)$.

6.3 Twist

Definition The **twist** $t\,(l_1, l_2)$ between the non-perpendicular lines $l_1 \equiv \langle a_1 : b_1 : c_1 \rangle$ and $l_2 \equiv \langle a_2 : b_2 : c_2 \rangle$ is the number

$$t\,(l_1, l_2) \equiv \frac{(a_1 b_2 - a_2 b_1)^2}{(a_1 a_2 + b_1 b_2)^2}.$$

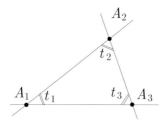

Figure 6.3: Twists of a triangle

The twist is not defined if l_1 and l_2 are perpendicular, as in this case $a_1 a_2 + b_1 b_2 = 0$. The twist is always a square number. Also $t\,(l_1, l_2) = t\,(l_2, l_1)$, and $t\,(l_1, l_2) = 0$ precisely when l_1 and l_2 are parallel. If l_1 and l_2 are non-parallel non-null lines then

$$t\,(l_1, l_2) = s\,(l_1, l_2)\,/c\,(l_1, l_2)\,.$$

Note that if one or both of l_1 and l_2 are null lines, then the twist between them may still be defined, although in this case neither the spread nor the cross is defined. The twist between two lines may be indicated by a double line segment, as in Figure 6.3.

6.4 Ratio theorems

Theorem 33 (Spread plus cross) For non-null lines l_1 and l_2, let s and c be respectively the spread and cross between them. Then

$$s + c = 1.$$

Proof. This follows from the definitions of spread and cross, together with Fibonacci's identity

$$(a_1 b_2 - a_2 b_1)^2 + (a_1 a_2 + b_1 b_2)^2 = (a_1^2 + b_1^2)(a_2^2 + b_2^2). \ \blacksquare$$

Over the rational or decimal number field, this theorem implies that both the spread and cross always take values in the interval $[0, 1]$, since they are both always positive.

Theorem 34 (Spread number) For non-null lines l_1 and l_2 the spread $s \equiv s(l_1, l_2)$ is a spread number, and every spread number is obtained as a spread between two lines.

Proof. If $l_1 \equiv \langle a_1 : b_1 : c_1 \rangle$ and $l_2 \equiv \langle a_2 : b_2 : c_2 \rangle$ then the definitions of the spread $s \equiv s(l_1, l_2)$ and cross $c \equiv c(l_1, l_2)$, together with the Spread plus cross theorem, gives

$$
\begin{aligned}
s(1-s) \ &= \ sc \\
&= \ \frac{(a_1 b_2 - a_2 b_1)^2}{(a_1^2 + b_1^2)(a_2^2 + b_2^2)} \frac{(a_1 a_2 + b_1 b_2)^2}{(a_1^2 + b_1^2)(a_2^2 + b_2^2)} \\
&= \ \left(\frac{(a_1 b_2 - a_2 b_1)(a_1 a_2 + b_1 b_2)}{(a_1^2 + b_1^2)(a_2^2 + b_2^2)} \right)^2.
\end{aligned}
$$

Since this is a square, s is a spread number.

Conversely, suppose that s is a spread number, so that $s(1-s) \equiv r^2$ for some number r. If $s = 1$, then it is the spread between the two lines $\langle 0 : 1 : 0 \rangle$ and $\langle 1 : 0 : 0 \rangle$. Otherwise, consider the two lines $l_1 = \langle 0 : 1 : 0 \rangle$ and $l_2 = \langle r : 1 - s : 0 \rangle$. The spread between them is, from the definition,

$$
\begin{aligned}
s(l_1, l_2) \ &= \ \frac{r^2}{1 \times \left(r^2 + (1-s)^2 \right)} \\
&= \ \frac{s(1-s)}{1-s} = s. \ \blacksquare
\end{aligned}
$$

Theorem 35 (Spread ratio) Suppose that $\overline{A_1A_2A_3}$ is a non-null right triangle with a right vertex at A_3, and quadrances Q_1, Q_2 and Q_3. Then the spread at the vertex A_1 is

$$s_1 \equiv s\,(A_1A_2, A_1A_3) = Q_1/Q_3.$$

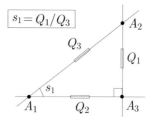

Figure 6.4: Spread ratio theorem

Proof. Assume the points are $A_1 \equiv [x_1, y_1]$, $A_2 \equiv [x_2, y_2]$ and $A_3 \equiv [x_3, y_3]$. Then

$$
\begin{aligned}
A_1A_2 &= \langle y_1 - y_2 : x_2 - x_1 : x_1y_2 - x_2y_1 \rangle \\
A_1A_3 &= \langle y_1 - y_3 : x_3 - x_1 : x_1y_3 - x_3y_1 \rangle \\
A_2A_3 &= \langle y_2 - y_3 : x_3 - x_2 : x_2y_3 - x_3y_2 \rangle
\end{aligned}
$$

so that

$$s_1 = \frac{\left((y_1 - y_2)(x_3 - x_1) - (y_1 - y_3)(x_2 - x_1)\right)^2}{\left((y_1 - y_2)^2 + (x_2 - x_1)^2\right)\left((y_1 - y_3)^2 + (x_3 - x_1)^2\right)}.$$

Since A_1A_3 and A_2A_3 are perpendicular

$$(y_1 - y_3)(y_2 - y_3) + (x_3 - x_1)(x_3 - x_2) = 0.$$

The following identity appeared in Exercise 2.6

$$
\begin{aligned}
&(y_1 - y_2)(x_3 - x_1) - (y_1 - y_3)(x_2 - x_1) \\
={}& (y_1 - y_3)(x_3 - x_2) - (y_2 - y_3)(x_3 - x_1).
\end{aligned}
$$

So the numerator of s_1 is

$$
\begin{aligned}
&\left((y_1 - y_2)(x_3 - x_1) - (y_1 - y_3)(x_2 - x_1)\right)^2 \\
={}& \left((y_1 - y_3)(x_3 - x_2) - (y_2 - y_3)(x_3 - x_1)\right)^2 \\
&+ \left((y_1 - y_3)(y_2 - y_3) + (x_3 - x_1)(x_3 - x_2)\right)^2 \\
={}& \left((y_1 - y_3)^2 + (x_3 - x_1)^2\right)\left((y_2 - y_3)^2 + (x_3 - x_2)^2\right)
\end{aligned}
$$

where Fibonacci's identity is used in the last step. Hence

$$s_1 = (Q_2Q_1)\,/\,(Q_3Q_2) = Q_1/Q_3. \quad \blacksquare$$

Theorem 36 (Cross ratio) Suppose that $\overline{A_1 A_2 A_3}$ is a non-null right triangle with a right vertex at A_3, and quadrances Q_1, Q_2 and Q_3. Then the cross at the vertex A_1 is

$$c_1 \equiv c\,(A_1 A_2, A_1 A_3) = \frac{Q_2}{Q_3}.$$

Proof. Use the Spread plus cross theorem, the Spread ratio theorem and Pythagoras' theorem to get

$$
\begin{aligned}
c_1 &\equiv c\,(A_1 A_2, A_1 A_3) \\
&= 1 - s\,(A_1 A_2, A_1 A_3) \\
&= 1 - \frac{Q_1}{Q_3} \\
&= \frac{Q_2}{Q_3}. \quad \blacksquare
\end{aligned}
$$

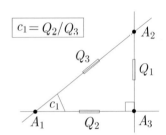

Theorem 37 (Twist ratio) Suppose that $\overline{A_1 A_2 A_3}$ is a right triangle with a right vertex at A_3, and quadrances Q_1, Q_2 and Q_3. Then the twist t_1 at the vertex A_1 is

$$t_1 \equiv t\,(A_1 A_2, A_1 A_3) = \frac{Q_1}{Q_2}.$$

Proof. If $Q_3 \neq 0$, this follows immediately from $t_1 = s_1/c_1$ together with the Spread ratio theorem $s_1 = Q_1/Q_3$ and the Cross ratio theorem $c_1 = Q_2/Q_3$.

However if $Q_3 = 0$ then neither s_1 nor c_1 are defined. In this case Pythagoras' theorem shows that $Q_1 = -Q_2$. It then suffices to show that $t_1 = -1$. By the Null line theorem (page 60) l_3 is a null line, so is of the form $\langle 1 : i : d \rangle$ for some number i satisfying $i^2 = -1$, and some number d.

The lines l_2 and l_3 are not perpendicular, since otherwise l_1 would be parallel to l_3. So if $l_2 \equiv \langle a : b : c \rangle$, then $a + bi \neq 0$, and the definition of the twist gives

$$t_1 = t\,(l_2, l_3) = \frac{(ai - b)^2}{(a + bi)^2} = -1. \quad \blacksquare$$

Exercise 6.1 Show that if the spread s, cross c and twist t are defined between two lines, then

$$t = s/c = s/\,(1 - s) = (1 - c)/c \qquad s = t/\,(1 + t) \qquad c = 1/\,(1 + t). \quad \diamond$$

6.5 Complementary spreads

Two spreads s_1 and s_2 are **complementary** precisely when $s_1 + s_2 = 1$.

Theorem 38 (Complementary spreads) If the non-null lines l_1 and l_2 are perpendicular, then for any non-null line l_3 the spreads $s_1 \equiv s(l_2, l_3)$ and $s_2 \equiv s(l_1, l_3)$ are complementary.

Proof. Suppose that l_1 and l_2 are perpendicular non-null lines. If l_3 is parallel to one of these lines, then it is perpendicular to the other, in which case s_1 and s_2 are 0 and 1 in some order, and so complementary.

Otherwise any two of the lines intersect, and since spreads are unchanged when lines are replaced by parallel lines, assume that the lines l_1, l_2 and l_3 are not concurrent. Let $A_1 \equiv l_2 l_3$, $A_2 \equiv l_1 l_3$ and $A_3 \equiv l_1 l_2$, and suppose that the quadrances of $\overline{A_1 A_2 A_3}$ are Q_1, Q_2 and Q_3. Then since $\overline{A_1 A_2 A_3}$ has a right vertex at A_3, the Spread ratio theorem states that

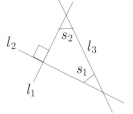

$$s_1 = Q_1/Q_3 \qquad \text{and} \qquad s_2 = Q_2/Q_3.$$

Thus

$$s_1 + s_2 = (Q_1 + Q_2)/Q_3 = 1$$

by Pythagoras' theorem. ■

Exercise 6.2 Show that the converse does not hold. ◇

Theorem 39 (Perpendicular spreads) If the non-null lines l_1 and l_2 are perpendicular, and the non-null lines m_1 and m_2 are perpendicular, then

$$s(l_1, m_1) = s(l_2, m_2).$$

Proof. Apply the Complementary spreads theorem to the lines m_1, m_2 and l_1 to get

$$s(l_1, m_1) + s(l_1, m_2) = 1.$$

Apply it to the lines l_1, l_2 and m_2 to get

$$s(l_1, m_2) + s(l_2, m_2) = 1.$$

Subtract these equations to conclude that

$$s(l_1, m_1) = s(l_2, m_2). ■$$

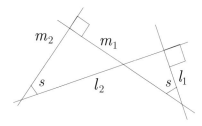

6.6 Spread law

Theorem 40 (Spread law) Suppose three points A_1, A_2 and A_3 form non-zero quadrances $Q_1 \equiv Q(A_2, A_3)$, $Q_2 \equiv Q(A_1, A_3)$ and $Q_3 \equiv Q(A_1, A_2)$. Define the spreads $s_1 \equiv s(A_1A_2, A_1A_3)$, $s_2 \equiv s(A_2A_1, A_2A_3)$ and $s_3 \equiv s(A_3A_1, A_3A_2)$. Then

$$\frac{s_1}{Q_1} = \frac{s_2}{Q_2} = \frac{s_3}{Q_3}.$$

Proof. If A_1, A_2 and A_3 are collinear, then $s_1 = s_2 = s_3 = 0$ and the theorem is immediate. Otherwise the three points form a triangle $\overline{A_1A_2A_3}$, which is not null, since the quadrances are non-zero. Suppose that D is the foot of the altitude from A_1 to A_2A_3. Define the quadrances

$$R_1 \equiv Q(A_1, D) \qquad R_2 \equiv Q(A_2, D) \qquad R_3 \equiv Q(A_3, D)$$

as illustrated in either of the diagrams in Figure 6.5.

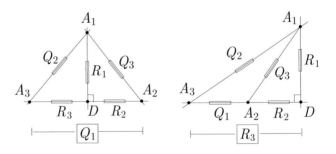

Figure 6.5: Spread law

Since $\overline{A_1A_2D}$ and $\overline{A_1A_3D}$ are right triangles, with right vertices at D, the Spread ratio theorem asserts that

$$s_2 = R_1/Q_3 \qquad s_3 = R_1/Q_2.$$

Solve for R_1 to get

$$R_1 = Q_3 s_2 = Q_2 s_3$$

so that

$$\frac{s_2}{Q_2} = \frac{s_3}{Q_3}.$$

In a similar manner

$$\frac{s_1}{Q_1} = \frac{s_2}{Q_2}. \quad \blacksquare$$

6.7 Cross law

The following result contains both Pythagoras' theorem and the Triple quad formula as special cases.

Theorem 41 (Cross law) Suppose three points A_1, A_2 and A_3 form quadrances $Q_1 \equiv Q(A_2, A_3)$, $Q_2 \equiv Q(A_1, A_3)$ and $Q_3 \equiv Q(A_1, A_2)$, and define the cross $c_3 \equiv c(A_3 A_1, A_3 A_2)$. Then

$$(Q_1 + Q_2 - Q_3)^2 = 4Q_1 Q_2 c_3.$$

Proof. If the three points A_1, A_2 and A_3 are collinear, then $c_3 = 1$, so then the statement follows from the Triple quad formula.

Otherwise the three points form a triangle $\overline{A_1 A_2 A_3}$. By the definition of the cross c_3, $A_1 A_3$ and $A_2 A_3$ are not null lines, so let D be the foot of the altitude from A_1 to the line $A_2 A_3$. As in Figure 6.5 define the quadrances

$$R_1 \equiv Q(A_1, D) \qquad R_2 \equiv Q(A_2, D) \qquad R_3 \equiv Q(A_3, D).$$

Since $\overline{A_1 A_2 D}$ and $\overline{A_1 A_3 D}$ are right triangles, with right vertices at D, use Pythagoras' theorem to get

$$Q_3 = R_1 + R_2$$
$$Q_2 = R_1 + R_3.$$

By the Cross ratio theorem (page 78)

$$c_3 = R_3/Q_2.$$

Solve sequentially for R_3, R_1 and then R_2 to get

$$R_3 = Q_2 c_3$$
$$R_1 = Q_2 (1 - c_3)$$
$$R_2 = Q_3 - Q_2 (1 - c_3).$$

Since A_2, A_3 and D are collinear, apply the Triple quad formula to the three quadrances Q_1, R_2 and R_3, yielding

$$(Q_1 + R_3 - R_2)^2 = 4Q_1 R_3.$$

Substitute the values of R_3 and R_2, to get

$$(Q_1 + Q_2 - Q_3)^2 = 4Q_1 Q_2 c_3. \quad \blacksquare$$

The next result is a consequence of the Cross law, and gives a convenient way to quickly calculate the spreads of a triangle from the quadrances.

Theorem 42 (Quadrea spread) Suppose three points A_1, A_2 and A_3 form quadrances Q_1, Q_2 and Q_3 as usual, and spread $s_3 \equiv s\,(A_3A_1, A_3A_2)$. Then the quadrea of $\{A_1, A_2, A_3\}$ is
$$\mathcal{A} = 4Q_1Q_2s_3.$$

Proof. From the Spread plus cross theorem and the Cross law

$$
\begin{aligned}
4Q_1Q_2s_3 &= 4Q_1Q_2\,(1 - c_3) \\
&= 4Q_1Q_2 - (Q_1 + Q_2 - Q_3)^2 \\
&= (Q_1 + Q_2 + Q_3)^2 - 2\left(Q_1^2 + Q_2^2 + Q_3^2\right) \\
&= \mathcal{A}. \quad\blacksquare
\end{aligned}
$$

Exercise 6.3 Use the Quadrea spread theorem to show that if a triangle $\overline{A_1A_2A_3}$ has quadrances Q_1, Q_2 and Q_3, spreads s_1, s_2 and s_3, and quadrea $\mathcal{A}$, then
$$\frac{s_1}{Q_1} = \frac{s_2}{Q_2} = \frac{s_3}{Q_3} = \frac{\mathcal{A}}{4Q_1Q_2Q_3}. \quad \diamond$$

Exercise 6.4 Suppose the null triangle $\overline{A_1A_2A_3}$ has quadrances Q_1, Q_2 and Q_3, with $Q_3 \equiv 0$. Show that the quadrea of the triangle is
$$\mathcal{A} = -\,(Q_1 - Q_2)^2$$
and that
$$s_3 = -\,(Q_1 - Q_2)^2 \,/4Q_1Q_2. \quad \diamond$$

Exercise 6.5 Suppose the null triangle $\overline{A_1A_2A_3}$ has quadrances $Q_1 \neq 0$ and $Q_2 = Q_3 \equiv 0$. Show that the quadrea is
$$\mathcal{A} = -Q_1^2. \quad \diamond$$

Exercise 6.6 (Triangle inequality) In the rational or decimal number fields, show that if a triangle has quadrances Q_1, Q_2 and Q_3, then

$$(Q_1 + Q_2 - Q_3)^2 \leq 4Q_1Q_2. \quad \diamond$$

Examples

Example 6.1 In the decimal number field, the triangle $\overline{A_1 A_2 A_3}$ with quadrances

$$Q_1 \equiv 16 \quad Q_2 \equiv 36 \quad Q_3 \equiv 9$$

has quadrea

$$\mathcal{A} = A\,(16, 36, 9) = (16 + 36 + 9)^2 - 2\,(16^2 + 36^2 + 9^2) = 455.$$

So by the Quadrea spread theorem

$$s_1 = \frac{\mathcal{A}}{4Q_2 Q_3} = \frac{455}{4 \times 36 \times 9} = \frac{455}{1296}$$
$$s_2 = \frac{\mathcal{A}}{4Q_1 Q_3} = \frac{455}{4 \times 16 \times 9} = \frac{455}{576}$$
$$s_3 = \frac{\mathcal{A}}{4Q_1 Q_2} = \frac{455}{4 \times 16 \times 36} = \frac{455}{2304}. \quad \diamond$$

Example 6.2 The Quadrea theorem (page 68) shows that there is no triangle over the rational numbers with quadrances

$$Q_1 \equiv 16 \quad Q_2 \equiv 36 \quad Q_3 \equiv 9$$

since in this field the quadrea $\mathcal{A} \equiv 455$ is not a square. $\diamond$

Example 6.3 In the field $\mathbb{F}_{11}$ the number $\mathcal{A} \equiv 455 = 4$ is a square, and every number is the sum of two squares, so by the Triangle quadrea theorem (page 69) there is a triangle with quadrances

$$Q_1 \equiv 16 = 5 \quad Q_2 \equiv 36 = 3 \quad Q_3 \equiv 9.$$

The spreads of this triangle are

$$s_1 = \frac{\mathcal{A}}{4Q_2 Q_3} = \frac{4}{4 \times 3 \times 9} = 9$$
$$s_2 = \frac{\mathcal{A}}{4Q_1 Q_3} = \frac{4}{4 \times 5 \times 9} = 1$$
$$s_3 = \frac{\mathcal{A}}{4Q_1 Q_2} = \frac{4}{4 \times 5 \times 3} = 3. \quad \diamond$$

Example 6.4 Over the complex numbers, the triangle $\overline{A_1 A_2 A_3}$ with quadrances

$$Q_1 \equiv 1 \quad Q_2 \equiv 2 \quad Q_3 \equiv i$$

has quadrea

$$\mathcal{A} \equiv A\,(1, 2, i) = (1 + 2 + i)^2 - 2\,(1 + 4 - 1) = 6i.$$

So by the Quadrea spread theorem

$$s_1 = 3/4 \quad s_2 = 3/2 \quad s_3 = 3i/4. \quad \diamond$$

6.8 Spreads in coordinates

The next theorems give the spread and cross in terms of points lying on lines.

Theorem 43 (Spread from points) Suppose that the non-null lines l_1 and l_2 intersect at the point $A_3 \equiv [x_3, y_3]$, and that $A_1 \equiv [x_1, y_1]$ is any other point on l_1 and $A_2 \equiv [x_2, y_2]$ is any other point on l_2. Then the spread s between l_1 and l_2 is

$$s = \frac{\left((y_1 - y_3)(x_3 - x_2) - (y_2 - y_3)(x_3 - x_1)\right)^2}{\left((x_1 - x_3)^2 + (y_1 - y_3)^2\right)\left((x_2 - x_3)^2 + (y_2 - y_3)^2\right)}.$$

Proof. The Line through two points theorem (page 38) shows that

$$\begin{aligned} l_1 &= \langle y_1 - y_3 : x_3 - x_1 : x_1 y_3 - x_3 y_1 \rangle \\ l_2 &= \langle y_2 - y_3 : x_3 - x_2 : x_2 y_3 - x_3 y_2 \rangle. \end{aligned}$$

Now use the definition of the spread. ∎

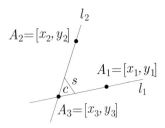

Figure 6.6: Spread and cross from points

Theorem 44 (Cross from points) Suppose that the non-null lines l_1 and l_2 intersect at the point $A_3 \equiv [x_3, y_3]$ and that $A_1 \equiv [x_1, y_1]$ is any other point on l_1 and that $A_2 \equiv [x_2, y_2]$ is any other point on l_2. Then the cross c between l_1 and l_2 is

$$c = \frac{\left((y_1 - y_3)(y_2 - y_3) + (x_3 - x_1)(x_3 - x_2)\right)^2}{\left((x_1 - x_3)^2 + (y_1 - y_3)^2\right)\left((x_2 - x_3)^2 + (y_2 - y_3)^2\right)}.$$

Proof. This is the same argument as the previous proof. ∎

Exercise 6.7 Formulate the corresponding result for twists. ◇

6.9 Vertex bisectors

Definition A **bisector** of the non-null vertex $\overline{l_1 l_2}$ is a line h which passes through $l_1 l_2$ and satisfies $s(l_1, h) = s(l_2, h)$.

Theorem 45 (Vertex bisector) A bisector of the non-null vertex $\overline{l_1 l_2}$ exists precisely when $s(l_1, l_2)$ is a square. In this case there are exactly two bisectors, and they are perpendicular. If $l_1 \equiv \langle a_1 : b_1 : c_1 \rangle$ and $l_2 \equiv \langle a_2 : b_2 : c_2 \rangle$, and $a_1 b_2 + a_2 b_1 = 0$ then the two bisectors of $\overline{l_1 l_2}$ always exists and are

$$\langle a_1 b_2 - a_2 b_1 : 0 : b_2 c_1 - b_1 c_2 \rangle \quad \text{and} \quad \langle 0 : a_1 b_2 - a_2 b_1 : c_2 a_1 - c_1 a_2 \rangle.$$

If $a_1 b_2 + a_2 b_1 \neq 0$ and $\left(a_1^2 + b_1^2\right)\left(a_2^2 + b_2^2\right) \equiv r^2$, then the two bisectors of $\overline{l_1 l_2}$ are given by

$$\left\langle \begin{array}{c} (a_1 a_2 - b_1 b_2 + r)(a_1 b_2 - a_2 b_1) : (a_1 b_2 + a_2 b_1)(a_1 b_2 - a_2 b_1) \\ \left(a_1^2 + b_1^2\right) b_2 c_2 - \left(a_2^2 + b_2^2\right) b_1 c_1 + r(b_2 c_1 - b_1 c_2) \end{array} \right\rangle$$

and

$$\left\langle \begin{array}{c} (a_1 a_2 - b_1 b_2 - r)(a_1 b_2 - a_2 b_1) : (a_1 b_2 + a_2 b_1)(a_1 b_2 - a_2 b_1) \\ \left(a_1^2 + b_1^2\right) b_2 c_2 - \left(a_2^2 + b_2^2\right) b_1 c_1 - r(b_2 c_1 - b_1 c_2) \end{array} \right\rangle.$$

Proof. If $s(l_1, h) = s(l_2, h) \equiv s$ then the Equal spreads theorem (page 94) shows that $s(l_1, l_2) = 4s(1 - s)$, since l_1 and l_2 are not parallel. The Spread number theorem (page 76) states that $s(1 - s)$ is a square, so that $s(l_1, l_2)$ is also a square.

Conversely suppose that $l_1 \equiv \langle a_1 : b_1 : c_1 \rangle$ and $l_2 \equiv \langle a_2 : b_2 : c_2 \rangle$, and that $s \equiv s(l_1, l_2)$ is a square. Since

$$s = \frac{(a_1 b_2 - a_2 b_1)^2}{\left(a_1^2 + b_1^2\right)\left(a_2^2 + b_2^2\right)}$$

this is equivalent to the condition that

$$\left(a_1^2 + b_1^2\right)\left(a_2^2 + b_2^2\right) = r^2$$

for some r. If $h \equiv \langle a : b : c \rangle$ then the equation $s(l_1, h) = s(l_2, h)$ is

$$\frac{(a_1 b - a b_1)^2}{\left(a_1^2 + b_1^2\right)\left(a^2 + b^2\right)} = \frac{(a_2 b - a b_2)^2}{\left(a_2^2 + b_2^2\right)\left(a^2 + b^2\right)}. \tag{6.1}$$

Verify the polynomial identity

$$(a_1 b - a b_1)^2 \left(a_2^2 + b_2^2\right) - (a_2 b - a b_2)^2 \left(a_1^2 + b_1^2\right)$$
$$= -(a_1 b_2 - a_2 b_1)\left(\left(a^2 - b^2\right)(a_1 b_2 + a_2 b_1) - 2ab(a_1 a_2 - b_1 b_2)\right). \tag{6.2}$$

Since l_1 and l_2 are not parallel, $a_1b_2 - a_2b_1 \neq 0$, so use (6.2) to replace (6.1) with the equivalent condition

$$a^2 (a_1b_2 + a_2b_1) - 2ab (a_1a_2 - b_1b_2) - b^2 (a_1b_2 + a_2b_1) = 0. \tag{6.3}$$

Suppose that $a_1b_2 + a_2b_1 = 0$. Then (6.3) reduces to

$$ab (a_1a_2 - b_1b_2) = 0.$$

If then $a_1a_2 - b_1b_2 = 0$, then the variant of Fibonacci's identity of Exercise 2.5,

$$(a_1a_2 - b_1b_2)^2 + (a_1b_2 + a_2b_1)^2 = (a_1^2 + b_1^2)(a_2^2 + b_2^2)$$

would imply that

$$(a_1^2 + b_1^2)(a_2^2 + b_2^2) = 0$$

which is impossible since neither l_1 nor l_2 is a null line. So instead $ab = 0$, and h is either of the form $\langle 1 : 0 : d_1 \rangle$ or $\langle 0 : 1 : d_2 \rangle$ for unique values of d_1 and d_2, determined by the fact that h passes through

$$l_1l_2 = \left[\frac{b_1c_2 - b_2c_1}{a_1b_2 - a_2b_1}, \frac{c_1a_2 - c_2a_1}{a_1b_2 - a_2b_1} \right].$$

This gives the two possibilities

$$h_1 \equiv \langle a_1b_2 - a_2b_1 : 0 : b_2c_1 - b_1c_2 \rangle$$

or

$$h_2 \equiv \langle 0 : a_1b_2 - a_2b_1 : c_2a_1 - c_1a_2 \rangle.$$

Note that s is automatically a square in this case, and in fact

$$s = \left(\frac{a_1b_2 - a_2b_1}{a_1a_2 - b_1b_2} \right)^2.$$

Suppose now that $a_1b_2 + a_2b_1 \neq 0$. In this case (6.3) shows that neither a nor b can be zero, since if one of them is zero, so is the other, which is impossible as $\langle a : b : c \rangle$ is a line. So by an appropriate non-zero scaling of a, b and c you can take

$$b \equiv a_1b_2 + a_2b_1 \neq 0.$$

In (6.3) complete the square in a using the variant of Fibonacci's identity to get

$$\begin{aligned}(a - (a_1a_2 - b_1b_2))^2 &= (a_1a_2 - b_1b_2)^2 + (a_1b_2 + a_2b_1)^2 \\ &= (a_1^2 + b_1^2)(a_2^2 + b_2^2) = r^2.\end{aligned}$$

So the possibilities for h are

$$h_1 \equiv \langle a_1a_2 - b_1b_2 + r : a_1b_2 + a_2b_1 : d_1 \rangle$$

or

$$h_2 \equiv \langle a_1a_2 - b_1b_2 - r : a_1b_2 + a_2b_1 : d_2 \rangle.$$

The numbers d_1 and d_2 are determined by the fact that h passes through $l_1 l_2$. A calculation shows that the possibilities for h can then be written

$$h_1 = \left\langle \begin{array}{c} (a_1 a_2 - b_1 b_2 + r)(a_1 b_2 - a_2 b_1) : (a_1 b_2 + a_2 b_1)(a_1 b_2 - a_2 b_1) \\ (a_1^2 + b_1^2) b_2 c_2 - (a_2^2 + b_2^2) b_1 c_1 + r(b_2 c_1 - b_1 c_2) \end{array} \right\rangle$$

or

$$h_2 = \left\langle \begin{array}{c} (a_1 a_2 - b_1 b_2 - r)(a_1 b_2 - a_2 b_1) : (a_1 b_2 + a_2 b_1)(a_1 b_2 - a_2 b_1) \\ (a_1^2 + b_1^2) b_2 c_2 - (a_2^2 + b_2^2) b_1 c_1 - r(b_2 c_1 - b_1 c_2) \end{array} \right\rangle .$$

These two lines are perpendicular since

$$((a_1 a_2 - b_1 b_2) + r)((a_1 a_2 - b_1 b_2) - r) + (a_1 b_2 + a_2 b_1)^2 = 0$$

by the variant of Fibonacci's identity and the definition of r. ∎

Definition The vertex $\overline{l_1 l_2}$ is a **square** vertex precisely when it has bisectors.

Example 6.5 Working over the rational number field, suppose that $l_1 \equiv \langle 2 : 1 : -1 \rangle$ and $l_2 \equiv \langle 11 : 2 : -4 \rangle$. Then

$$(a_1^2 + b_1^2)(a_2^2 + b_2^2) = 625 = (25)^2$$

is a square, so the vertex $\overline{l_1 l_2}$ has bisectors. Set $r \equiv 25$, and observe that $a_1 b_2 + a_2 b_1 \neq 0$. Then

$$\left\langle \begin{array}{c} (a_1 a_2 - b_1 b_2 \pm r)(a_1 b_2 - a_2 b_1) : (a_1 b_2 + a_2 b_1)(a_1 b_2 - a_2 b_1) \\ (a_1^2 + b_1^2) b_2 c_2 - (a_2^2 + b_2^2) b_1 c_1 \pm r(b_2 c_1 - b_1 c_2) \end{array} \right\rangle$$

evaluate to give bisectors $h_1 \equiv \langle 1 : -3 : 1 \rangle$ and $h_2 \equiv \langle 21 : 7 : -9 \rangle$. These lines are perpendicular and you may check that

$$\begin{aligned} s(l_1, h_1) &= s(l_2, h_1) = 49/50 \\ s(l_1, h_2) &= s(l_2, h_2) = 1/50. \end{aligned} \diamond$$

Example 6.6 Over the rational number field, suppose that $l_1 \equiv \langle 3 : 1 : 5 \rangle$ and $l_2 \equiv \langle -3 : 1 : 2 \rangle$. Then $s(l_1, l_2) = 9/25$ is a square, so the vertex $\overline{l_1 l_2}$ has bisectors. In this case $a_1 b_2 + a_2 b_1 = 0$, so the bisectors are given by the theorem as

$$h_1 \equiv \langle 6 : 0 : 3 \rangle = \langle 2 : 0 : 1 \rangle \qquad \text{and} \qquad h_2 \equiv \langle 0 : 6 : 21 \rangle = \langle 0 : 2 : 7 \rangle .$$

You may check that

$$\begin{aligned} s(l_1, h_1) &= s(l_2, h_1) = 1/10 \\ s(l_1, h_2) &= s(l_2, h_2) = 9/10. \end{aligned} \diamond$$

Theorem 46 (Equal quadrance to two lines) If $\overline{l_1 l_2}$ is a square vertex, then any point A lying on a vertex bisector h of $\overline{l_1 l_2}$ satisfies

$$Q(A, l_1) = Q(A, l_2)$$

and conversely any point satisfying this equation lies on one of the vertex bisectors of $\overline{l_1 l_2}$.

Proof. Suppose that $\overline{l_1 l_2}$ is a square vertex and that A is a point on one of the vertex bisectors h of $\overline{l_1 l_2}$. Suppose that $A_0 \equiv l_1 l_2$ and that F_1 and F_2 are the feet of the altitudes from A to l_1 and l_2 respectively as in Figure 6.7.

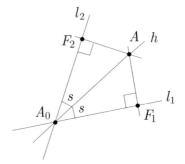

Figure 6.7: Equal quadrance to two lines

Then both $\overline{A_0 A F_1}$ and $\overline{A_0 A F_2}$ are right triangles, and by assumption

$$s(l_1, h) = \frac{Q(A, F_1)}{Q(A, A_0)} = s(l_2, h) = \frac{Q(A, F_2)}{Q(A, A_0)}.$$

Thus

$$Q(A, l_1) = Q(A, F_1) = Q(A, F_2) = Q(A, l_2).$$

Conversely if $A \neq l_1 l_2$ and $Q(A, l_1) = Q(A, l_2)$, then with F_1 and F_2 the feet of the altitudes from A to l_1 and l_2 respectively, you have

$$Q(A, F_1) = Q(A, F_2).$$

Let $A_0 \equiv l_1 l_2$ and $h \equiv AA_0$. Then

$$s(l_1, h) = \frac{Q(A, F_1)}{Q(A, A_0)} = \frac{Q(A, F_2)}{Q(A, A_0)} = s(l_2, h)$$

so that h is indeed a vertex bisector of $\overline{l_1 l_2}$. In particular $\overline{l_1 l_2}$ is a square vertex by the Vertex bisector theorem. ∎

Triple spread formula

This chapter introduces the Triple spread formula, the analogue in rational trigonometry to the fact that the sum of the angles in a triangle in the decimal number field is 180°. It differs from the Triple quad formula only by a single cubic term. There are a number of related results, including the Triple cross formula and the Triple twist formula, and an extension to four spreads. A particular application is the Equal spreads theorem, in which the logistic map of chaos theory makes an appearance.

7.1 Triple spread formula

Theorem 47 (Triple spread formula) Suppose that l_1, l_2 and l_3 are non-null lines, with $s_1 \equiv s\,(l_2, l_3)$, $s_2 \equiv s\,(l_1, l_3)$ and $s_3 \equiv s\,(l_1, l_2)$. Then

$$(s_1 + s_2 + s_3)^2 = 2\left(s_1^2 + s_2^2 + s_3^2\right) + 4s_1 s_2 s_3.$$

Proof. If at least two of the lines are parallel, then one of the spreads is zero, and the other two spreads must be equal. In this case the formula holds automatically. If the three lines are concurrent, then replace one of the lines with a line parallel to it, to obtain a triangle $\overline{A_1 A_2 A_3}$ with spreads s_1, s_2 and s_3 and quadrances Q_1, Q_2 and Q_3.

From the Spread law, there is a non-zero number D such that

$$\frac{s_1}{Q_1} = \frac{s_2}{Q_2} = \frac{s_3}{Q_3} \equiv \frac{1}{D}. \tag{7.1}$$

The Cross law can be expressed as

$$(Q_1 + Q_2 - Q_3)^2 = 4Q_1 Q_2 \,(1 - s_3)\,.$$

Rewrite this as

$$(Q_1 + Q_2 + Q_3)^2 = 2\left(Q_1^2 + Q_2^2 + Q_3^2\right) + 4Q_1 Q_2 s_3. \qquad (7.2)$$

Use (7.1) to replace Q_1 by $s_1 D$, Q_2 by $s_2 D$ and Q_3 by $s_3 D$ in (7.2), and then divide by D^2. The result is

$$(s_1 + s_2 + s_3)^2 = 2\left(s_1^2 + s_2^2 + s_3^2\right) + 4 s_1 s_2 s_3. \quad \blacksquare$$

Definition The **Triple spread function** S is defined by

$$S(a, b, c) \equiv (a + b + c)^2 - 2\left(a^2 + b^2 + c^2\right) - 4abc.$$

Note that $S(a, b, c)$ is a symmetric function of a, b and c. This motivates and justifies the following definition, in analogy with the definition of a quad triple (page 64).

Definition A set $\{a, b, c\}$ of numbers is a **spread triple** precisely when

$$S(a, b, c) = 0.$$

Exercise 7.1 In analogy with Exercise 5.7, show that

$$
\begin{aligned}
S(a, b, c) &= A(a, b, c) - 4abc \\
&= 2(ac + bc + ab) - \left(a^2 + b^2 + c^2\right) - 4abc \\
&= 4(ab + bc + ca) - (a + b + c)^2 - 4abc \\
&= 4(1 - a)(1 - b)(1 - c) - (a + b + c - 2)^2 \\
&= -\begin{vmatrix} 0 & a & b & 1 \\ a & 0 & c & 1 \\ b & c & 0 & 1 \\ 1 & 1 & 1 & 2 \end{vmatrix}. \quad \diamond
\end{aligned}
$$

Exercise 7.2 Demonstrate the following identity, of importance for the Triangle spread rules (page 219)

$$
\begin{aligned}
S(a, b, c) &= ((a + b - c)c + (c - a + b)(c - b + a))(1 - c) \\
&\quad - c(c - (a + b))(1 - (a + b)). \quad \diamond
\end{aligned}
$$

Exercise 7.3 Show that if $\{a, b, 0\}$ is a spread triple then $a = b$. Show that if $\{a, b, 1\}$ is a spread triple then $a + b = 1$. $\diamond$

Exercise 7.4 Show that in the rational or decimal number fields

$$0 \leq S(a, a, a)$$

precisely when $a \leq 3/4$. $\diamond$

Exercise 7.5 Show that for any numbers u and v with $u^2 \neq -1$ and $v^2 \neq -1$,

$$\left\{ \frac{u^2}{1+u^2}, \frac{v^2}{1+v^2}, \frac{(u-v)^2}{(1+u^2)(1+v^2)} \right\}$$

is a spread triple. Give an example where not every spread triple is of this form. ◇

Exercise 7.6 Show that as a quadratic equation in s_3, the Triple spread formula is

$$s_3^2 - 2s_3 (s_1 + s_2 - 2s_1 s_2) + (s_1 - s_2)^2 = 0.$$

Show that it can also be written as

$$(s_3 - s_1 + s_2)^2 = 4(1 - s_1) s_2 s_3$$
$$(s_3 - s_2 + s_1)^2 = 4s_1 (1 - s_2) s_3$$
$$(s_3 - s_1 - s_2)^2 = 4s_1 s_2 (1 - s_3)$$

and that in normal form it is

$$(s_3 - (s_1 + s_2 - 2s_1 s_2))^2 = 4s_1 s_2 (1 - s_1)(1 - s_2). \quad ◇$$

The next result shows how to determine a spread triple if one of the elements and the ratio of the other two is known.

Theorem 48 (Spread from ratio) Suppose that $\{s_1, s_2, s_3\}$ is a spread triple with s_2, s_3 both non-zero and $s_1/s_2 \equiv a$. Then $a(1 - s_3)$ is a square, and if $a(1 - s_3) \equiv r^2$ for some r, then

$$s_2 = s_3/(a + 1 \pm 2r).$$

Proof. Use the previous exercise to write the Triple spread formula in the form

$$(s_3 - s_1 - s_2)^2 = 4s_1 s_2 (1 - s_3).$$

By assumption s_2 is non-zero, so divide by s_2^2 to get

$$\left(\frac{s_3}{s_2} - a - 1 \right)^2 = 4a(1 - s_3).$$

Thus $a(1 - s_3)$ is a square, so that

$$a(1 - s_3) \equiv r^2$$

for some r. Then

$$s_3/s_2 = a + 1 \pm 2r$$

is non-zero, so that

$$s_2 = s_3/(a + 1 \pm 2r). \quad \blacksquare$$

7.2 Triple cross formula

A corresponding relationship to the Triple spread formula exists for three crosses.

Theorem 49 (Triple cross formula) Suppose that l_1, l_2 and l_3 are non-null lines, with $c_1 \equiv c\,(l_2, l_3)$, $c_2 \equiv c\,(l_1, l_3)$ and $c_3 \equiv c\,(l_1, l_2)$. Then

$$(c_1 + c_2 + c_3 - 1)^2 = 4c_1 c_2 c_3.$$

Proof. Use the Spread plus cross theorem to substitute $s_1 = 1 - c_1$, $s_2 = 1 - c_2$ and $s_3 = 1 - c_3$ into the Triple spread formula written as

$$(s_1 + s_2 + s_3 - 2)^2 = 4\,(1 - s_1)\,(1 - s_2)\,(1 - s_3). \quad \blacksquare$$

Example 7.1 In the complex number field, the Cross law shows that a triangle with quadrances $Q_1 \equiv 1$, $Q_2 \equiv -1$ and $Q_3 \equiv i$ has crosses

$$
\begin{aligned}
c_1 &= \frac{(Q_2 + Q_3 - Q_1)^2}{4Q_2 Q_3} = 1 + \frac{3}{4}i \\[2mm]
c_2 &= \frac{(Q_3 + Q_1 - Q_2)^2}{4Q_3 Q_1} = 1 - \frac{3}{4}i \\[2mm]
c_3 &= \frac{(Q_1 + Q_2 - Q_3)^2}{4Q_1 Q_2} = \frac{1}{4}.
\end{aligned}
$$

Both sides of the Triple cross formula become $25/16$. $\diamond$

Exercise 7.7 Show that as a quadratic equation in c_3, the Triple cross formula in normal form is

$$(c_3 + c_1 + c_2 - 2c_1 c_2 - 1)^2 = 4c_1 c_2\,(1 - c_1)\,(1 - c_2)$$

or also incorporating the spreads,

$$(c_3 - (c_1 c_2 + s_1 s_2))^2 = 4c_1 c_2 s_1 s_2. \quad \diamond$$

Exercise 7.8 Following Exercises 5.7 and 7.1, show that

$$(c_1 + c_2 + c_3 - 1)^2 - 4c_1 c_2 c_3 = -
\begin{vmatrix}
1 & c_1 & c_2 & 1 \\
c_1 & 1 & c_3 & 1 \\
c_2 & c_3 & 1 & 1 \\
1 & 1 & 1 & 2
\end{vmatrix}. \quad \diamond$$

Exercise 7.9 Show that in the rational and decimal number fields, the crosses c_1, c_2 and c_3 of any triangle satisfy

$$c_1 c_2 c_3 \leq 1/64 \qquad \text{and} \qquad 3/4 \leq c_1 + c_2 + c_3 \leq 5/4. \quad \diamond$$

7.3 Triple twist formula

The corresponding relation between the three twists of a triangle is somewhat more complicated. It will be seen to be closely connected to the addition of velocities in Einstein's special theory of relativity (page 242). A simpler version of this formula is suggested by Exercise 7.12 below, and realized by the Triple turn formula (page 115).

Theorem 50 (Triple twist formula) Suppose that l_1, l_2 and l_3 are lines, with the twists $t_1 \equiv t(l_2, l_3)$, $t_2 \equiv t(l_1, l_3)$ and $t_3 \equiv t(l_1, l_2)$. Then

$$(t_1 + t_2 + t_3 - t_1 t_2 t_3)^2 = 4(t_1 t_2 + t_1 t_3 + t_2 t_3 + 2t_1 t_2 t_3).$$

Proof. Suppose first that all the lines are non-null lines. Then use the Triple cross formula

$$(c_1 + c_2 + c_3 - 1)^2 = 4c_1 c_2 c_3$$

and the relation $c = 1/(1 + t)$ between a cross and twist to get

$$\left(\frac{1}{1+t_1} + \frac{1}{1+t_2} + \frac{1}{1+t_3} - 1 \right)^2 = \frac{4}{(1+t_1)(1+t_2)(1+t_3)}.$$

Expand this to get

$$
\begin{aligned}
t_1^2 + t_2^2 + t_3^2 + t_1^2 t_2^2 t_3^2 &= 2t_1 t_2 + 2t_2 t_3 + 2t_1 t_3 \\
&\quad + 2t_1 t_2 t_3 (t_1 + t_2 + t_3) + 8t_1 t_2 t_3
\end{aligned}
$$

and rewrite as

$$(t_1 + t_2 + t_3 - t_1 t_2 t_3)^2 = 4(t_1 t_2 + t_1 t_3 + t_2 t_3 + 2t_1 t_2 t_3).$$

If one of the lines, say l_3, is a null line, then by the proof of the Twist ratio theorem $t_1 = t_2 = -1$ and the required formula becomes the equation $4 = 4$. ∎

Exercise 7.10 Rewrite the Triple twist formula as a quadratic equation in t_3 in normal form. ◇

Exercise 7.11 Show that the Triple twist formula can be rewritten as

$$(t_1 + t_2 - t_3 - t_1 t_2 t_3)^2 = 4t_1 t_2 (1 + t_3)^2. \quad ◇$$

Exercise 7.12 Show that if three numbers r_1, r_2 and r_3 satisfy

$$r_1 + r_2 + r_3 = r_1 r_2 r_3$$

and $t_1 \equiv r_1^2$, $t_2 \equiv r_2^2$ and $t_3 \equiv r_3^2$, then $\{t_1, t_2, t_3\}$ satisfy the Triple twist formula. ◇

7.4 Equal spreads

Theorem 51 (Equal spreads) If l_1, l_2 and l_3 are non-null lines with $s(l_1, l_2) = s(l_2, l_3) \equiv s$ as in either of the diagrams, then $s(l_1, l_3) = 0$ or

$$s(l_1, l_3) = 4s(1 - s).$$

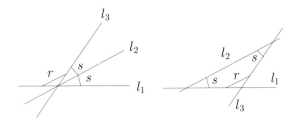

Figure 7.1: Equal spreads theorem

Proof. If $s(l_1, l_3) \equiv r$ then from the Triple spread formula

$$(2s + r)^2 = 2(2s^2 + r^2) + 4s^2 r$$

which becomes

$$r(r - 4s(1 - s)) = 0.$$

Thus $r = 0$ or $r = 4s(1 - s)$. ∎

In the decimal number field the quadratic polynomial function

$$S_2(s) \equiv 4s(1 - s)$$

is the **logistic map**, and is important in chaos theory. This is an example of a *spread polynomial* (see page 102). The graph of $S_2(s)$ for s near the range $0 \le s \le 1$ is given in Figure 7.2.

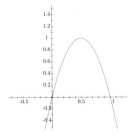

Figure 7.2: Logistic map $S_2(s) \equiv 4s(1 - s)$

7.5 Spread reflection theorem

Recall the definition of the reflection lineation Σ_l for a non-null line l on page 54.

Theorem 52 (Spread reflection) If l_1, l_2 and l are concurrent non-null lines with l_1 and l_2 distinct, then $\Sigma_l(l_1) = l_2$ precisely when

$$s(l_1, l) = s(l_2, l).$$

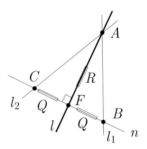

Figure 7.3: Spread reflection theorem

Proof. Suppose that l_1, l_2 and l are non-null lines intersecting at A, with l_1 and l_2 distinct. The reflection $\Sigma_l(l_1)$ of the line l_1 in the line l was defined in terms of the reflection σ_l in l of points. Suppose that $l_2 = \Sigma_l(l_1)$. If $B \neq A$ lies on l_1, then by definition l_2 is the line passing through A and $C \equiv \sigma_l(B)$.

If n is the altitude from B to l, with foot F, then define the quadrances

$$Q \equiv Q(B, F) = Q(F, C) \qquad \text{and} \qquad R \equiv Q(A, F)$$

as in Figure 7.3. Then by the Spread ratio theorem (page 77)

$$s(l_1, l) = Q/(Q + R) = s(l_2, l).$$

Conversely suppose that $s(l_1, l) = s(l_2, l) \equiv s$. Then $s \neq 1$, since otherwise l_1 and l_2 would both be perpendicular to l, which is impossible. Thus the two twists $t(l_1, l)$ and $t(l, l_2)$ are both equal to $t \equiv s/(1 - s)$. If B is any point on l_1 other than A, F the foot of the altitude n from B to l and $C \equiv nl_2$, then by the Twist ratio theorem (page 78)

$$t = \frac{Q(B, F)}{Q(F, A)} = \frac{Q(F, C)}{Q(F, A)}.$$

Thus

$$Q(B, F) = Q(F, C).$$

But then by the Midpoint theorem, (page 60) F is the midpoint of $\overline{BC}$, so that $C = \sigma_l(B)$. Thus $l_2 = \Sigma_l(l_1)$. ∎

7.6 Examples using different fields

To gain confidence in the formulas of this chapter, let's verify them in particular cases involving different fields. This will also bring out some of the rich number theoretical possibilities in the subject.

Example 7.2 Over a general field, consider the triangle $\overline{A_1 A_2 A_3}$ where

$$A_1 \equiv [1, 1] \quad A_2 \equiv [5, 2] \quad A_3 \equiv [3, -1].$$

The quadrances are $Q_1 = 13$, $Q_2 = 8$ and $Q_3 = 17$ and so the quadrea is

$$\mathcal{A} = (13 + 8 + 17)^2 - 2\left(13^2 + 8^2 + 17^2\right) = 400.$$

Use the Quadrea spread theorem to obtain the spreads $s_1 = 25/34$, $s_2 = 100/221$ and $s_3 = 25/26$, so that the crosses are $c_1 = 9/34$, $c_2 = 121/221$ and $c_3 = 1/26$. Check the Spread law, the Triple spread and Triple cross formulas as follows

$$\frac{25/34}{13} = \frac{100/121}{8} = \frac{25/26}{17} = \frac{25}{442}$$

$$(s_1 + s_2 + s_3)^2 = \frac{225\,625}{48\,841} = 2\left(s_1^2 + s_2^2 + s_3^2\right) + 4s_1 s_2 s_3$$

$$(c_1 + c_2 + c_3 - 1)^2 = \frac{1089}{48\,841} = 4c_1 c_2 c_3.$$

Since $221 = 13 \times 17$, $442 = 2 \times 13 \times 17$ and $48\,841 = (13)^2 \times (17)^2$, these formulas are valid in any field not of characteristic 13 or 17. If in addition the field is not of characteristic 3 or 11, the crosses are all non-zero, and so the twists are $t_1 = 25/9$, $t_2 = 100/121$ and $t_3 = 25$. The Triple twist formula is then

$$(t_1 + t_2 + t_3 - t_1 t_2 t_3)^2 = \frac{902\,500}{1089} = 4\left(t_1 t_2 + t_1 t_3 + t_2 t_3 + 2t_1 t_2 t_3\right). \quad \diamond$$

Example 7.3 In the field $\mathbb{F}_{11}$ consider the triangle $\overline{A_1 A_2 A_3}$ where

$$A_1 \equiv [1, 1] \qquad A_2 \equiv [3, 4] \qquad A_3 \equiv [9, 5].$$

The lines of the triangle are $l_1 \equiv \langle 10 : 6 : 1 \rangle$ (small black circles), $l_2 \equiv \langle 1 : 9 : 1 \rangle$ (large open circles) and $l_3 \equiv \langle 8 : 2 : 1 \rangle$ (gray boxes) as shown in Figure 7.4.

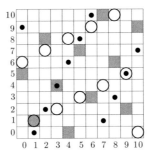

Figure 7.4: A triangle in $\mathbb{F}_{11}$

The quadrances are $Q_1 = 4$, $Q_2 = 3$ and $Q_3 = 2$, so the quadrea is

$$A = (4 + 3 + 2)^2 - 2(16 + 9 + 4) = 1.$$

The Quadrea spread theorem gives the spreads $s_1 = 6$, $s_2 = 10$ and $s_3 = 3$. The Spread law takes the form

$$6/4 = 10/3 = 3/2 = 7.$$

The Triple spread formula is

$$(s_1 + s_2 + s_3)^2 = 9 = 2\left(s_1^2 + s_2^2 + s_3^2\right) + 4s_1 s_2 s_3. \quad \diamond$$

Example 7.4 In the complex number field, consider the triangle $\overline{A_1 A_2 A_3}$ where

$$A_1 \equiv [0, 0] \quad A_2 \equiv [3, -i] \quad A_3 \equiv [1 + i, 2i].$$

The quadrances are

$$Q_1 = (-2 + i)^2 + (3i)^2 = -6 - 4i$$
$$Q_2 = (1 + i)^2 + (2i)^2 = -4 + 2i$$
$$Q_3 = (-3)^2 + i^2 = 8.$$

and the quadrea is

$$A = (-6 - 4i - 4 + 2i + 8)^2 - 2\left((-6 - 4i)^2 + (-4 + 2i)^2 + (8)^2\right)$$
$$= -192 - 56i.$$

Compute the spreads, using for example the Quadrea spread theorem,

$$s_1 = \frac{41}{40} + \frac{19}{20}i \qquad s_2 = \frac{43}{52} - \frac{27}{104}i \qquad s_3 = -\frac{199}{130} - \frac{16}{65}i$$

and verify the Spread law

$$\frac{\frac{41}{40} + \frac{19}{20}i}{-6 - 4i} = \frac{\frac{43}{52} - \frac{27}{104}i}{-4 + 2i} = \frac{-\frac{199}{130} - \frac{16}{65}i}{8}$$
$$= -\frac{199}{1040} - \frac{2}{65}i.$$

The Triple spread formula is

$$(s_1 + s_2 + s_3)^2 = -\frac{398}{4225} + \frac{38\,577}{135\,200}i = 2\left(s_1^2 + s_2^2 + s_3^2\right) + 4s_1 s_2 s_3.$$

The Triple twist formula is

$$(t_1 + t_2 + t_3 - t_1 t_2 t_3)^2 = -\frac{1293\,148}{4372\,281} + \frac{389\,312}{1457\,427}i = 4\left(t_1 t_2 + t_1 t_3 + t_2 t_3 + 2t_1 t_2 t_3\right). \quad \diamond$$

7.7 Quadruple spread formula

The next theorems extend the Triple spread and Triple cross formulas to four lines.
They should be compared to the results of Section 5.7.

Theorem 53 (Two spread triples) Suppose that $\{a, b, x\}$ and $\{c, d, x\}$ are both
spread triples. Then a, b, c and d satisfy the condition

$$\left(\begin{array}{c} (a + b + c + d)^2 - 2\left(a^2 + b^2 + c^2 + d^2\right) \\ -4\left(abc + abd + acd + bcd\right) + 8abcd \end{array} \right)^2$$
$$= 64abcd\left(1 - a\right)\left(1 - b\right)\left(1 - c\right)\left(1 - d\right).$$

Furthermore if $a + b - 2ab \neq c + d - 2cd$ then

$$x = \frac{(a - b)^2 - (c - d)^2}{2\left(a + b - c - d - 2ab + 2cd\right)}.$$

Proof. Suppose that $\{a, b, x\}$ and $\{c, d, x\}$ are both spread triples. Then the Triple
spread formula gives quadratic equations in x which may be written as

$$(x - a - b + 2ab)^2 = 4ab\left(1 - a\right)\left(1 - b\right)$$
$$(x - c - d + 2cd)^2 = 4cd\left(1 - c\right)\left(1 - d\right).$$

Then the Quadratic compatibility theorem (page 33) states that a, b, c and d must
satisfy

$$\left(\begin{array}{c} (a + b - 2ab - c - d + 2cd)^2 \\ -4\left(ab\left(1 - a\right)\left(1 - b\right) + cd\left(1 - c\right)\left(1 - d\right)\right) \end{array} \right)^2$$
$$= 64abcd\left(1 - a\right)\left(1 - b\right)\left(1 - c\right)\left(1 - d\right).$$

This compatibility condition may be rewritten more symmetrically as

$$\left(\begin{array}{c} (a + b + c + d)^2 - 2\left(a^2 + b^2 + c^2 + d^2\right) \\ -4\left(abc + abd + acd + bcd\right) + 8abcd \end{array} \right)^2$$
$$= 64abcd\left(1 - a\right)\left(1 - b\right)\left(1 - c\right)\left(1 - d\right).$$

The same theorem also asserts that if $a + b - 2ab \neq c + d - 2cd$ then

$$x = \frac{(a + b - 2ab) + (c + d - 2cd)}{2} - \frac{4ab\left(1 - a\right)\left(1 - b\right) - 4cd\left(1 - c\right)\left(1 - d\right)}{2\left(a + b - c - d - 2ab + 2cd\right)}$$

$$= \frac{(a - b)^2 - (c - d)^2}{2\left(a + b - c - d - 2ab + 2cd\right)}. \blacksquare$$

Definition The **Quadruple spread function** $R(a, b, c, d)$ is defined for numbers a, b, c and d by

$$R(a, b, c, d) \equiv \left(\frac{(a+b+c+d)^2 - 2(a^2+b^2+c^2+d^2)}{-4(abc+abd+acd+bcd)+8abcd} \right)^2 - 64abcd(1-a)(1-b)(1-c)(1-d).$$

Theorem 54 (Quadruple spread formula) Suppose l_1, l_2, l_3 and l_4 are non-null lines with $s_{ij} = s(l_i, l_j)$ for all $i, j = 1, 2, 3$ and 4. Then

$$R(s_{12}, s_{23}, s_{34}, s_{14}) = 0.$$

Furthermore

$$s_{13} = \frac{(s_{12} - s_{23})^2 - (s_{34} - s_{14})^2}{2(s_{12} + s_{23} - s_{34} - s_{14} - 2s_{12}s_{23} + 2s_{34}s_{14})}$$

$$s_{24} = \frac{(s_{23} - s_{34})^2 - (s_{12} - s_{14})^2}{2(s_{23} + s_{34} - s_{12} - s_{14} - 2s_{23}s_{34} + 2s_{12}s_{14})}$$

provided the denominators are non-zero.

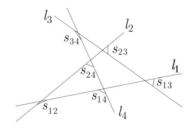

Figure 7.5: Four lines and their spreads

Proof. Since $\{s_{12}, s_{23}, s_{13}\}$ and $\{s_{14}, s_{34}, s_{13}\}$ are both spread triples, and $\{s_{23}, s_{34}, s_{24}\}$ and $\{s_{12}, s_{14}, s_{24}\}$ are also both spread triples, the formulas follow from the Two spread triples theorem. ∎

The Quadruple spread formula expresses s_{13} and s_{24} in terms of the four spreads s_{12}, s_{23}, s_{34} and s_{14}. Note that by symmetry it can also be restated to express s_{12} and s_{34} in terms of the four spreads s_{13}, s_{14}, s_{23} and s_{24}, or to express s_{14} and s_{23} in terms of the four spreads s_{12}, s_{13}, s_{24} and s_{34}.

Theorem 55 (Quadruple cross formula) Suppose l_1, l_2, l_3 and l_4 are non-null lines with $c_{ij} \equiv c(l_i, l_j)$ for all $i, j = 1, 2, 3$ and 4. Then

$$R(c_{12}, c_{23}, c_{34}, c_{14}) = 0.$$

Proof. The polynomial identity

$$(a + b + c + d)^2 - 2\left(a^2 + b^2 + c^2 + d^2\right)$$
$$- 4(abc + abd + acd + bcd) + 8abcd$$
$$= 4abcd + 4(1 - a)(1 - b)(1 - c)(1 - d)$$
$$- (a + b + c + d - 2)^2$$

has the property that the right hand side is unchanged if each of the numbers a, b, c and d is replaced by $1 - a, 1 - b, 1 - c$ and $1 - d$ respectively. That means the same is true for the left hand side, so that the Quadruple spread formula

$$R(s_{12}, s_{23}, s_{34}, s_{14}) = 0$$

remains true if each spread s_{ij} is replaced by the corresponding cross $c_{ij} = 1 - s_{ij}$. ∎

Note: This has exactly the same form as the Quadruple spread formula! This is an unexpected symmetry, not occurring in the analogous Triple spread and Triple cross formulas.

Exercise 7.13 Show that if $\{a, b, x\}$ and $\{b, c, x\}$ are spread triples with $a \neq c$ and $b \neq 1/2$ then

$$x = \frac{a + c - 2b}{2(1 - 2b)}. \quad \diamond$$

Exercise 7.14 Suppose l_1, l_2, l_3 and l_4 are non-null lines with $c_{ij} \equiv c(l_i, l_j)$ for all $i, j = 1, 2, 3$ and 4. Then show that

$$c_{13} = \frac{(c_{12} - c_{23})^2 - (c_{34} - c_{14})^2}{2(c_{12} + c_{23} - c_{34} - c_{14} - 2c_{12}c_{23} + 2c_{34}c_{14})}$$

$$c_{24} = \frac{(c_{23} - c_{34})^2 - (c_{12} - c_{14})^2}{2(c_{23} + c_{34} - c_{12} - c_{14} - 2c_{23}c_{34} + 2c_{12}c_{14})}. \quad \diamond$$

Exercise 7.15 (Harder) Is there a Quintuple spread formula? Generalize. ◇

8

Spread polynomials

Spread polynomials are the rational equivalents of the Chebyshev polynomials of the first kind, to which they are closely related. However they are defined in any field, suggesting an underlying 'universal' phenomenon behind aspects of the theory of special functions. In particular there is an interesting appearance of orthogonality in finite fields. The analogous cross polynomials are also discussed.

8.1 Combining equal spreads

Theorem 56 (Three equal spreads) Suppose that the lines l_0, l_1, l_2 and l_3 satisfy $s(l_0, l_1) = s(l_1, l_2) = s(l_2, l_3) \equiv s$, and that l_0 and l_2 are not parallel. Then

$$s(l_0, l_3) = s \qquad \text{or} \qquad s(l_0, l_3) = s(3 - 4s)^2.$$

Proof. By the Equal spreads theorem (page 94), $s(l_0, l_2) = 4s(1 - s)$. If $r \equiv s(l_0, l_3)$, then $\{4s(1 - s), s, r\}$ is a spread triple so that

$$(4s(1 - s) + r - s)^2 = 16s(1 - s)r(1 - s).$$

Simplify and factor to obtain

$$\left(r - s(3 - 4s)^2\right)(r - s) = 0$$

so that $r = s$ or

$$r = s(3 - 4s)^2. \quad \blacksquare$$

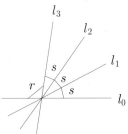

101

Exercise 8.1 Show that if the lines l_0, l_3 and l_4 form spreads $s(l_3, l_4) = s$ and $s(l_0, l_3) = s(3 - 4s)^2$, then

$$s(l_0, l_4) = 4s(1 - s) \qquad \text{or} \qquad s(l_0, l_4) = 16s(1 - s)(1 - 2s)^2. \quad \diamond$$

8.2 Spread polynomials

The above pattern gives rise to an important family of polynomials. The following recursive definition shows that these polynomials are defined with integer coefficients, so have an unambiguous meaning in any field, not of characteristic two.

Definition The **spread polynomial** $S_n(s)$ is defined recursively by

$$S_0(s) \equiv 0 \qquad \text{and} \qquad S_1(s) \equiv s$$

and the rule

$$S_n(s) \equiv 2(1 - 2s)S_{n-1}(s) - S_{n-2}(s) + 2s.$$

The coefficient of s^n in $S_n(s)$ is a power of four, so the degree of the polynomial $S_n(s)$ is n.

Theorem 57 (Recursive spreads) The polynomials $S_n(s)$ have the property that $\{S_{n-1}(s), s, S_n(s)\}$ is a spread triple for any $n \geq 1$ and any number s.

Proof. Fix a number s and use induction on n. For $n = 1$ the statement is immediate. For a general $n \geq 1$, $\{S_{n-1}(s), s, S_n(s)\}$ is a spread triple precisely when

$$(S_{n-1}(s) + s + S_n(s))^2 = 2(S_{n-1}^2(s) + s^2 + S_n^2(s)) + 4sS_{n-1}(s)S_n(s) \qquad (8.1)$$

while $\{S_n(s), s, S_{n+1}(s)\}$ is a spread triple precisely when

$$(S_n(s) + s + S_{n+1}(s))^2 = 2(S_n^2(s) + s^2 + S_{n+1}^2(s)) + 4sS_n(s)S_{n+1}(s). \qquad (8.2)$$

The difference between (8.1) and (8.2) can be rearranged and factored as

$$(S_{n+1}(s) - S_{n-1}(s))(S_{n+1}(s) - 2(1 - 2s)S_n(s) + S_{n-1}(s) - 2s) = 0.$$

Thus (8.2) follows from (8.1) if

$$S_{n+1}(s) = 2(1 - 2s)S_n(s) - S_{n-1}(s) + 2s.$$

This is the induction step of the proof. ∎

Theorem 58 (Consecutive spreads) Suppose that l_0 and l_1 are intersecting non-null lines with $s(l_0, l_1) \equiv s$, and define $l_{n+1} \equiv \Sigma_{l_n}(l_{n-1})$ for $n = 1, 2, 3, \cdots$. Then for any $n = 0, 1, 2, \cdots$

$$s(l_0, l_n) = S_n(s).$$

Proof. First note by the Spread reflection theorem (page 95) that

$$s = s(l_0, l_1) = s(l_1, l_2) = s(l_2, l_3) = \cdots.$$

To show that $s(l_0, l_n) = S_n(s)$ for all $n = 0, 1, 2, \cdots$ proceed by induction on n, with the cases $n = 0$ and 1 immediate.

For a general $n \geq 1$ assume that $s(l_0, l_k) = S_k(s)$ for all $k \leq n$. Let $s(l_0, l_{n+1}) \equiv r$. Then apply the Triple spread formula to the spreads made by the lines l_0, l_n and l_{n+1} to deduce that $\{S_n(s), s, r\}$ is a spread triple.

But by the Recursive spreads theorem

$$\{S_n(s), s, S_{n-1}(s)\} \qquad \text{and} \qquad \{S_n(s), s, S_{n+1}(s)\}$$

are both spread triples. Thus since a quadratic equation has at most two solutions, $r = S_{n+1}(s)$ or $r = S_{n-1}(s)$. If $r = S_{n+1}(s)$ then the induction is complete.

If $r = S_{n-1}(s)$ then

$$r = s(l_0, l_{n-1}) = s(l_0, l_{n+1})$$

so l_0 is a bisector of the vertex $\overline{l_{n-1}l_{n+1}}$, as is l_n. By the Vertex bisector theorem (page 85), l_0 and l_n are then either parallel or perpendicular, so that $S_n(s)$ is either 0 or 1. Let's consider both cases.

If $S_n(s) = 0$ then $\{0, s, r\}$ is a spread triple, and by the Recursive spreads theorem, so is $\{0, s, S_{n+1}(s)\}$. Then by Exercise 7.3

$$r = s = S_{n+1}(s).$$

If $S_n(s) = 1$ then $\{1, s, r\}$ is a spread triple, as is $\{1, s, S_{n+1}(s)\}$. Then by the same exercise,

$$1 = r + s = S_{n+1}(s) + s$$

so that again $r = S_{n+1}(s)$.

Thus if $r = S_{n-1}(s)$ then $r = S_{n+1}(s)$. So $s(l_0, l_{n+1}) = S_{n+1}(s)$ and the induction is complete. ∎

Definition The **order** of the spread s is the least natural number $n \geq 1$ such that $s_n \equiv S_n(s) = 0$, if it exists.

Definition If the order of the spread s is n, then the **spread sequence** of s is the list

$$[0, s_1, s_2, \cdots, s_{n-1}]$$

where $s_k \equiv S_k(s)$, for $k = 1, \cdots, n-1$.

Example 8.1 In $\mathbb{F}_{13}$ the non-zero spread numbers are $1, 4, 6, 7, 8$ and 10. The order of $s \equiv 6$ is 12, and the spread sequence of s is

$$[0, 6, 10, 7, 4, 8, 1, 8, 4, 7, 10, 6].$$

Since this spread sequence contains all the spreads, the other spread sequences can be easily determined from this one by stepping through the sequence in a circular fashion. This is a consequence of the Cyclic reflection theorem (page 56). (The situation is analogous to that of subgroups of the cyclic group with twelve elements). For example, the spread sequence for $s \equiv 10$ is

$$[0, 10, 4, 1, 4, 10]. \quad \diamond$$

Example 8.2 In $\mathbb{F}_{19}$ the non-zero spread numbers are $1, 2, 4, 8, 9, 10, 11, 12, 16$ and 18. The order of $s \equiv 8$ is 20 and the spread sequence of s is

$$[0, 8, 4, 2, 9, 10, 11, 18, 16, 12, 1, 12, 16, 18, 11, 10, 9, 2, 4, 8].$$

As in the previous example, all other spread sequences can be determined easily from this one by stepping cyclically through it. For example the spread sequence for $s \equiv 4$ is

$$[0, 4, 9, 11, 16, 1, 16, 11, 9, 4]$$

while that for $s \equiv 9$ (particularly important for five-fold symmetry) is

$$[0, 9, 16, 16, 9]. \quad \diamond$$

8.3   Special cases

The first few spread polynomials are

$$S_0(s) = 0$$
$$S_1(s) = s$$
$$S_2(s) = 4s - 4s^2 = 4s(1-s)$$
$$S_3(s) = 9s - 24s^2 + 16s^3 = s(3 - 4s)^2$$
$$S_4(s) = 16s - 80s^2 + 128s^3 - 64s^4 = 16s(1-s)(1-2s)^2$$
$$S_5(s) = 25s - 200s^2 + 560s^3 - 640s^4 + 256s^5 = s(5 - 20s + 16s^2)^2$$
$$S_6(s) = 36s - 420s^2 + 1792s^3 - 3456s^4 + 3072s^5 - 1024s^6$$
$$= 4s(1-s)(1-4s)^2(3-4s)^2$$
$$S_7(s) = 49s - 784s^2 + 4704s^3 - 13\,440s^4 + 19\,712s^5 - 14\,336s^6 + 4096s^7$$
$$= s(7 - 56s + 112s^2 - 64s^3)^2.$$

The spread polynomials make sense in any field. In the decimal number field, here are the graphs of $S_1(s)$, $S_2(s)$, $S_3(s)$, $S_4(s)$ and $S_5(s)$, both separately and together, in the interval $[0, 1]$. The function $S_2(s)$ is called the **logistic map** in chaos theory.

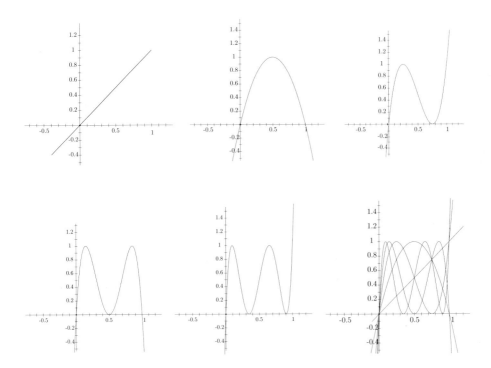

Example 8.3 Here is a table of values of spread polynomials in the field $\mathbb{F}_5$. Recall that the spread numbers in this field are $0, 1$ and 3.

s	0	1	2	3	4
$S_0(s)$	0	0	0	0	0
$S_1(s)$	0	1	2	3	4
$S_2(s)$	0	0	2	1	2
$S_3(s)$	0	1	0	3	1
$S_4(s)$	0	0	2	0	2
$S_5(s)$	0	1	2	3	4
$S_6(s)$	0	0	0	1	0
$S_7(s)$	0	1	2	3	4
$S_8(s)$	0	0	2	0	2
$S_9(s)$	0	1	0	3	1
$S_{10}(s)$	0	0	2	1	2
$S_{11}(s)$	0	1	2	3	4
$S_{12}(s)$	0	0	0	0	0

The pattern repeats with period 12, that is $S_n(s) = S_{n+12}(s)$ for all n and for all s. However for values of s which are spread numbers, $S_n(s) = S_{n+4}(s)$ for all n. ◇

Example 8.4 Here is a table of values of spread polynomials in the field $\mathbb{F}_7$. Recall that the spread numbers in this field are $0, 1, 3, 4$ and 5.

s	0	1	2	3	4	5	6
$S_0(s)$	0	0	0	0	0	0	0
$S_1(s)$	0	1	2	3	4	5	6
$S_2(s)$	0	0	6	4	1	4	6
$S_3(s)$	0	1	1	5	4	3	0
$S_4(s)$	0	0	6	1	0	1	6
$S_5(s)$	0	1	2	5	4	3	6
$S_6(s)$	0	0	0	4	1	4	0
$S_7(s)$	0	1	2	3	4	5	6
$S_8(s)$	0	0	6	0	0	0	6
$S_9(s)$	0	1	1	3	4	5	0
$S_{10}(s)$	0	0	6	4	1	4	6
$S_{11}(s)$	0	1	2	5	4	3	6
$S_{12}(s)$	0	0	0	1	0	1	0

s	0	1	2	3	4	5	6
$S_{13}(s)$	0	1	2	5	4	3	6
$S_{14}(s)$	0	0	6	4	1	4	6
$S_{15}(s)$	0	1	1	3	4	5	0
$S_{16}(s)$	0	0	6	0	0	0	6
$S_{17}(s)$	0	1	2	3	4	5	6
$S_{18}(s)$	0	0	0	4	1	4	0
$S_{19}(s)$	0	1	2	5	4	3	6
$S_{20}(s)$	0	0	6	1	0	1	6
$S_{21}(s)$	0	1	1	5	4	3	0
$S_{22}(s)$	0	0	6	4	1	4	6
$S_{23}(s)$	0	1	2	3	4	5	6
$S_{24}(s)$	0	0	0	0	0	0	0
$S_{25}(s)$	0	1	2	3	4	5	6

The pattern repeats with period 24, that is $S_n(s) = S_{n+24}(s)$ for all n and for all s. For values of s which are spread numbers, $S_n(s) = S_{n+8}(s)$ for all n. ◇

Exercise 8.2 (S. Goh) Show that in the field $\mathbb{F}_p$, if $k = (p-1)(p+1)/2$ then
$$S_n(s) = S_{n+k}(s)$$
for all n and for all s. ◇

Exercise 8.3 In the rational or decimal number fields, show that the spread polynomials satisfy $0 \leq S_n(s) \leq 1$ for $0 \leq s \leq 1$ and all n. ◇

Exercise 8.4 (Uses Chebyshev polynomials) In the decimal number field, show that if $T_n(x)$ is the nth Chebyshev polynomial of the first kind then
$$
\begin{aligned}
S_n(s) &= 1 - T_n^2\left(\sqrt{1-s}\right) \\
&= \frac{1 - T_n(1-2s)}{2}.
\end{aligned}
$$ ◇

8.4 Explicit formulas

Theorem 59 (Spread polynomial formula) Suppose that $4s(1-s) = r^2$ and that the field contains a number i satisfying $i^2 = -1$. Then for any $n = 0, 1, 2, \cdots$
$$S_n(s) = \frac{2 - (1 - 2s + ir)^n - (1 - 2s - ir)^n}{4}.$$

Proof. Use induction on n. For $n = 0$ and $n = 1$ the formula in the theorem agrees with the values $S_0(s) = 0$ and $S_1(s) = s$. Assume that the formula holds for values up to and including n. Then set

$$C \equiv 1 - 2s + ir \qquad D \equiv 1 - 2s - ir$$

so that

$$
\begin{aligned}
S_{n+1}(s) &\equiv 2(1 - 2s) S_n(s) - S_{n-1}(s) + 2s \\
&= 2(1 - 2s)\left(\frac{2 - (1 - 2s + ir)C^{n-1} - (1 - 2s - ir)D^{n-1}}{4}\right) \\
&\quad - \left(\frac{2 - C^{n-1} - D^{n-1}}{4}\right) + 2s \\
&= \frac{1}{2} - \frac{C^{n-1}}{4}\left(1 - 8s + 8s^2 + 2ir - 4irs\right) \\
&\quad - \frac{D^{n-1}}{4}\left(1 - 8s + 8s^2 - 2ir + 4irs\right).
\end{aligned}
$$

But the assumption on r means that

$$
\begin{aligned}
(1 - 2s + ir)^2 &= 1 - 8s + 8s^2 + 2ir - 4irs = C^2 \\
(1 - 2s - ir)^2 &= 1 - 8s + 8s^2 - 2ir + 4irs = D^2
\end{aligned}
$$

so that indeed

$$
\begin{aligned}
S_{n+1}(s) &= \frac{1}{2} - \frac{C^{n+1}}{4} - \frac{D^{n+1}}{4} \\
&= \frac{2 - (1 - 2s + ir)^{n+1} - (1 - 2s - ir)^{n+1}}{4}. \qquad \blacksquare
\end{aligned}
$$

Note that even if the field does not contain a number i satisfying $i^2 = -1$, a quadratic extension of it does, so the formula in the previous theorem works quite generally.

Exercise 8.5 Show that in the field $\mathbb{F}_p$, $S_p(s) = s$ for all s. $\diamond$

Exercise 8.6 Use the Spread polynomial theorem and the Binomial theorem to show that if $a \equiv 1 - 2s$ and $b \equiv 4s(1 - s)$ then

$$1 - 2S_n(s) = a^n - \binom{n}{2}a^{n-2}b + \binom{n}{4}a^{n-4}b^2 - \cdots$$

ending either in $(-b)^l$ if $n = 2l$ or $na(-b)^l$ if $n = 2l + 1$. $\diamond$

The next exercise is motivated by Problem 222 in [Shklarsky-Chentzov-Yaglom].

Exercise 8.7 (Harder) Show that if $n = 2l + 1$ is an odd natural number then

$$S_n(s) = s\left(\binom{n}{1}(1 - s)^l - \binom{n}{3}(1 - s)^{l-1}s + \binom{n}{5}(1 - s)^{l-2}s^2 - \cdots + (-1)^l s^l\right)^2. \quad \diamond$$

Exercise 8.8 (S. Goh) Show that $S_1(s)$, $S_2(s)$, $S_3(s)$, $S_4(s) \cdots$ can be written as

$$
\left|s\right|, \quad
\begin{vmatrix} 2-4s & 1 \\ -2s & s \end{vmatrix}, \quad
\begin{vmatrix} 2-4s & -1 & 1 \\ -1 & 2-4s & 1 \\ 0 & -2s & s \end{vmatrix},
$$

$$
\begin{vmatrix}
2-4s & -1 & 0 & 1 \\
-1 & 2-4s & -1 & 1 \\
0 & -1 & 2-4s & 1 \\
0 & 0 & -2s & s
\end{vmatrix} \cdots . \ \diamond
$$

Exercise 8.9 (M. Hirschhorn, S. Goh) Show that for any natural number n

$$
S_n(s) = s \sum_{k=0}^{n-1} \frac{n}{n-k} \binom{2n-1-k}{k} (-4s)^{n-k-1}. \ \diamond
$$

Define the **scaled spread polynomials** $S_n^*(r) = 4S_n(r/4)$. As observed by M. Hirschhorn, they can be evaluated as follows. Write Pascal's triangle so that the usual 'rows' are appearing diagonally, and each entry is the sum of the number above it and the number diagonally above it to its left, as in the left-most array below.

$$
\begin{bmatrix}
1 \\
1 & 1 \\
1 & 2 & 1 \\
1 & 3 & 3 & 1 \\
1 & 3 & 6 & 4 & 1 \\
1 & 4 & 10 & 10 & 5 & 1 \\
1 & 10 & 15 & 20 & 15 & 6 & 1 \\
\vdots & & \vdots & & & \ddots
\end{bmatrix}
\qquad
\begin{bmatrix}
1 \\
1 & 1 \\
3 & 4 & 1 \\
5 & 9 & 5 & 1 \\
7 & 16 & 14 & 6 & 1 \\
& & & 20 & 7 & 1 \\
\vdots & & \vdots & & & \ddots
\end{bmatrix}
$$

Now slide Pascal's array down two steps, add the result to the original array, and disregard the first column, to get the **spread array**, as in the right-most array above. Every entry outside of the first column of the spread array is still the sum of the entry above it and the entry diagonally above it to the left. The first column of the spread array contains all the odd numbers, and the second column contains all the non-zero squares. Then those rows of the spread array beginning with the square numbers in the second column give the coefficients of the scaled spread polynomials, beginning with r, then r^2 and so on. For example the row beginning with the third square 9 yields

$$
S_3^*(r) = 9r - 6r^2 + r^3.
$$

Exercise 8.10 (M. Hirschhorn) Show that a generating function for the spread polynomials is

$$
\sum_{n=1}^{\infty} S_n(s) x^n = \frac{sx(1+x)}{(1-x)^3 + 4sx(1-x)}. \ \diamond
$$

8.5 Orthogonality

This is a brief introduction to a phenomenon that requires more study. In the field $\mathbb{F}_5$ the array of values

$$\sum_{k=0}^{4} S_m(k) S_n(k) \equiv a_{m,n}$$

where m and n are indexed by $0, 1, 2, 3$ and 4 is

$m\backslash n$	0	1	2	3	4
0	0	0	0	0	0
1	0	0	0	4	2
2	0	0	4	0	3
3	0	4	0	1	2
4	0	2	3	2	3

In the field $\mathbb{F}_7$ the array of values

$$\sum_{k=0}^{6} S_m(k) S_n(k) \equiv a_{m,n}$$

where m and n are indexed by $0, 1, \cdots, 6$ is

$m\backslash n$	0	1	2	3	4	5	6
0	0	0	0	0	0	0	0
1	0	0	0	0	0	3	1
2	0	0	0	0	3	0	5
3	0	0	0	3	0	4	1
4	0	0	3	0	4	0	1
5	0	3	0	4	0	0	1
6	0	1	5	1	1	1	5

Exercise 8.11 (Harder) In the field $\mathbb{F}_p$ show that for $1 \le m, n \le p - 2$

$$\sum_{k=0}^{p-1} S_m(k) S_n(k) = 0$$

unless $m + n = p \pm 1$. What are the values of the sum in these latter cases? ◇

Exercise 8.12 (Uses Chebyshev polynomials) Show that over the decimal number field, if $m \ne n$ then

$$\int_0^1 \frac{(S_m(s) - 1/2)(S_n(s) - 1/2)}{\sqrt{s(1-s)}} ds = 0$$

while if $m = n$ the integral equals $\pi/4$. Hint: See Exercise 8.4 and Example 27.1. ◇

8.6   Composition of spread polynomials

Define the **composition** $S_n \circ S_m$ of spread polynomials S_n and S_m by the rule

$$(S_n \circ S_m)(s) = S_n(S_m(s)).$$

Theorem 60 (Spread composition) For any natural numbers n and m

$$S_n \circ S_m = S_{nm}.$$

Proof. Since the spread polynomials have integer coefficients, it suffices to prove this over the rational number field. Suppose that s is a spread number, so that by the Spread number theorem (page 76) there are lines l_0 and l_1 with $s(l_0, l_1) = s$. Consider the reflection sequence

$$\cdots, l_{-2}, l_{-1}, l_0, l_1, l_2, \cdots \qquad (8.3)$$

characterized by the condition that for any integer n

$$\Sigma_{l_n}(l_{n-1}) = l_{n+1}.$$

The Consecutive spreads theorem (page 103) states that for any natural number k

$$S_k(s) = s(l_0, l_k)$$

and in particular for any natural numbers n and m,

$$S_{nm}(s) = s(l_0, l_{nm}).$$

Suppose that $S_m(s) = s(l_0, l_m) \equiv r$. Now consider the two sided subsequence

$$\cdots, l_{-2m}, l_{-m}, l_0, l_m, l_{2m}, \cdots \qquad (8.4)$$

of (8.3). The Cyclic reflection theorem (page 56) shows that

$$\Sigma_{l_m}(l_0) = l_{2m} \qquad \Sigma_{l_{2m}}(l_m) = l_{3m}$$

and so on, so that more generally

$$\Sigma_{l_{km}}(l_{jm}) = l_{(2k-j)m}.$$

This means that (8.4) is itself a reflection sequence with common spread r. But then

$$S_{nm}(s) = s(l_0, l_{nm}) = S_n(r) = S_n(S_m(s)) = (S_n \circ S_m)(s).$$

Since $(S_n \circ S_m)(s)$ and $S_{nm}(s)$ agree for any spread numbers s, and there are more spread numbers than the degree nm, the two polynomials are equal. ∎

It follows that the values of S_n for prime values of n are particularly basic, and to calculate S_n for large values of n this theorem is more effective than the recursive definition. Another consequence is a pleasant commutativity and associativity of composition for spread polynomials; that is

$$S_n \circ S_m = S_m \circ S_n$$
$$(S_n \circ S_m) \circ S_k = S_n \circ (S_m \circ S_k).$$

Example 8.5 Using
$$S_3(s) = s(3 - 4s)^2$$
and
$$S_5(s) = s(5 - 20s + 16s^2)^2$$
you find that

$$S_{15}(s) = S_3(S_5(s)) = s(5 - 20s + 16s^2)^2(3 - 4s(5 - 20s + 16s^2)^2)^2$$
$$= s(3 - 4s)^2(5 - 20s + 16s^2)^2(1 - 32s + 224s^2 - 448s^3 + 256s^4)^2.$$

In the same vein

$$S_{30}(s) = S_2(S_{15}(s)) = 4S_{15}(s)(1 - S_{15}(s))$$
$$= 4s(1 - s)(3 - 4s)^2(5 - 20s + 16s^2)^2(1 - 32s + 224s^2 - 448s^3 + 256s^4)^2$$
$$\times (1 - 4s)^2(1 - 12s + 16s^2)^2(1 - 96s + 416s^2 - 576s^3 + 256s)^2. \quad \diamond$$

Exercise 8.13 (S. Goh) Show that for every $k = 1, 2, 3, \cdots$ there is a polynomial $\Phi_k(s)$ with integer coefficients of degree $\phi(k)$, where ϕ is Euler's totient function, such that for any $n = 1, 2, 3, \cdots$
$$S_n(s) = \prod_{k|n} \Phi_k(s).$$
The first few values of these 'spread-cyclotomic' polynomials are

$$\Phi_1(s) = s \qquad\qquad \Phi_2(s) = 4(1 - s)$$
$$\Phi_3(s) = (3 - 4s)^2 \qquad\qquad \Phi_4(s) = 4(1 - 2s)^2$$
$$\Phi_5(s) = (5 - 20s + 16s^2)^2 \qquad\qquad \Phi_6(s) = (1 - 4s)^2$$
$$\Phi_7(s) = (7 - 56s + 112s^2 - 64s^3)^2 \qquad\qquad \Phi_8(s) = 4(1 - 8s + 8s^2)^2.$$

So for example since also $\Phi_{12}(s) = (1 - 16s + 16s^2)^2$,

$$S_{12}(s) = \Phi_1(s)\Phi_2(s)\Phi_3(s)\Phi_4(s)\Phi_6(s)\Phi_{12}(s)$$
$$= 16s(1 - s)(3 - 4s)^2(1 - 2s)^2(1 - 4s)^2(1 - 16s + 16s^2)^2. \quad \diamond$$

8.7 Cross polynomials

Definition The **cross polynomials** $C_n (c)$ are defined recursively by

$$C_0 (c) \equiv 1 \qquad \text{and} \qquad C_1 (c) \equiv c$$

and the rule

$$C_n (c) \equiv 2 (2c - 1) C_{n-1} (c) - C_{n-2} (c) + 2 (1 - c).$$

The properties of the cross polynomials are analogous and closely related to those of the spread polynomials. They will be developed here in the form of a number of exercises.

Exercise 8.14 Show that the polynomials $C_n (c)$ have the property that for any $n \geq 1$ and any c, the numbers $C_{n-1} (c) , c$ and $C_n (c)$ satisfy the Triple cross formula. $\diamond$

Exercise 8.15 Verify that the first few cross polynomials are

$$C_0 (c) = 1$$
$$C_1 (c) = c$$
$$C_2 (c) = 1 - 4c + 4c^2 = (1 - 2c)^2$$
$$C_3 (c) = 9c - 24c^2 + 16c^3 = c (3 - 4c)^2$$
$$C_4 (c) = 1 - 16c + 80c^2 - 128c^3 + 64c^4 = \left(1 - 8c + 8c^2\right)^2$$
$$C_5 (c) = c \left(5 - 20c + 16c^2\right)^2$$
$$C_6 (c) = (1 - 2c)^2 \left(1 - 16c + 16c^2\right)^2 . \diamond$$

Exercise 8.16 Show that for any natural numbers n and m

$$C_n (C_m (c)) = C_{nm} (c) . \diamond$$

Exercise 8.17 Show that if $c + s = 1$ then $C_n (c) + S_n (s) = 1.$ $\diamond$

Exercise 8.18 Show that if n is odd then $C_n (t) = S_n (t)$, and that if n is even then $C_n (t) = 1 - S_n (t).$ $\diamond$

Exercise 8.19 Show that for any n

$$(C_n (t) - S_n (1 - t))^2 = C_{2n} (t)$$

and

$$4S_n (t) C_n (1 - t) = S_{2n} (t) .$$

Generalize. $\diamond$

Exercise 8.20 Show how the coefficients of the **scaled cross polynomials** $C_n^* (r) = 4C_n (r/4)$ can be read off from the rows of the spread array. $\diamond$

Oriented triangles and turns

There is an alternative way to develop rational trigonometry, where the fundamental object is not a triangle $\overline{A_1 A_2 A_3}$, but rather an *oriented triangle* $\overrightarrow{A_1 A_2 A_3}$. In this book, which emphasizes geometry, the unoriented approach takes precedence, but the oriented version is useful in applications to calculus, and is simpler in some situations.

This chapter introduces the more refined notions of oriented sides and vertices, oriented triangles and oriented n-gons. This allows a definition of *signed area*, so that the quadrea $\mathcal{A}$ of a triangle becomes sixteen times the square of the signed area, and allows the extension of quadrea to n-gons.

The twist of a vertex can be written as the square of the *turn* of one of the associated oriented vertices. The *Triple turn formula* then turns out to be linear in any of the three turns. Instead of turn polynomials one finds *turn rational functions*, which are well-known. Bretschneider's formula for the quadrea of a quadrilateral is established.

9.1 Oriented sides, vertices and triangles

Definition An **oriented side** $\overrightarrow{A_1 A_2}$ is an ordered pair $[A_1, A_2]$ of distinct points. An **oriented vertex** $\overrightarrow{l_1 l_2}$ is an ordered pair $[l_1, l_2]$ of distinct intersecting lines.

Definition An **oriented triangle** $\overrightarrow{A_1 A_2 A_3}$ is a list $[A_1, A_2, A_3]$ of distinct non-collinear points, with the convention that

$$\overrightarrow{A_1 A_2 A_3} \equiv \overrightarrow{A_2 A_3 A_1} \equiv \overrightarrow{A_3 A_1 A_2}.$$

The points A_1, A_2 and A_3 are the **points**, and the lines $l_1 \equiv A_2A_3$, $l_2 \equiv A_1A_3$ and $l_3 \equiv A_1A_2$ are the **lines** of the oriented triangle $\overrightarrow{A_1A_2A_3}$. Also $\overrightarrow{A_1A_2}$, $\overrightarrow{A_2A_3}$ and $\overrightarrow{A_3A_1}$ are the **oriented sides** of the oriented triangle $\overrightarrow{A_1A_2A_3}$, while $\overrightarrow{l_1l_2}$, $\overrightarrow{l_2l_3}$ and $\overrightarrow{l_3l_1}$ are the **oriented vertices** of $\overrightarrow{A_1A_2A_3}$.

An oriented side $\overrightarrow{A_1A_2}$ determines a side $\overline{A_1A_2}$, and similarly an oriented vertex $\overrightarrow{l_1l_2}$ determines a vertex $\overline{l_1l_2}$. An oriented triangle $\overrightarrow{A_1A_2A_3}$ determines a triangle $\overline{A_1A_2A_3}$, and to every triangle $\overline{A_1A_2A_3}$ there are correspondingly two oriented triangles, namely $\overrightarrow{A_1A_2A_3}$ and the **opposite** oriented triangle $\overrightarrow{A_3A_2A_1}$.

Definition An **oriented quadrilateral** $\overrightarrow{A_1A_2A_3A_4}$ is a cyclical list $[A_1, A_2, A_3, A_4]$ of distinct points, meaning that

$$\overrightarrow{A_1A_2A_3A_4} \equiv \overrightarrow{A_2A_3A_4A_1} = \overrightarrow{A_3A_4A_1A_2} \equiv \overrightarrow{A_4A_1A_2A_3}$$

and such that no three consecutive points are collinear (including A_3, A_4, A_1 and A_4, A_1, A_2).

Define $l_{ij} \equiv A_iA_j$ for $i \neq j$. The points A_1, A_2, A_3 and A_4 are the **points** of the oriented quadrilateral, and the lines l_{12}, l_{23}, l_{34} and l_{41} are the **lines** of the oriented quadrilateral. Also $\overrightarrow{A_1A_2}$, $\overrightarrow{A_2A_3}$, $\overrightarrow{A_3A_4}$ and $\overrightarrow{A_4A_1}$ are the **oriented sides** of the oriented quadrilateral $\overrightarrow{A_1A_2A_3A_4}$, while $\overrightarrow{l_{12}l_{23}}$, $\overrightarrow{l_{23}l_{34}}$, $\overrightarrow{l_{34}l_{41}}$ and $\overrightarrow{l_{41}l_{12}}$ are the **oriented vertices** of $\overrightarrow{A_1A_2A_3A_4}$.

These definitions extend to an oriented 5-gon $\overrightarrow{A_1A_2A_3A_4A_5}$ and beyond in the obvious fashion. As with triangles, an oriented n-gon $\overrightarrow{A_1A_2 \cdots A_n}$ has associated to it the n-gon $\overline{A_1A_2 \cdots A_n}$, and to any such n-gon there are correspondingly two oriented n-gons, namely $\overrightarrow{A_1A_2 \cdots A_n}$ and its **opposite** oriented n-gon $\overrightarrow{A_nA_n \cdots A_1}$.

9.2   Turns of oriented vertices

Definition If $l_1 \equiv \langle a_1 : b_1 : c_1 \rangle$ and $l_2 \equiv \langle a_2 : b_2 : c_2 \rangle$ are non-perpendicular lines then the **turn** of the oriented vertex $\overrightarrow{l_1l_2}$ is the number

$$u\left(\overrightarrow{l_1l_2}\right) \equiv u\left(l_1, l_2\right) \equiv \frac{a_1b_2 - a_2b_1}{a_1a_2 + b_1b_2}.$$

Comparing with the definition of twist $t\left(l_1, l_2\right)$, observe that

$$t\left(l_1, l_2\right) = \left(u\left(l_1, l_2\right)\right)^2.$$

Note also that $u\left(l_1, l_2\right) = -u\left(l_2, l_1\right)$ so that order matters with turns.

If the triangle $\overline{A_1 A_2 A_3}$ has points $A_1 \equiv [x_1, y_1]$, $A_2 \equiv [x_2, y_2]$ and $A_3 \equiv [x_3, y_3]$, then by the Line through two points theorem (page 38) the lines $l_1 \equiv A_2 A_3$ and $l_2 \equiv A_1 A_3$ are

$$
\begin{aligned}
l_1 &= \langle y_2 - y_3 : x_3 - x_2 : x_2 y_3 - x_3 y_2 \rangle \\
l_2 &= \langle y_1 - y_3 : x_3 - x_1 : x_1 y_3 - x_3 y_1 \rangle .
\end{aligned}
$$

The turn $u(l_1, l_2)$ can therefore be written as

$$
u(l_1, l_2) = \frac{(y_2 - y_3)(x_3 - x_1) - (y_1 - y_3)(x_3 - x_2)}{(y_2 - y_3)(y_1 - y_3) + (x_3 - x_2)(x_3 - x_1)}.
$$

The following lovely result is closely related to the Triple twist formula (page 115), but is clearly more elementary. This is an example where the oriented theory is simpler than the unoriented one.

Theorem 61 (Triple turn formula) Suppose that l_1, l_2 and l_3 are lines, no two perpendicular, with the turns $u_1 \equiv u(l_2, l_3)$, $u_2 \equiv u(l_3, l_1)$ and $u_3 \equiv u(l_1, l_2)$. Then

$$
u_1 + u_2 + u_3 = u_1 u_2 u_3.
$$

Proof. Suppose that $l_1 \equiv \langle a_1 : b_1 : c_1 \rangle$, $l_2 \equiv \langle a_2 : b_2 : c_2 \rangle$ and $l_3 \equiv \langle a_3 : b_3 : c_3 \rangle$. Then

$$
\begin{aligned}
u_1 &= \frac{a_2 b_3 - a_3 b_2}{a_2 a_3 + b_2 b_3} \\
u_2 &= \frac{a_3 b_1 - a_1 b_3}{a_3 a_1 + b_3 b_1} \\
u_3 &= \frac{a_1 b_2 - a_2 b_1}{a_1 a_2 + b_1 b_2}.
\end{aligned}
$$

The polynomial identity

$$
\begin{aligned}
&(a_2 b_3 - a_3 b_2)(a_3 a_1 + b_3 b_1)(a_1 a_2 + b_1 b_2) \\
&+ (a_3 b_1 - a_1 b_3)(a_2 a_3 + b_2 b_3)(a_1 a_2 + b_1 b_2) \\
&+ (a_1 b_2 - a_2 b_1)(a_2 a_3 + b_2 b_3)(a_3 a_1 + b_3 b_1) \\
&= (a_1 b_2 - a_2 b_1)(a_2 b_3 - a_3 b_2)(a_3 b_1 - a_1 b_3)
\end{aligned}
$$

implies that

$$
u_1 + u_2 + u_3 = u_1 u_2 u_3. \quad \blacksquare
$$

Note that the Triple turn formula is linear in any one of the variables u_1, u_2 and u_3, so that for example if u_1 and u_2 are known then

$$
u_3 = \frac{u_1 + u_2}{u_1 u_2 - 1}.
$$

Exercise 9.1 (Triple coturn formula) If $l_1 \equiv \langle a_1 : b_1 : c_1 \rangle$ and $l_2 \equiv \langle a_2 : b_2 : c_2 \rangle$ are non-parallel lines then define the **coturn** $o(l_1, l_2)$ to be

$$o(l_1, l_2) = \frac{a_1 a_2 + b_1 b_2}{a_1 b_2 - a_2 b_1}.$$

Show that

$$o_1 o_2 + o_2 o_3 + o_3 o_1 = 1. \quad \diamond$$

Exercise 9.2 Show that if $u \equiv u(l_0, l_1)$ and $v \equiv u(l_1, l_2)$ then

$$w \equiv u(l_0, l_2) = \frac{u + v}{1 - uv}.$$

Deduce that if $u = v$ then

$$w = \frac{2u}{1 - u^2}. \quad \diamond$$

Exercise 9.3 Carrying on from the previous exercise, suppose that

$$u(l_0, l_1) = u(l_1, l_2) = \cdots = u(l_{n-1}, l_n) \equiv u$$

for some reflection sequence of lines $l_0, l_1, \cdots, l_n$. For a natural number n, define the **turn (rational) function** U_n by the rule $U_n(u) \equiv u(l_0, l_n)$. Show that

$$
\begin{aligned}
U_1(u) &= u \\
U_2(u) &= \frac{2u}{1 - u^2} \\
U_3(u) &= \frac{3u - u^3}{1 - 3u^2} \\
U_4(u) &= \frac{4u - 4u^3}{1 - 6u^2 + u^4} \\
U_5(u) &= \frac{5u - 10u^3 + u^5}{1 - 10u^2 + 5u^4}.
\end{aligned}
$$

State and prove the general form for $U_n(u)$. $\diamond$

9.3   Signed areas

Definition The **signed area** a of the oriented triangle $\overrightarrow{A_1 A_2 A_3}$ with points $A_1 \equiv [x_1, y_1]$, $A_2 \equiv [x_2, y_2]$ and $A_3 \equiv [x_3, y_3]$ is the number

$$a \equiv a\left(\overrightarrow{A_1 A_2 A_3}\right) \equiv \frac{x_1 y_2 - x_2 y_1 + x_2 y_3 - x_3 y_2 + x_3 y_1 - x_1 y_3}{2} = \frac{1}{2} \begin{vmatrix} x_1 & y_1 & 1 \\ x_2 & y_2 & 1 \\ x_3 & y_3 & 1 \end{vmatrix}.$$

This formula makes sense even if the points are collinear, in which case it gives the value 0. Note that the convention for ordering the six terms involved in a is different than in previous chapters. If $\mathcal{A}$ is the quadrea of $\overline{A_1 A_2 A_3}$ then by the Quadrea theorem (page 68)

$$\mathcal{A} = 16a^2.$$

Theorem 62 (Signed area) For an oriented n-gon $\overrightarrow{A_1 A_2 \cdots A_n}$ and a point P, the sum

$$a \equiv a\left(\overrightarrow{PA_1 A_2}\right) + a\left(\overrightarrow{PA_2 A_3}\right) + \cdots + a\left(\overrightarrow{PA_{n-1} A_n}\right) + a\left(\overrightarrow{PA_n A_1}\right)$$

is independent of P. If $A_i \equiv [x_i, y_i]$ for $i = 1, 2, \cdots, n$ then

$$a = \frac{x_1 y_2 - x_2 y_1 + x_2 y_3 - x_3 y_2 + \cdots + x_{n-1} y_n - x_n y_{n-1} + x_n y_1 - x_1 y_n}{2}.$$

Proof. Suppose that $P \equiv [x_0, y_0]$ and $A_i \equiv [x_i, y_i]$ for $i = 1, 2, \cdots, n$. Note that

$$a\left(\overrightarrow{PA_1 A_2}\right) = \frac{1}{2} x_0 \left(y_1 - y_2\right) + \frac{1}{2} y_0 \left(x_2 - x_1\right) + \frac{1}{2} x_1 y_2 - \frac{1}{2} x_2 y_1.$$

Thus in the sum

$$a \equiv a\left(\overrightarrow{PA_1 A_2}\right) + a\left(\overrightarrow{PA_2 A_3}\right) + \cdots + a\left(\overrightarrow{PA_{n-1} A_n}\right) + a\left(\overrightarrow{PA_n A_1}\right)$$

all the terms involving x_0 and y_0 cancel, and what is left is

$$a = \frac{x_1 y_2 - x_2 y_1 + x_2 y_3 - x_3 y_2 + \cdots + x_{n-1} y_n - x_n y_{n-1} + x_n y_1 - x_1 y_n}{2}. \quad \blacksquare$$

Definition The expression a in the above theorem is the **signed area** of the oriented n-gon $\overrightarrow{A_1 A_2 \cdots A_n}$ and is denoted $a\left(\overrightarrow{A_1 A_2 \cdots A_n}\right)$.

In particular the signed area of the oriented quadrilateral $\overrightarrow{A_1 A_2 A_3 A_4}$ with points $A_1 \equiv [x_1, y_1]$, $A_2 \equiv [x_2, y_2]$, $A_3 \equiv [x_3, y_3]$ and $A_4 \equiv [x_4, y_4]$ is

$$a \equiv a\left(\overrightarrow{A_1 A_2 A_3 A_4}\right) = \frac{x_1 y_2 - x_2 y_1 + x_2 y_3 - x_3 y_2 + x_3 y_4 - x_4 y_3 + x_4 y_1 - x_1 y_4}{2}. \quad (9.1)$$

Exercise 9.4 Show that the signed area of the oriented quadrilateral $\overrightarrow{A_1 A_2 A_3 A_4}$ with points

$$A_1 \equiv [k, 0] \qquad A_2 \equiv [l, 0] \qquad A_3 \equiv [l, n] \qquad A_4 \equiv [k, m]$$

is

$$a = (m + n)(l - k)/2. \quad \diamond$$

Exercise 9.5 Show that for any oriented n-gon $\overrightarrow{A_1 A_2 \cdots A_n}$

$$a\left(\overrightarrow{A_1 A_2 \cdots A_n}\right) = a\left(\overrightarrow{A_1 A_2 A_3}\right) + a\left(\overrightarrow{A_1 A_3 A_4}\right) + \cdots + a\left(\overrightarrow{A_1 A_{n-1} A_n}\right). \quad \diamond$$

Exercise 9.6 Show that if $3 \le m < n$, then for any oriented n-gon $\overrightarrow{A_1 A_2 \cdots A_n}$

$$a\left(\overrightarrow{A_1 A_2 \cdots A_n}\right) = a\left(\overrightarrow{A_1 A_2 \cdots A_m}\right) + a\left(\overrightarrow{A_1 A_m A_{m+1} \cdots A_n}\right). \quad \diamond$$

Exercise 9.7 Show that $a\left(\overrightarrow{A_n A_{n-1} \cdots A_1}\right) = -a\left(\overrightarrow{A_1 A_2 \cdots A_n}\right). \quad \diamond$

Definition For $n \ge 4$ the **quadrea** $\mathcal{A}$ of an n-gon $\overrightarrow{A_1 A_2 \cdots A_n}$ is

$$\mathcal{A} \equiv 16a^2$$

where a is the signed area of the oriented n-gon $\overrightarrow{A_1 A_2 \cdots A_n}$.

This is well-defined by the previous exercise, and extends the definition of quadrea of a triangle.

Theorem 63 (Bretschneider's formula) Suppose that $\overrightarrow{A_1 A_2 A_3 A_4}$ is a quadrilateral with $Q_{ij} \equiv Q(A_i, A_j)$ for all $i, j = 1, 2, 3$ and 4. Then the quadrea $\mathcal{A}$ of $\overrightarrow{A_1 A_2 A_3 A_4}$ is

$$\mathcal{A} = 4Q_{13}Q_{24} - (Q_{12} + Q_{34} - Q_{23} - Q_{14})^2.$$

Proof. Suppose that $A_1 \equiv [x_1, y_1]$, $A_2 \equiv [x_2, y_2]$, $A_3 \equiv [x_3, y_3]$ and $A_4 \equiv [x_4, y_4]$, so that

$$Q_{ij} = (x_j - x_i)^2 + (y_j - y_i)^2$$

for all $i, j = 1, 2, 3$ and 4. Then

$$(Q_{12} + Q_{34} - Q_{23} - Q_{14})^2 = 4(x_1 x_2 + x_3 x_4 - x_1 x_4 - x_2 x_3 + y_1 y_2 + y_3 y_4 - y_1 y_4 - y_2 y_3)^2$$

while from (9.1) and the definition of quadrea,

$$\mathcal{A} = 4(x_1 y_2 - x_2 y_1 + x_2 y_3 - x_3 y_2 + x_3 y_4 - x_4 y_3 + x_4 y_1 - x_1 y_4)^2.$$

Add these two expressions and factor to obtain the surprising relation

$$\begin{aligned}
&(Q_{12} + Q_{34} - Q_{23} - Q_{14})^2 + \mathcal{A} \\
= \ &4\left((x_1 - x_3)^2 + (y_1 - y_3)^2\right)\left((x_2 - x_4)^2 + (y_2 - y_4)^2\right) \\
= \ &4Q_{13}Q_{24}.
\end{aligned}$$

Thus

$$\mathcal{A} = 4Q_{13}Q_{24} - (Q_{12} + Q_{34} - Q_{23} - Q_{14})^2. \quad \blacksquare$$

Part III

Universal Geometry

Triangles

Universal geometry parallels Euclidean geometry, except that all theorems in the subject are necessarily valid over a general field, excluding characteristic two. In this chapter, basic and useful facts about isosceles, equilateral and right triangles are derived, and congruent and similar triangles are defined.

10.1 Isosceles triangles

Definition A triangle is **isosceles** precisely when at least two of its quadrances are equal.

Theorem 64 (Null isosceles) An isosceles triangle has either zero or two null lines.

Proof. As in Exercise 3.12, a triangle cannot have three null lines, for by the Null line theorem (page 60) this would imply that all three quadrances are zero, in which case the quadrea is zero, which is impossible by the Quadrea theorem (page 68).

Suppose that $\overline{A_1 A_2 A_3}$ is isosceles, with quadrances $Q_1 = Q_2 \equiv Q$ and Q_3, and with exactly one null line. If this line is $A_1 A_3$ or $A_2 A_3$ then $Q = 0$ which means that both $A_1 A_3$ and $A_2 A_3$ are null which is a contradiction. Otherwise $A_1 A_2$ is null, so $Q_3 = 0$ and $Q \neq 0$. The Cross law (page 81) then states that

$$(Q + Q - 0)^2 = 4Q^2 c_3$$

from which $c_3 = 1$, and so $A_1 A_3$ and $A_2 A_3$ are parallel, which is impossible for a triangle. ■

Theorem 65 (Pons Asinorum) In a non-null triangle $Q_1 = Q_2$ precisely when $s_1 = s_2$.

Proof. This follows from the Spread law

$$\frac{s_1}{Q_1} = \frac{s_2}{Q_2} = \frac{s_3}{Q_3}. \quad \blacksquare$$

Theorem 66 (Isosceles triangle) Suppose a non-null triangle $\overline{A_1 A_2 A_3}$ has quadrances $Q_1 = Q_2 \equiv Q$ and Q_3, and corresponding spreads $s_1 = s_2 \equiv s$ and s_3. Then

$$Q_3 = 4Q (1 - s)$$

and

$$s_3 = \frac{Q_3}{Q} \left(1 - \frac{Q_3}{4Q} \right).$$

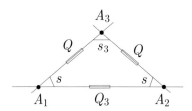

Figure 10.1: Isosceles triangle theorem

Proof. Combine the Equal spreads theorem (page 94)

$$s_3 = 4s (1 - s)$$

and the Spread law

$$\frac{s}{Q} = \frac{s_3}{Q_3}$$

to get

$$Q_3 = 4Q (1 - s).$$

Then

$$s = 1 - Q_3/4Q \qquad \text{and} \qquad 1 - s = Q_3/4Q$$

so that

$$s_3 = \frac{Q_3}{Q} \left(1 - \frac{Q_3}{4Q} \right). \quad \blacksquare$$

Theorem 67 (Isosceles median) Suppose that $\overline{A_1 A_2 A_3}$ is non-null and isosceles, with quadrances $Q_1 = Q_2 \equiv Q$ and Q_3, and corresponding spreads $s_1 = s_2 \equiv s$ and s_3, with l a line passing through A_3. The following are equivalent

i) l is the altitude from A_3 to $A_1 A_2$.

ii) l is the median passing through the midpoint M_3 of $\overline{A_1 A_2}$.

iii) l is a bisector of the vertex of $\overline{A_1 A_2 A_3}$ at A_3 which intersects $A_1 A_2$.

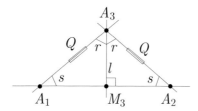

Figure 10.2: Isosceles median theorem

Proof. i)$\Longleftrightarrow$ ii) If $l = A_3 M_3$ is the median through A_3, then by the Equal quadrance to two points theorem (page 66), A_3 is on the perpendicular bisector of $\overline{A_1 A_2}$, so l is the altitude from A_3 to $A_1 A_2$. Conversely if l is the altitude from A_3 to $A_1 A_2$, with foot F lying on $A_1 A_2$, then Pythagoras' theorem shows that

$$Q(A_1, F) = Q - Q(A_3, F) = Q(A_2, F).$$

Thus by the Midpoint theorem (page 60), $F = M_3$ and so l is the median passing through M_3.

i)$\Longleftrightarrow$ iii) If l is the altitude from A_3 to $A_1 A_2$ then it meets $A_1 A_2$ at the foot F. By Pons Asinorum and the Complementary spreads theorem (page 79)

$$s(A_3 A_1, A_3 F) = s(A_3 A_2, A_3 F).$$

So l is then a bisector of the vertex of $\overline{A_1 A_2 A_3}$ at A_3 which intersects $A_1 A_2$.

Conversely, suppose l is a bisector of the vertex at A_3 which intersects $A_1 A_2$ at a point B with $s(A_3 A_1, A_3 B) = s(A_3 A_2, A_3 B) \equiv r$. Then by the Spread law in the triangles $\overline{A_1 A_3 B}$ and $\overline{A_2 A_3 B}$

$$\frac{r}{Q(A_1, B)} = \frac{s}{Q(A_3, B)} = \frac{r}{Q(A_2, B)}.$$

So $Q(A_1, B) = Q(A_2, B)$ and by the Midpoint theorem $B = M_3$. Therefore by the first part of the proof, l is also the altitude from A_3 to $A_1 A_2$. ∎

Theorem 68 (Isosceles reflection) Suppose a non-null triangle $\overline{A_1A_2A_3}$ has quadrances $Q_1 = Q_2 \equiv Q$ and Q_3, and that the altitude from A_3 to A_1A_2 with foot M_3 makes (necessarily) equal spreads

$$s\left(A_3A_1, A_3M_3\right) = s\left(A_3A_2, A_3M_3\right) \equiv r.$$

Then
$$Q_3 = 4rQ.$$

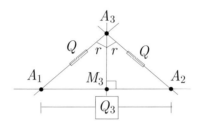

Figure 10.3: Isosceles reflection theorem

Proof. In the right triangle $\overline{A_1A_3M_3}$ the Spread ratio theorem (page 77) states that

$$r = \frac{Q\left(A_1, M_3\right)}{Q}.$$

By the Isosceles median theorem, M_3 is the midpoint of the side $\overline{A_1A_2}$, so that the Midpoint theorem (page 60) shows that

$$Q\left(A_1, M_3\right) = Q_3/4.$$

Thus
$$Q_3 = 4rQ. \quad \blacksquare$$

Exercise 10.1 If a triangle has crosses $c_1 = c_2 \equiv c$ and c_3, and twists $t_1 = t_2 \equiv t$ and t_3, then show that

$$c_3 = (2c - 1)^2 \qquad t_3 = 4t/(1 - t)^2. \quad \diamond$$

Exercise 10.2 Show that in the notation of the Isosceles triangle theorem, the quadrea of the isosceles triangle $\overline{A_1A_2A_3}$ is

$$\mathcal{A} = 16Q^2 s\left(1 - s\right) = Q_3\left(4Q - Q_3\right). \quad \diamond$$

Exercise 10.3 What happens to the previous theorems if isosceles triangles with two null lines are considered? $\diamond$

10.2 Equilateral triangles

Definition A triangle is **equilateral** precisely when all three of its quadrances are equal.

By Pons Asinorum, this is equivalent to all three spreads being equal.

Theorem 69 (Equilateral triangle) In an equilateral triangle $\overline{A_1A_2A_3}$, each spread has the value $3/4$, and each cross has the value $1/4$. If all quadrances are equal to Q, then the quadrea is $\mathcal{A} = 3Q^2$.

Proof. If $s_1 = s_2 = s_3 \equiv s$ then the Triple spread formula becomes
$$(3s)^2 = 2\left(3s^2\right) + 4s^3$$
so $3s^2 = 4s^3$. Since $s = 0$ is impossible, deduce that $s = 3/4$. Thus by the Spread plus cross theorem each cross has value $1 - 3/4 = 1/4$. Use the definition of the quadrea to find that
$$\mathcal{A} = (3Q)^2 - 2\left(3Q^2\right) = 3Q^2. \quad \blacksquare$$

Exercise 10.4 Suppose the characteristic of the field is not three. In an equilateral triangle $\overline{A_1A_2A_3}$ with all quadrances Q, show that the quadrance from A_3 to the centroid G is $Q/3$, that the quadrance from G to the midpoint M_3 of $\overline{A_1A_2}$ is $Q/12$, and that the quadrance from A_3 to the midpoint M_3 is $3Q/4$, as in Figure 10.4.

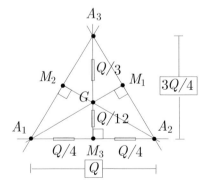

Figure 10.4: Medians in an equilateral triangle ◇

Exercise 10.5 Show that an equilateral triangle with common quadrance $Q = 1$ exists precisely when 3 is a non-zero square number. ◇

10.3   Right triangles

This is the second most important result about right triangles (after Pythagoras' theorem).

Theorem 70 (Right midpoint) Suppose that M is the midpoint of the side $\overline{A_1 A_2}$ of the triangle $\overline{A_1 A_2 A_3}$. Then the vertex at A_3 is a right vertex precisely when

$$Q(M, A_1) = Q(M, A_3).$$

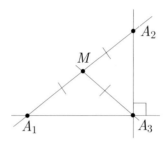

Figure 10.5: Right midpoint theorem

Proof. Suppose the points are $A_1 \equiv [x_1, y_1]$, $A_2 \equiv [x_2, y_2]$ and $A_3 \equiv [x_3, y_3]$ so that $M = [(x_1 + x_2)/2, (y_1 + y_2)/2]$. Then $Q(M, A_1) = Q(M, A_3)$ precisely when

$$\left((x_2 - x_1)^2 + (y_2 - y_1)^2\right)/4 = (x_3 - (x_1 + x_2)/2)^2 + (y_3 - (y_1 + y_2)/2)^2.$$

Expand to obtain the condition

$$x_3^2 - x_3 x_1 - x_3 x_2 + x_1 x_2 + y_3^2 - y_3 y_1 - y_3 y_2 + y_1 y_2 = 0$$

which can be rewritten as

$$(x_3 - x_1)(x_3 - x_2) + (y_1 - y_3)(y_2 - y_3) = 0.$$

By the Cross from points theorem (page 84) this is exactly the condition that $A_1 A_3$ is perpendicular to $A_2 A_3$. ■

Suppose the right triangle $\overline{A_1 A_2 A_3}$ has quadrances Q_1, Q_2 and Q_3, and spreads s_1, s_2 and s_3, with $s_3 \equiv 1$. Then any two of the five quantities Q_1, Q_2, Q_3, s_1 and s_2 determine the other three quantities unambiguously, with the exception of s_1 and s_2.

If you know two of the quadrances, the third follows from Pythagoras' theorem, so that s_1 and s_2 can then be determined from the Spread ratio theorem (page 77) to be

$$s_1 = Q_1/Q_3 \qquad s_2 = Q_2/Q_3.$$

If you know one quadrance and one spread, say s_1, then by the Complementary spreads theorem (page 79) $s_1 + s_2 = 1$ gives s_2, and then the equations

$$Q_1 = Q_3 s_1 \qquad Q_2 = Q_3 s_2$$

allow you to determine the other two quadrances. So with rational trigonometry there are a wealth of right triangles that can be completely analysed by elementary means.

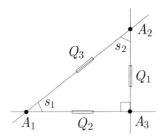

Figure 10.6: Right triangle

Exercise 10.6 Suppose that $\overline{A_1 A_2 A_3}$ is a right triangle with a right vertex at A_3, quadrances Q_1, Q_2 and Q_3, and that F is the foot of the altitude from A_3 to $A_1 A_2$. Show that

$$Q(A_1, F) = Q_1^2/Q_3 \qquad Q(A_2, F) = Q_2^2/Q_3 \qquad Q(A_3, F) = Q_1 Q_2/Q_3. \quad \diamond$$

10.4 Congruent and similar triangles

Definition Two triangles $\overline{A_1 A_2 A_3}$ and $\overline{B_1 B_2 B_3}$ are **congruent** precisely when they have identical quadrances.

Note that this information does not tell you which sides of the two triangles have equal quadrances.

Exercise 10.7 In the rational number field, show that the triangle with points $A_1 \equiv [2, 3]$, $A_2 \equiv [3, 1]$ and $A_3 \equiv [10, 2]$ is congruent to the triangle with points $B_1 \equiv [0, 1]$, $B_2 \equiv [-2, 2]$ and $B_3 \equiv [5, 6]$. $\diamond$

Definition Two triangles $\overline{A_1 A_2 A_3}$ and $\overline{B_1 B_2 B_3}$ are **similar** precisely when they have identical spreads.

Since the quadrances of a triangle determine the spreads, congruent triangles are similar.

Exercise 10.8 In the rational number field, show that the triangle with points $A_1 \equiv [-4, 3]$, $A_2 \equiv [6, 5]$ and $A_3 \equiv [-1, 1]$ is similar to, but not congruent to, the triangle with points $B_1 \equiv [4, -7]$, $B_2 \equiv [-2, -11]$ and $B_3 \equiv [2, 9]$. ◇

Exercise 10.9 Show that if two triangles are similar, then there is a non-zero number λ such that the quadrances of one triangle are all λ times the quadrances of the other. ◇

Exercise 10.10 In $\mathbb{F}_3$ show that any two triangles are similar, and that any triangle is both isosceles and right. ◇

Exercise 10.11 In $\mathbb{F}_5$ show that any two non-null triangles are similar, and are isosceles. Show that up to similarity there are two types of null triangles. ◇

Theorem 71 (Median triangle) Suppose that $\overline{A_1 A_2 A_3}$ is a triangle with M_1, M_2 and M_3 the midpoints of the sides $\overline{A_2 A_3}$, $\overline{A_1 A_3}$ and $\overline{A_1 A_2}$ respectively. Then $\overline{M_1 M_2 M_3}$ is similar to $\overline{A_1 A_2 A_3}$, and

$$Q(M_1, M_2) = Q(A_1, A_2)/4.$$

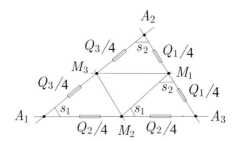

Figure 10.7: Median triangle theorem

Proof. From Thales' theorem (page 48) $M_1 M_2$ is parallel to $A_1 A_2$, $M_2 M_3$ is parallel to $A_2 A_3$ and $M_1 M_3$ is parallel to $A_1 A_3$. Thus $\overline{M_1 M_2 M_3}$ has the same spreads as $\overline{A_1 A_2 A_3}$, so these triangles are similar. Also $\overline{A_1 M_3 M_1 M_2}$ is a parallelogram, so by the Parallelogram quadrance theorem (page 62) and the Midpoint theorem (page 60)

$$Q(M_1, M_2) = Q(A_1, M_3) = Q(A_1, A_2)/4. \quad \blacksquare$$

The triangle $\overline{M_1 M_2 M_3}$ is the **median triangle** of $\overline{A_1 A_2 A_3}$.

10.5   Solving triangles

Generally speaking if you know three of the six possible quadrances and spreads of a triangle then you can determine a small number of possibilities for the other unknown quantities. The exception is knowing three spreads, which determines the triangle only up to similarity.

Three quadrances

The quadrances Q_1, Q_2 and Q_3 of a non-null triangle $\overline{A_1 A_2 A_3}$ determine the quadrea $\mathcal{A}$, and then the spreads s_1, s_2 and s_3 by the Quadrea spread theorem (page 82).

Two quadrances and a spread

If two quadrances and a spread, say s_3, of a non-null triangle are known, then the Cross law

$$(Q_1 + Q_2 - Q_3)^2 = 4Q_1Q_2 \left(1 - s_3\right)$$

gives a quadratic equation for the third unknown quadrance. If the unknown quadrance is Q_3, then this is already in normal form. If the unknown quadrance is Q_1 or Q_2, then first complete the square.

For each value of the third quadrance you can determine the other spreads by the Spread law.

Example 10.1 In the rational number field a triangle $\overline{A_1 A_2 A_3}$ has $s_3 \equiv 81/130$, $Q_1 \equiv 5$ and $Q_3 \equiv 17$. Then use the Cross law to get

$$(Q_2 - 12)^2 = 4 \times 5 \times Q_2 \times \frac{49}{130} = \frac{98}{13} \times Q_2.$$

Rearrange to find

$$(13Q_2 - 72)(Q_2 - 26) = 0$$

so that

$$\text{i) } Q_2 = 72/13 \qquad \text{or} \qquad \text{ii) } Q_2 = 26.$$

i) If $Q_2 = 72/13$, then the Spread law is

$$\frac{s_1}{5} = \frac{s_2}{72/13} = \frac{81/130}{17}$$

so that

$$s_1 = 81/442 \qquad s_2 = 2916/14\,365 \qquad s_3 = 81/130.$$

This is illustrated to scale on the left in Figure 10.8.

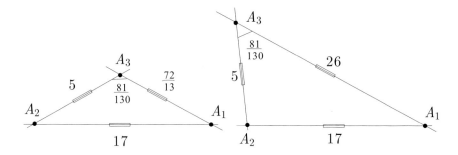

Figure 10.8: Two possibilities

ii) If $Q_2 = 26$, then the Spread law is

$$\frac{s_1}{5} = \frac{s_2}{26} = \frac{81/130}{17}$$

so that

$$s_1 = 81/442 \qquad s_2 = 81/85 \qquad s_3 = 81/130.$$

This is illustrated to scale on the right in Figure 10.8. ◇

One quadrance and two spreads

If one quadrance and two spreads, say s_1 and s_2 are known, then the Triple spread formula gives a quadratic equation for the third spread s_3. For each of the generally two solutions s_3, the two unknown quadrances may be found using the Spread law.

Exercise 10.12 Suppose that in the complex number field a triangle $\overline{A_1 A_2 A_3}$ has quadrance $Q_3 \equiv -3$, and spreads $s_1 \equiv 4/15 + 2i/15$ and $s_2 \equiv 1/24 + 7i/24$. Then show that either

$$Q_1 = 8 - 8i \qquad Q_2 = 11 + 2i$$

or

$$Q_1 = 10\,872/11\,881 + 2232i/11\,881 \qquad Q_2 = 7929/11\,881 - 7578i/11\,881. ◇$$

Three spreads

Knowledge of the three spreads of a triangle determines the triangle only up to similarity. Although the quadrances are not determined, the Spread law

$$\frac{s_1}{Q_1} = \frac{s_2}{Q_2} = \frac{s_3}{Q_3}$$

determines the proportion $Q_1 : Q_2 : Q_3$.

11

Laws of proportion

This chapter introduces useful results when triangles and quadrilaterals are augmented by additional lines. These lead to generalizations of the classical theorems of Stewart, Menelaus and Ceva.

11.1 Triangle proportions

Theorem 72 (Triangle proportions) Suppose that $\overline{A_1 A_2 A_3}$ is a triangle with quadrances Q_1, Q_2 and Q_3, corresponding spreads s_1, s_2 and s_3, and that D is a point lying on the line $A_1 A_2$ distinct from A_1 and A_2. Define the quadrances $R_1 \equiv Q(A_1, D)$ and $R_2 \equiv Q(A_2, D)$, and the spreads $r_1 \equiv s(A_3 A_1, A_3 D)$ and $r_2 \equiv s(A_3 A_2, A_3 D)$. Then

$$\frac{r_1}{r_2} = \frac{s_1}{s_2} \frac{R_1}{R_2} = \frac{Q_1}{Q_2} \frac{R_1}{R_2}.$$

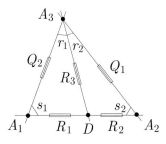

Figure 11.1: Triangle proportions theorem

Proof. Define also $R_3 \equiv Q(A_3, D)$ as in Figure 11.1. In $\overline{DA_2A_3}$ use the Spread law to get

$$\frac{s_2}{R_3} = \frac{r_2}{R_2}.$$

In $\overline{DA_1A_3}$ use the Spread law to get

$$\frac{s_1}{R_3} = \frac{r_1}{R_1}.$$

Thus

$$R_3 = \frac{s_2 R_2}{r_2} = \frac{s_1 R_1}{r_1}$$

and rearrange to obtain

$$\frac{r_1}{r_2} = \frac{s_1}{s_2}\frac{R_1}{R_2}.$$

Since

$$\frac{s_1}{s_2} = \frac{Q_1}{Q_2}$$

this can be rewritten as

$$\frac{r_1}{r_2} = \frac{Q_1}{Q_2}\frac{R_1}{R_2}. \quad \blacksquare$$

Special cases

- If $r_1 = r_2$ then the line DA_3 bisects the vertex of $\overline{A_1A_2A_3}$ at A_3. The theorem then reduces to

$$\frac{R_1}{R_2} = \frac{s_2}{s_1} = \frac{Q_2}{Q_1}.$$

  Recall that in general there are two possible vertex bisectors.

- If $s_1 = s_2$ then the triangle $\overline{A_1A_2A_3}$ is isosceles. The theorem then reduces to

$$\frac{r_1}{r_2} = \frac{R_1}{R_2}.$$

- If $R_1 = R_2$ then the line DA_3 is a median of $\overline{A_1A_2A_3}$. The theorem then reduces to

$$\frac{r_1}{r_2} = \frac{s_1}{s_2} = \frac{Q_1}{Q_2}.$$

Exercise 11.1 Show that with the same notation as in the theorem, if $s_3 = 1$ then

$$s_1 = \left(1 + \frac{r_2 R_1}{r_1 R_2}\right)^{-1}. \quad \diamond$$

11.2 Quadrilateral proportions

Theorem 73 (Quadrilateral proportions) Suppose that $\overline{ABCD}$ is a quadrilateral with spreads $s_1 \equiv s\,(AB, AD)$ and $s_2 \equiv s\,(CB, CD)$ at A and C respectively. Define the spreads $r_1 \equiv s\,(BA, BD)$ and $r_2 \equiv s\,(BC, BD)$, and the quadrances $R_1 \equiv Q\,(A, D)$ and $R_2 \equiv Q\,(C, D)$. Then

$$\frac{r_1}{r_2} = \frac{s_1}{s_2} \frac{R_1}{R_2}.$$

In the rational or decimal number fields, both diagrams in Figure 11.2 illustrate the theorem.

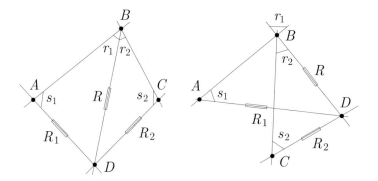

Figure 11.2: Quadrilateral proportions theorem

Proof. Define $R \equiv Q\,(B, D)$. Use the Spread law in $\overline{ABD}$ to obtain

$$\frac{r_1}{R_1} = \frac{s_1}{R}$$

and in $\overline{BCD}$ to obtain

$$\frac{r_2}{R_2} = \frac{s_2}{R}.$$

Solve for R

$$R = \frac{s_1 R_1}{r_1} = \frac{s_2 R_2}{r_2}$$

and rearrange to obtain

$$\frac{r_1}{r_2} = \frac{s_1}{s_2} \frac{R_1}{R_2}. \quad \blacksquare$$

11.3 Two struts theorem

This theorem illustrates a quadratic aspect of barycentric coordinates.

Theorem 74 (Two struts) Suppose that $\overline{A_1 A_2 A_3}$ is a triangle and that the points B_1 and B_2 are distinct from A_1, A_2 and A_3 and lie on the lines $A_2 A_3$ and $A_1 A_3$ respectively, with $A_1 B_1$ and $A_2 B_2$ intersecting at the point C. Suppose the quadrances

$$
\begin{aligned}
P_1 &\equiv Q\left(A_1, B_2\right) & P_2 &\equiv Q\left(B_2, A_3\right) \\
R_1 &\equiv Q\left(A_2, B_1\right) & R_2 &\equiv Q\left(B_1, A_3\right) \\
N_1 &\equiv Q\left(A_1, C\right) & N_2 &\equiv Q\left(C, B_1\right) \\
M_1 &\equiv Q\left(A_2, C\right) & M_2 &\equiv Q\left(C, B_2\right)
\end{aligned}
$$

are all non-zero, and define the corresponding numbers

$$
\begin{aligned}
p &\equiv P_1/P_2 & r &\equiv R_1/R_2 \\
n &\equiv N_1/N_2 & m &\equiv M_1/M_2.
\end{aligned}
$$

Then $\{r, rp, mp\}$ and $\{p, rp, nr\}$ are both quad triples.

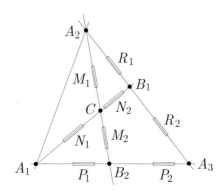

Figure 11.3: Two struts theorem

Proof. Suppose the quadrances of the triangle $\overline{A_1 A_2 A_3}$ are Q_1, Q_2 and Q_3 as usual. Use the Triangle proportions theorem in the triangles $\overline{A_1 A_2 A_3}$ and $\overline{A_1 A_2 B_2}$, together with the line $A_1 B_1$, to get

$$
\frac{s\left(A_1 B_1, A_1 A_2\right)}{s\left(A_1 B_1, A_1 A_3\right)} = \frac{Q_2}{Q_3} \frac{R_1}{R_2} = \frac{P_1}{Q_3} \frac{M_1}{M_2}
$$

so that

$$
\frac{Q_2}{P_1} = \frac{m}{r}. \tag{11.1}
$$

Since $\{Q_2, P_1, P_2\}$ is a quad triple, the Triple quad formula gives

$$(Q_2 + P_1 + P_2)^2 = 2\left(Q_2^2 + P_1^2 + P_2^2\right).$$

Divide by P_1^2 and use (11.1) to obtain

$$\left(\frac{m}{r} + 1 + \frac{1}{p}\right)^2 = 2\left(\frac{m^2}{r^2} + 1 + \frac{1}{p^2}\right).$$

Now remove denominators to get

$$(mp + rp + r)^2 = 2\left(m^2p^2 + r^2p^2 + r^2\right).$$

This is the statement that $\{r, rp, mp\}$ is a quad triple. The situation with $\{p, rp, nr\}$ is similar. ∎

Note that the ratio p for example does not determine the point B_2 uniquely on the line A_1A_3, and in fact there are generally two possible choices. Similarly given r there are two possible choices for B_1 on A_2A_3. This might suggest that given p and r there should be four possible values for m, and also for n. However the theorem shows that only two occur in each case.

Example 11.1 Suppose that $p \equiv 1/4$ and $r \equiv 9/64$. Then the theorem gives two quadratic equations, the one for m factoring as

$$(64m - 9)(64m - 81) = 0$$

and the one for n factoring as

$$(36n - 25)(36n - 121) = 0. \quad \diamond$$

Exercise 11.2 Suppose that $r = p$ in the above theorem. Show that n and m must both be solutions to the quadratic equation $(x - r - 1)^2 = 4r$. $\diamond$

Exercise 11.3 Suppose that $m = r$ in the above theorem. Show that then $p = 1/4$. $\diamond$

Exercise 11.4 In the notation of the above theorem, suppose that A_1B_1 and A_2B_2 are bisectors of the vertices of $\overline{A_1A_2A_3}$ at A_1 and A_2 respectively. Suppose that the spreads of the triangle $\overline{A_1A_2A_3}$ are s_1, s_2 and s_3 as usual. Show that m and n satisfy respectively the quadratic equations

$$\left(m + \frac{s_1 + s_3}{s_2}\right)^2 = \frac{2\left(s_1^2 + s_3^2\right)}{s_2^2}$$

$$\left(n + \frac{s_2 + s_3}{s_1}\right)^2 = \frac{2\left(s_2^2 + s_3^2\right)}{s_1^2}. \quad \diamond$$

11.4 Stewart's theorem

The decimal number version of this result was published by Matthew Stewart in 1745.

Theorem 75 (Stewart's theorem) Suppose that $\overline{A_1 A_2 A_3}$ is a non-null triangle with quadrances Q_1, Q_2 and Q_3, with D a point lying on $A_1 A_2$. Define

$$R_1 \equiv Q(A_1, D) \qquad R_2 \equiv Q(A_2, D) \qquad R_3 \equiv Q(A_3, D).$$

Then

$$R_2 (R_3 + R_1 - Q_2)^2 = R_1 (R_3 + R_2 - Q_1)^2.$$

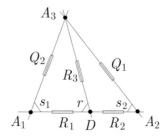

Figure 11.4: Stewart's theorem

Proof. If $R_3 \neq 0$ then define $r \equiv s(DA_1, DA_3)$. Then the Cross law in the triangles $\overline{A_1 A_3 D}$ and $\overline{A_2 A_3 D}$ yields

$$\begin{aligned}
(R_3 + R_1 - Q_2)^2 &= 4R_1 R_3 (1 - r) \\
(R_3 + R_2 - Q_1)^2 &= 4R_2 R_3 (1 - r).
\end{aligned}$$

Combine these two to get the result. If $R_3 = 0$ then use Exercise 6.4 and the Spread law to get

$$\frac{s_1}{s_2} = \frac{(R_1 - Q_2)^2 R_2 Q_1}{(R_2 - Q_1)^2 R_1 Q_2} = \frac{Q_1}{Q_2}$$

from which the result follows. ∎

Exercise 11.5 Suppose that $Q_1 = Q_2 \equiv Q$ in Stewart's theorem. Show that

$$(Q - R_3)^2 = R_1 R_2. \quad \diamond$$

Exercise 11.6 Suppose that $Q_1 = Q_2 = Q_3 \equiv Q$ in Stewart's theorem. Show that Q equals

$$2R_3 - R_1 - R_2 \qquad \text{or} \qquad (2R_3 + R_1 + R_2)/3. \quad \diamond$$

11.5 Median quadrance and spread

Theorem 76 (Median quadrance) Suppose a triangle $\overline{A_1 A_2 A_3}$ has quadrances Q_1, Q_2 and Q_3, with $Q_1 \neq 0$. Let P_1 denote the quadrance from A_1 to the midpoint M_1 of $\overline{A_2 A_3}$. Then

$$P_1 = \frac{2(Q_2 + Q_3) - Q_1}{4}.$$

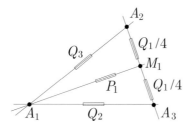

Figure 11.5: Median quadrance theorem

Proof. By Stewart's theorem,

$$\frac{Q_1}{4}\left(P_1 + \frac{Q_1}{4} - Q_2\right)^2 = \frac{Q_1}{4}\left(P_1 + \frac{Q_1}{4} - Q_3\right)^2$$

or

$$Q_1\left(Q_3 - Q_2\right)\left(4P_1 + Q_1 - 2Q_2 - 2Q_3\right) = 0.$$

By assumption $Q_1 \neq 0$. If $Q_3 - Q_2 = 0$ then the triangle $\overline{A_1 A_2 A_3}$ is isosceles and so from the Equal quadrance to two points theorem (page 66), $A_1 M_1$ is the perpendicular bisector of the side $\overline{A_2 A_3}$. Then Pythagoras' theorem implies that

$$P_1 = Q_2 - \frac{Q_1}{4} = \frac{2(Q_2 + Q_3) - Q_1}{4}.$$

Otherwise

$$4P_1 + Q_1 - 2Q_2 - 2Q_3 = 0$$

so that also

$$P_1 = \frac{2(Q_2 + Q_3) - Q_1}{4}. \quad \blacksquare$$

Exercise 11.7 If P_2 and P_3 are defined analogously to P_1, show that

$$P_1 + P_2 + P_3 = \frac{3}{4}(Q_1 + Q_2 + Q_3). \quad \diamond$$

Theorem 77 (Median spreads) Suppose the triangle $\overline{A_1 A_2 A_3}$ has quadrances Q_1, Q_2 and Q_3, and spreads s_1, s_2 and s_3, with M_1 the midpoint of the non-null side $\overline{A_2 A_3}$. If $A_1 M_1$ is a non-null line then

$$s(M_1 A_2, M_1 A_1) = \frac{4 s_2 s_3}{2(s_2 + s_3) - s_1}$$

$$s(A_1 A_2, A_1 M_1) = \frac{s_1 s_2}{2(s_2 + s_3) - s_1}$$

$$s(A_1 A_3, A_1 M_1) = \frac{s_1 s_3}{2(s_2 + s_3) - s_1}.$$

Proof. As in Figure 11.6 define the quadrance $P_1 \equiv Q(A_1, M_1) \neq 0$ and the spreads

$$r_1 \equiv s(M_1 A_1, M_1 A_2) \qquad u_1 \equiv s(A_1 A_2, A_1 M_1) \qquad v_1 \equiv s(A_1 A_3, A_1 M_1).$$

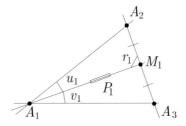

Figure 11.6: Median spreads

Since $Q(A_2, M_1) = Q_1/4$, the Spread law in $\overline{A_1 A_2 M_1}$ gives

$$\frac{r_1}{Q_3} = \frac{s_2}{P_1} = \frac{u_1}{Q_1/4}.$$

Use the Median quadrance theorem and the Spread law in $\overline{A_1 A_2 A_3}$ to get

$$r_1 = \frac{4 s_2 Q_3}{2(Q_2 + Q_3) - Q_1}$$

$$= \frac{4 s_2 s_3}{2(s_2 + s_3) - s_1}.$$

Thus

$$u_1 = \frac{r_1 Q_1}{4 Q_3} = \frac{s_1 r_1}{4 s_3} = \frac{s_1 s_2}{2(s_2 + s_3) - s_1}.$$

Similarly from the Spread law in $\overline{A_1 A_3 M_1}$

$$v_1 = \frac{r_1 Q_1}{4 Q_2} = \frac{s_1 r_1}{4 s_2} = \frac{s_1 s_3}{2(s_2 + s_3) - s_1}. \quad \blacksquare$$

11.6 Menelaus' and Ceva's theorems

The results in this section include rational analogues of the famous theorems of Menelaus (about 100 A.D.) and Ceva (1678). These theorems properly belong to affine geometry, but they can also be viewed metrically.

Theorem 78 (Menelaus' theorem) Suppose that l is a non-null line not parallel to any of the lines of the triangle $\overline{A_1 A_2 A_3}$, and intersecting $A_2 A_3$, $A_1 A_3$ and $A_1 A_2$ at the points B_1, B_2 and B_3 respectively. Define the quadrances

$$\begin{array}{ll} R_1 \equiv Q\left(A_2, B_1\right) & P_1 \equiv Q\left(B_1, A_3\right) \\ R_2 \equiv Q\left(A_3, B_2\right) & P_2 \equiv Q\left(B_2, A_1\right) \\ R_3 \equiv Q\left(A_1, B_3\right) & P_3 \equiv Q\left(B_3, A_2\right). \end{array}$$

Then

$$R_1 R_2 R_3 = P_1 P_2 P_3.$$

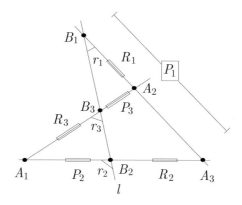

Figure 11.7: Menelaus' theorem

Proof. If $\overline{A_1 A_2 A_3}$ is a null triangle then both sides of the equation are zero. Otherwise define the spreads between l and the lines $A_2 A_3$, $A_1 A_3$ and $A_1 A_2$ to be respectively r_1, r_2 and r_3, as in Figure 11.7. Then use the Spread law in the triangles $\overline{B_1 B_2 A_3}$, $\overline{B_2 B_3 A_1}$ and $\overline{B_3 B_1 A_2}$ to get

$$r_1/r_2 = R_2/P_1 \qquad r_2/r_3 = R_3/P_2 \qquad r_3/r_1 = R_1/P_3.$$

Multiply these three equations to obtain

$$R_1 R_2 R_3 = P_1 P_2 P_3. \quad \blacksquare$$

Exercise 11.8 Show that the converse of Menelaus' theorem does not hold: the relation $R_1R_2R_3 = P_1P_2P_3$ does not necessarily imply that the points B_1, B_2 and B_3 are collinear. $\diamond$

Theorem 79 (Alternate spreads) Suppose that A_0 is a point distinct from the points of a non-null triangle $\overline{A_1A_2A_3}$, with the spreads

$$\begin{aligned}
r_1 &\equiv s\,(A_1A_2, A_1A_0) & p_1 &\equiv s\,(A_1A_3, A_1A_0) \\
r_2 &\equiv s\,(A_2A_3, A_2A_0) & p_2 &\equiv s\,(A_2A_1, A_2A_0) \\
r_3 &\equiv s\,(A_3A_1, A_3A_0) & p_3 &\equiv s\,(A_3A_2, A_3A_0)\,.
\end{aligned}$$

Then

$$r_1r_2r_3 = p_1p_2p_3.$$

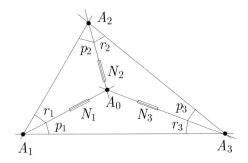

Figure 11.8: Alternate spreads theorem

Proof. If A_0 lies on one of the lines of the triangle then both sides of the required equation equal zero. Otherwise, define the quadrances

$$\begin{aligned}
N_1 &\equiv Q\,(A_0, A_1) \\
N_2 &\equiv Q\,(A_0, A_2) \\
N_3 &\equiv Q\,(A_0, A_3)\,.
\end{aligned}$$

Then the Spread law applied to the triangles $\overline{A_0A_2A_3}$, $\overline{A_0A_3A_1}$ and $\overline{A_0A_1A_2}$ yields

$$r_2/p_3 = N_3/N_2 \qquad r_3/p_1 = N_1/N_3 \qquad r_1/p_2 = N_2/N_1.$$

Multiply these three equations to get

$$r_1r_2r_3 = p_1p_2p_3. \quad \blacksquare$$

Theorem 80 (Ceva's theorem) Suppose that A_0 is a point distinct from the points A_1, A_2 and A_3 of a non-null triangle $\overline{A_1 A_2 A_3}$, and that the non-null lines $A_0 A_1$, $A_0 A_2$ and $A_0 A_3$ meet $A_2 A_3$, $A_1 A_3$ and $A_1 A_2$ respectively at the points B_1, B_2 and B_3. Define the quadrances

$$\begin{array}{ll} R_1 \equiv Q(A_2, B_1) & P_1 \equiv Q(B_1, A_3) \\ R_2 \equiv Q(A_3, B_2) & P_2 \equiv Q(B_2, A_1) \\ R_3 \equiv Q(A_1, B_3) & P_3 \equiv Q(B_3, A_2). \end{array}$$

Then

$$R_1 R_2 R_3 = P_1 P_2 P_3.$$

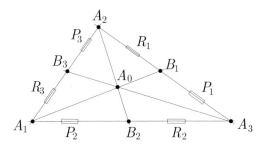

Figure 11.9: Ceva's theorem

Proof. Let s_1, s_2 and s_3 be the usual spreads of the triangle $\overline{A_1 A_2 A_3}$. Define the spreads

$$\begin{array}{ll} r_1 \equiv s(A_1 A_2, A_1 A_0) & p_1 \equiv s(A_1 A_3, A_1 A_0) \\ r_2 \equiv s(A_2 A_3, A_2 A_0) & p_2 \equiv s(A_2 A_1, A_2 A_0) \\ r_3 \equiv s(A_3 A_1, A_3 A_0) & p_3 \equiv s(A_3 A_2, A_3 A_0). \end{array}$$

as in the Alternate spreads theorem. Then use the Triangle proportions theorem (page 131) with the triangle $\overline{A_1 A_2 A_3}$ and the respective lines $A_1 B_1$, $A_2 B_2$ and $A_3 B_3$ to obtain

$$\begin{aligned} \frac{r_1}{p_1} &= \frac{s_2}{s_3} \frac{R_1}{P_1} \\ \frac{r_2}{p_2} &= \frac{s_3}{s_1} \frac{R_2}{P_2} \\ \frac{r_3}{p_3} &= \frac{s_1}{s_2} \frac{R_3}{P_3}. \end{aligned}$$

Multiply these three equations and use the Alternate spreads theorem to get

$$\frac{R_1 R_2 R_3}{P_1 P_2 P_3} = \frac{r_1 r_2 r_3}{p_1 p_2 p_3} = 1. \ \blacksquare$$

Exercise 11.9 Show that the Alternate spreads theorem extends to a quadrilateral $\overline{A_1 A_2 A_3 A_4}$, so that if A_0 is any point distinct from A_1, A_2, A_3 and A_4, and the spreads are as shown in Figure 11.10, then

$$r_1 r_2 r_3 r_4 = p_1 p_2 p_3 p_4.$$

Generalize further to an n-gon.

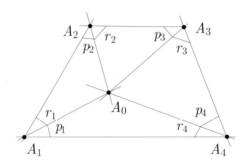

Figure 11.10: Alternate spreads (quadrilateral) ⋄

Exercise 11.10 Show that the converse of Ceva's theorem does not hold: the relation $R_1 R_2 R_3 = P_1 P_2 P_3$ does not necessarily imply that the lines $A_1 B_1$, $A_2 B_2$ and $A_3 B_3$ are concurrent. ⋄

Exercise 11.11 What happens when the conditions of the theorems in this chapter are relaxed to allow null triangles and null lines? ⋄

12

Centers of triangles

In this chapter the circumcenter, orthocenter and incenters of a triangle are studied. Typically the existence of incenters depends on number theoretic considerations, and if incenters exist, then there are four which play a symmetrical role.

12.1 Perpendicular bisectors and circumcenter

Theorem 81 (Circumcenter) For any triangle $\overline{A_1 A_2 A_3}$ the three perpendicular bisectors of the sides are concurrent at a point C.

Proof. Since two lines of a triangle are never parallel, the respective perpendicular bisectors always intersect. If C is the intersection of the perpendicular bisectors p_1 and p_2 of $\overline{A_2 A_3}$ and $\overline{A_1 A_3}$ respectively, then it follows from the Equal quadrance to two points theorem (page 66) that $Q(C, A_2) = Q(C, A_3)$ and $Q(C, A_1) = Q(C, A_3)$.

But then $Q(C, A_1) = Q(C, A_2)$ so that C must lie on the perpendicular bisector p_3 of $\overline{A_1 A_2}$. ∎

Definition The **circumcenter** C of the triangle $\overline{A_1 A_2 A_3}$ is the common intersection of the three perpendicular bisectors of the sides of the triangle. The **circumquadrance** K of the triangle $\overline{A_1 A_2 A_3}$ is the common quadrance

$$K \equiv Q(C, A_1) = Q(C, A_2) = Q(C, A_3).$$

Theorem 82 (Extended spread law) Suppose a non-null triangle $\overline{A_1A_2A_3}$ has quadrances Q_1, Q_2 and Q_3, corresponding spreads s_1, s_2 and s_3, and circumquadrance K. Then

$$\frac{s_1}{Q_1} = \frac{s_2}{Q_2} = \frac{s_3}{Q_3} = \frac{1}{4K}.$$

Proof. Suppose that C is the circumcenter of $\overline{A_1A_2A_3}$, and that M_1, M_2 and M_3 are the midpoints of the sides $\overline{A_2A_3}$, $\overline{A_1A_3}$ and $\overline{A_1A_2}$ respectively. Since by the Median triangle theorem (page 128) M_1, M_2 and M_3 are distinct, you may assume without loss of generality that C is distinct from M_1 and M_2, and does not lie on M_1M_2. Define the quadrances

$$R_1 \equiv Q\left(M_1, C\right) \qquad R_2 \equiv Q\left(M_2, C\right)$$

as in Figure 12.1.

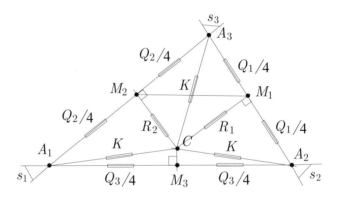

Figure 12.1: Circumcenter of a triangle

Since A_3M_2 is perpendicular to M_2C and A_3M_1 is perpendicular to M_1C, the Perpendicular spreads theorem (page 79) gives

$$s\left(CM_1, CM_2\right) = s\left(A_3M_1, A_3M_2\right) = s_3.$$

The Median triangle theorem (page 128) states that

$$Q\left(M_1, M_2\right) = Q_3/4.$$

From Thales' theorem (page 48), M_1M_2 is parallel to A_1A_2, so that

$$s\left(M_2M_1, M_2A_3\right) = s_1 \qquad \text{and} \qquad s\left(M_1M_2, M_1A_3\right) = s_2.$$

Use the Complementary spreads theorem (page 79) to see that

$$s\left(M_2M_1, M_2C\right) = 1 - s_1 \qquad \text{and} \qquad s\left(M_1M_2, M_1C\right) = 1 - s_2.$$

Now solve the triangle $\overline{M_1 M_2 C}$, since you know one quadrance and all three spreads. Use the Spread law to get

$$R_1 = \frac{Q_3 (1 - s_1)}{4 s_3}$$

$$R_2 = \frac{Q_3 (1 - s_2)}{4 s_3}.$$

Pythagoras' theorem in the right triangle $\overline{A_3 M_1 C}$ gives

$$K = R_1 + \frac{Q_1}{4} = \frac{Q_3 (1 - s_1)}{4 s_3} + \frac{Q_1}{4}.$$

From the Spread law in $\overline{A_1 A_2 A_3}$

$$\frac{Q_3}{s_3} = \frac{Q_1}{s_1}$$

so that

$$K = \frac{Q_1 (1 - s_1)}{4 s_1} + \frac{Q_1}{4} = \frac{Q_1}{4 s_1}.$$

By symmetry

$$\frac{s_1}{Q_1} = \frac{s_2}{Q_2} = \frac{s_3}{Q_3} = \frac{1}{4K}. \quad \blacksquare$$

Exercise 12.1 Using the notation of the previous proof, show that

$$s (A_3 C, A_3 A_2) = 1 - s_1 \qquad s (A_3 C, A_3 A_1) = 1 - s_2$$

and

$$s (C A_3, C M_1) = s_1 = s (C A_2, C M_1). \quad \diamond$$

Exercise 12.2 Show that if the triangle $\overline{A_1 A_2 A_3}$ has quadrances Q_1, Q_2 and Q_3, spreads s_1, s_2 and s_3, quadrea $\mathcal{A}$ and circumquadrance K, then

$$\mathcal{A} = \frac{Q_1 Q_2 Q_3}{K} = 64 K^2 s_1 s_2 s_3. \quad \diamond$$

Exercise 12.3 Show that with the notation of the previous exercise,

$$s_1 + s_2 = (Q_1 + Q_2) / 4K \qquad \text{and} \qquad s_1 + s_2 + s_3 = (Q_1 + Q_2 + Q_3) / 4K. \quad \diamond$$

Exercise 12.4 Show that if $A_2 A_3$ is a null line, then the circumcenter of $\overline{A_1 A_2 A_3}$ lies on $A_2 A_3$. Deduce that if $A_1 A_3$ and $A_2 A_3$ are both null lines, then the circumcenter is A_3. $\diamond$

Exercise 12.5 Verify the polynomial identity

$$\left((x_1 + x_2 + x_3)^2 - 2 \left(x_1^2 + x_2^2 + x_3^2 \right) \right) (x_1 + x_2 + x_3) - 8 x_1 x_2 x_3$$
$$= (x_1 + x_2 - x_3) (x_2 + x_3 - x_1) (x_3 + x_1 - x_2).$$

Deduce that $Q_1 + Q_2 + Q_3 = 8K$ precisely when the triangle $\overline{A_1 A_2 A_3}$ is a right triangle. $\diamond$

12.2 Formulas for the circumcenter

Theorem 83 (Circumcenter formula) If $A_1 \equiv [x_1, y_1]$, $A_2 \equiv [x_2, y_2]$ and $A_3 \equiv [x_3, y_3]$, then the circumcenter C of the triangle $\overline{A_1 A_2 A_3}$ is

$$C = \left[\frac{\left[x_1^2 y_2\right]_3^- + \left[y_1^2 y_2\right]_3^-}{2\left[x_1 y_2\right]_3^-}, \; \frac{\left[x_1 x_2^2\right]_3^- + \left[x_1 y_2^2\right]_3^-}{2\left[x_1 y_2\right]_3^-} \right].$$

Proof. By the Circumcenter theorem, it suffices to find the intersection of the perpendicular bisectors p_3 and p_1 of the sides $\overline{A_1 A_2}$ and $\overline{A_2 A_3}$, which by the Perpendicular bisector theorem (page 50) are

$$p_3 = \left\langle x_1 - x_2 : y_1 - y_2 : \left(x_2^2 - x_1^2 + y_2^2 - y_1^2\right)/2 \right\rangle$$
$$p_1 = \left\langle x_2 - x_3 : y_2 - y_3 : \left(x_3^2 - x_2^2 + y_3^2 - y_2^2\right)/2 \right\rangle.$$

Use the Point on two lines theorem (page 40) to deduce that p_1 and p_3 intersect at the point $C \equiv [x_0, y_0]$ where

$$x_0 \equiv \frac{\left(\begin{array}{c} x_1^2 y_2 - x_1^2 y_3 + x_2^2 y_3 - x_3^2 y_2 + x_3^2 y_1 - x_2^2 y_1 \\ +y_1^2 y_2 - y_1^2 y_3 + y_2^2 y_3 - y_3^2 y_2 + y_3^2 y_1 - y_2^2 y_1 \end{array} \right)}{2\left(x_1 y_2 - x_1 y_3 + x_2 y_3 - x_3 y_2 + x_3 y_1 - x_2 y_1\right)}$$

and

$$y_0 \equiv \frac{\left(\begin{array}{c} x_1 x_2^2 - x_1 x_3^2 + x_2 x_3^2 - x_3 x_2^2 + x_3 x_1^2 - x_2 x_1^2 \\ +x_1 y_2^2 - x_1 y_3^2 + x_2 y_3^2 - x_3 y_2^2 + x_3 y_1^2 - x_2 y_1^2 \end{array} \right)}{2\left(x_1 y_2 - x_1 y_3 + x_2 y_3 - x_3 y_2 + x_3 y_1 - x_2 y_1\right)}.$$

Express C using the conventions for anti-symmetric polynomials (page 29). ∎

Theorem 84 (Affine circumcenter) If the quadrances of the triangle $\overline{A_1 A_2 A_3}$ are Q_1, Q_2 and Q_3, and the quadrea is $\mathcal{A}$, then the circumcenter C can be written as the affine combination

$$C = \gamma_1 A_1 + \gamma_2 A_2 + \gamma_3 A_3$$

where

$$\gamma_1 \equiv Q_1 \left(Q_2 + Q_3 - Q_1\right)/\mathcal{A}$$
$$\gamma_2 \equiv Q_2 \left(Q_3 + Q_1 - Q_2\right)/\mathcal{A}$$
$$\gamma_3 \equiv Q_3 \left(Q_1 + Q_2 - Q_3\right)/\mathcal{A}.$$

Proof. This is a straightforward but laborious verification using the previous theorem. Note that Exercise 5.14 (page 69) shows that $\gamma_1 + \gamma_2 + \gamma_3 = 1$. ∎

12.3 Altitudes and orthocenter

Definition An **altitude** of a triangle $\overline{A_1 A_2 A_3}$ is an altitude from a point of the triangle to the line of the opposite side.

Theorem 85 (Orthocenter) For any non-null triangle $\overline{A_1 A_2 A_3}$ the three altitudes are concurrent at a point O.

Proof. In the special case when the triangle is a right triangle, the theorem is immediate, since then the altitudes intersect at the point of the right vertex.

Since the lines $A_1 A_3$ and $A_2 A_3$ of the triangle are not parallel, the altitudes n_1 from A_1 to $A_2 A_3$ and n_2 from A_2 to $A_1 A_3$ are not parallel, so intersect at some point O. Suppose that F_1 and F_2 are the feet of the altitudes n_1 and n_2 lying on $A_2 A_3$ and $A_1 A_3$ respectively. If O lies either on $A_1 A_3$ or $A_2 A_3$ then it must coincide with one of the feet, in which case $\overline{A_1 A_2 A_3}$ has a right vertex at A_3.

Otherwise assume that O does not lie on $A_1 A_3$ or $A_2 A_3$. Suppose that the quadrances of $\overline{A_1 A_2 A_3}$ are Q_1, Q_2 and Q_3, and the corresponding spreads are s_1, s_2 and s_3. It suffices to show that $A_1 A_2$ and $O A_3$ are perpendicular.

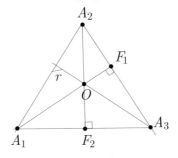

Figure 12.2: Two altitudes intersecting

By properties of right triangles

$$s\left(A_1 A_3, A_1 F_1\right) = 1 - s_3 \qquad s\left(A_2 A_3, A_2 F_2\right) = 1 - s_3$$
$$s\left(A_1 A_2, A_1 F_1\right) = 1 - s_2 \qquad s\left(A_2 A_1, A_2 F_2\right) = 1 - s_1.$$

Use the Spread ratio theorem (page 77) to get

$$Q\left(A_1, F_2\right) = \left(1 - s_1\right) Q_3 \qquad Q\left(A_2, F_1\right) = \left(1 - s_2\right) Q_3$$
$$Q\left(A_3, F_1\right) = \left(1 - s_3\right) Q_2 \qquad Q\left(A_3, F_2\right) = \left(1 - s_3\right) Q_1.$$

Use the Spread law in $\overline{A_1OF_2}$ and $\overline{A_2OF_1}$ to obtain

$$
\begin{aligned}
Q\left(O, F_2\right) &= \left(1 - s_1\right)\left(1 - s_3\right)Q_3/s_3 \\
Q\left(O, F_1\right) &= \left(1 - s_2\right)\left(1 - s_3\right)Q_3/s_3.
\end{aligned}
$$

Apply Pythagoras' theorem

$$
\begin{aligned}
Q\left(O, A_3\right) &= Q\left(O, F_1\right) + Q\left(F_1, A_3\right) \\
&= \left(1 - s_2\right)\left(1 - s_3\right)Q_3/s_3 + \left(1 - s_3\right)Q_2 \\
&= \left(1 - s_2\right)\left(1 - s_3\right)Q_3/s_3 + \left(1 - s_3\right)s_2Q_3/s_3 \\
&= \left(1 - s_3\right)Q_3/s_3.
\end{aligned}
$$

Thus OA_3 is a non-null line and so define the spread $r \equiv s\left(A_1A_2, OA_3\right)$. From the Spread ratio theorem

$$
s\left(A_3O, A_3F_1\right) = 1 - s_2 \qquad \text{and} \qquad s\left(A_3O, A_3F_2\right) = 1 - s_1. \tag{12.1}
$$

Now apply the Triple spread formula to the three lines A_1A_2, A_1A_3 and A_3O to see that $\{r, s_1, 1 - s_1\}$ is a spread triple. Similarly $\{r, s_2, 1 - s_2\}$ is a spread triple. The Two spread triples theorem (page 98) shows that if

$$
1 - 2s_1\left(1 - s_1\right) \neq 1 - 2s_2\left(1 - s_2\right) \tag{12.2}
$$

then

$$
r = \frac{\left(2s_1 - 1\right)^2 - \left(2s_2 - 1\right)^2}{2\left(1 - 1 - 2s_1\left(1 - s_1\right) + 2s_2\left(1 - s_2\right)\right)} = 1.
$$

But the condition (12.2) occurs precisely when either $s_1 = s_2$ or $s_1 = 1 - s_2$, in which case the triangle is either an isosceles or a right triangle respectively. The case of a right triangle has already been considered.

If $s_1 = s_2 \equiv s$ then (12.1) shows that

$$
s\left(A_3O, A_3F_1\right) = s\left(A_3O, A_3F_2\right)
$$

and so A_3O is a vertex bisector of $\overline{A_1A_2A_3}$. If A_3O is parallel to A_1A_2, then both A_3 and O lie on the perpendicular bisector of A_1A_2, the latter since $s\left(A_1O, A_1A_2\right) = s\left(A_2O, A_2A_1\right) = 1 - s$. Then O must coincide with A_3, and this case has already been excluded. Thus A_3O intersects A_1A_2, and so the Isosceles median theorem (page 123) shows it to be the altitude from A_3 to A_1A_2. ∎

Definition The **orthocenter** O of the triangle $\overline{A_1A_2A_3}$ is the common intersection of the altitudes of the triangle.

If a triangle $\overline{A_1A_2A_3}$ is a null triangle with exactly one line a null line, say A_1A_2, then the altitudes from A_1 and A_2 to the opposite sides are still defined, as is the orthocenter.

The next theorem provides another computational proof of the previous one.

12.4 Formulas for the orthocenter

Theorem 86 (Orthocenter formula) If $A_1 \equiv [x_1, y_1]$, $A_2 \equiv [x_2, y_2]$ and $A_3 \equiv [x_3, y_3]$, then the orthocenter O of the triangle $\overline{A_1 A_2 A_3}$ is

$$O = \left[\frac{[x_1 x_2 y_2]_3^- + [y_1 y_2^2]_3^-}{[x_1 y_2]_3^-}, \frac{[x_1 y_1 y_2]_3^- + [x_1^2 x_2]_3^-}{[x_1 y_2]_3^-} \right].$$

Proof. The altitudes n_1 and n_2 from A_1 and A_2 respectively are given by the Altitude to a line theorem (page 41) as

$$n_1 = \langle x_3 - x_2 : y_3 - y_2 : x_1 (x_2 - x_3) + y_1 (y_2 - y_3) \rangle$$
$$n_2 = \langle x_3 - x_1 : y_3 - y_1 : x_2 (x_1 - x_3) + y_2 (y_1 - y_3) \rangle .$$

The intersection of these lines is the point $O \equiv [x_0, y_0]$ where

$$x_0 \equiv \frac{\left(\begin{array}{c} x_1 x_2 y_2 - x_1 x_3 y_3 + x_2 x_3 y_3 - x_3 x_2 y_2 + x_3 x_1 y_1 - x_2 x_1 y_1 \\ + y_1 y_2^2 - y_1 y_3^2 + y_2 y_3^2 - y_3 y_2^2 + y_3 y_1^2 - y_2 y_1^2 \end{array} \right)}{x_1 y_2 - x_1 y_3 + x_2 y_3 - x_3 y_2 + x_3 y_1 - x_2 y_1}$$

and

$$y_0 \equiv \frac{\left(\begin{array}{c} x_1 y_1 y_2 - x_1 y_1 y_3 + x_2 y_2 y_3 - x_3 y_3 y_2 + x_3 y_3 y_1 - x_2 y_2 y_1 \\ + x_1^2 x_2 - x_1^2 x_3 + x_2^2 x_3 - x_3^2 x_2 + x_3^2 x_1 - x_2^2 x_1 \end{array} \right)}{x_1 y_2 - x_1 y_3 + x_2 y_3 - x_3 y_2 + x_3 y_1 - x_2 y_1} .$$

Use the conventions for anti-symmetric polynomials to rewrite O as stated. Since x_0 and y_0 are quotients of anti-symmetric polynomials, they are symmetric in the indices $1, 2$ and 3, showing that in fact O is the intersection of all three altitudes. ∎

Theorem 87 (Affine orthocenter) Suppose the quadrances of the triangle $\overline{A_1 A_2 A_3}$ are Q_1, Q_2 and Q_3 as usual, and the quadrea is $\mathcal{A}$. Then the orthocenter O can be written as the affine combination

$$O = \beta_1 A_1 + \beta_2 A_2 + \beta_3 A_3$$

where

$$\beta_1 \equiv (Q_3 + Q_1 - Q_2)(Q_1 + Q_2 - Q_3)/\mathcal{A}$$
$$\beta_2 \equiv (Q_1 + Q_2 - Q_3)(Q_2 + Q_3 - Q_1)/\mathcal{A}$$
$$\beta_3 \equiv (Q_2 + Q_3 - Q_1)(Q_3 + Q_1 - Q_2)/\mathcal{A}.$$

Proof. This is a straightforward but laborious verification using the previous theorem. Note that Exercise 5.15 (page 69) shows that $\beta_1 + \beta_2 + \beta_3 = 1$. ∎

12.5 Incenters

Theorem 88 (Incenter) Suppose that in the triangle $\overline{A_1 A_2 A_3}$ the vertices at A_1 and A_2 are bisected by the lines h_1 and h_2 respectively. Then h_1 and h_2 intersect at a point I, and $A_3 I$ is a bisector of the vertex at A_3.

Proof. By the Spread reflection theorem (page 95) the line $l_2 \equiv A_1 A_3$ is the reflection of the line $l_3 \equiv A_1 A_2$ in the bisector h_1, and $l_1 \equiv A_2 A_3$ is the reflection of l_3 in the bisector h_2. If h_1 and h_2 are parallel, then it follows that l_2 and l_1 are parallel, which they are not, since they intersect at A_3. So h_1 and h_2 intersect, say at the point I.

The Equal quadrance to two lines theorem (page 88) shows that

$$Q(I, l_2) = Q(I, l_3)$$
$$Q(I, l_1) = Q(I, l_3)$$

so that $Q(I, l_1) = Q(I, l_2)$. That means that $A_3 I$ is a bisector of the vertex at A_3. ∎

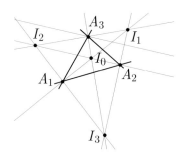

Figure 12.3: Incenters of a triangle

From the Vertex bisector theorem (page 85), if a vertex has a bisector, then it has exactly two bisectors and they are perpendicular. So there are four possible choices for the ordered pair $[h_1, h_2]$ where h_1 is a bisector of the vertex at A_1 and h_2 is a bisector of the vertex at A_2. This gives in general four intersection points I_0, I_1, I_2 and I_3 of the possible bisectors, the **incenters** of $\overline{A_1 A_2 A_3}$. If one incenter exists, so do all four.

Each of these four incenters lies on a bisector of each of the three vertices of $\overline{A_1 A_2 A_3}$. By the Equal quadrance to two lines theorem the quadrances from a particular incenter I_i to each of the three lines of the triangle are equal, and have the common value R_i, the associated **inquadrance** of the triangle $\overline{A_1 A_2 A_3}$. In general there are four inquadrances, R_0, R_1, R_2 and R_3.

The following theorem is surprisingly tricky to prove, especially when compared to the usual decimal number result involving angles. One should remember that the version here covers the case of all four incenters at once.

Theorem 89 (Incenter spread) Suppose that I is an incenter of $\overline{A_1A_2A_3}$, with $s(A_1I, A_1A_2) \equiv u_1$, $s(A_2I, A_2A_3) \equiv u_2$ and $s(A_3I, A_3A_1) \equiv u_3$. Then

$$s(IA_1, IA_2) = 1 - u_3. \qquad (12.3)$$

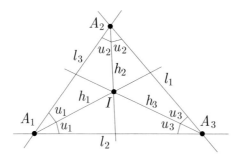

Figure 12.4: Incenter spread theorem

Proof. (Using a computer) To simplify matters, suppose that the coordinates of all points have been translated so that $I \equiv [0,0]$, and that $A_1 \equiv [x_1, y_1]$ and $A_2 \equiv [x_2, y_2]$. The general case follows the same lines. Suppose that l_1, l_2 and l_3 are the usual lines of the triangle $\overline{A_1A_2A_3}$, and that the vertex bisectors through I and A_1 and A_2 are respectively h_1 and h_2. Then using the Line through two points theorem (page 38)

$$l_3 = A_1A_2 = \langle y_1 - y_2 : x_2 - x_1 : x_1y_2 - x_2y_1 \rangle$$
$$h_1 = IA_1 = \langle y_1 : -x_1 : 0 \rangle$$
$$h_2 = IA_2 = \langle y_2 : -x_2 : 0 \rangle .$$

Since l_2 is the reflection of l_3 in h_1, the Reflection of a line in a line theorem (page 54) gives

$$l_2 = \left\langle \begin{array}{c} (y_1^2 - x_1^2)(y_1 - y_2) - 2y_1x_1(x_2 - x_1) : -2y_1x_1(y_1 - y_2) - (y_1^2 - x_1^2)(x_2 - x_1) \\ - (y_1^2 + x_1^2)(x_1y_2 - x_2y_1) \end{array} \right\rangle$$

Similarly

$$l_1 = \left\langle \begin{array}{c} (y_2^2 - x_2^2)(y_2 - y_1) - 2y_2x_2(x_1 - x_2) : -2y_2x_2(y_2 - y_1) - (y_2^2 - x_2^2)(x_1 - x_2) \\ - (y_2^2 + x_2^2)(x_2y_1 - x_1y_2) \end{array} \right\rangle .$$

Now use the Point on two lines theorem (page 40) to find $A_3 \equiv l_1l_2 \equiv [x_3, y_3]$.

The result is

$$
x_3 = \frac{\left(x_1^2 y_2 - x_2^2 y_1 + y_1^2 y_2 - y_1 y_2^2\right)(x_1 y_2 - x_2 y_1)}{\left((x_2 - x_1)^2 + (y_2 - y_1)^2\right)(x_1 x_2 + y_1 y_2)}
$$

$$
y_3 = \frac{\left(x_1 x_2^2 - x_1^2 x_2 + x_1 y_2^2 - x_2 y_1^2\right)(x_1 y_2 - x_2 y_1)}{\left((x_2 - x_1)^2 + (y_2 - y_1)^2\right)(x_1 x_2 + y_1 y_2)}.
$$

Then use a computer to calculate $s(A_3 I, A_3 A_1)$ using the Spread from points theorem (page 84). The result is

$$
s(A_3 I, A_3 A_1) = u_3 = \frac{(x_1 x_2 + y_1 y_2)^2}{(x_1^2 + y_1^2)(x_2^2 + y_2^2)}.
$$

By Fibonacci's identity

$$
1 - u_3 = \frac{(x_1 y_2 - x_2 y_1)^2}{(x_1^2 + y_1^2)(x_2^2 + y_2^2)} = s(I A_1, I A_2). \quad \blacksquare
$$

Note that since the triangle $\overline{A_1 A_2 I}$ has spreads u_1, u_2 and $1 - u_3$, the Triple spread theorem shows that $\{u_1, u_2, 1 - u_3\}$ is a spread triple.

Exercise 12.6 Verify that for any a, b and c

$$
S(a, b, 1 - c) = 2(a + b + c) - 2\left(a^2 + b^2 + c^2\right) - 1 - S(a, b, c)
$$

and hence deduce that

$$
S(a, b, 1 - c) = S(a, 1 - b, c) = S(1 - a, b, c). \quad \diamond
$$

Exercise 12.7 With notation as in the previous theorem, show that if $u_1 \neq 1/2$ then

$$
r_1 = s(A_1 I, A_2 A_3) = \frac{u_1 - 2u_2 - 2u_3 + 2u_2^2 + 2u_3^2}{2u_1 - 1}. \quad \diamond
$$

Example 12.1 Suppose that the field is $\mathbb{F}_{13}$, and that $A_1 \equiv [3, 7]$ and $A_2 \equiv [-2, -4]$ with $I \equiv [0, 0]$. Then proceeding as in the previous theorem, $A_3 \equiv [5, 7]$ and

$$
u_1 = 6 \qquad u_2 = 7 \qquad u_3 = 4.
$$

You may then check that $\{6, 7, -3\}$, $\{-5, 7, 4\}$ and $\{6, -6, 4\}$ are all spread triples. The spread between $A_1 I = \langle 2 : 1 : 0 \rangle$ and $A_2 A_3 = \langle 4 : 1 : -1 \rangle$ is

$$
r_1 = \frac{(2 \times 1 - 4 \times 1)^2}{(2^2 + 1^1)(4^2 + 1^2)} = 8 = \frac{6 - 2 \times 7 - 2 \times 4 + 2 \times 7^2 + 2 \times 4^2}{2 \times 6 - 1}
$$

as stated in the previous exercise. While r_3 may be determined in a similar way, some care must be taken with r_2 since $7 = 1/2$. $\diamond$

Theorem 90 (Inquadrance) Suppose that I is an incenter of $\overline{A_1 A_2 A_3}$, and that $s(A_1 I, A_1 A_2) \equiv u_1$, $s(A_2 I, A_2 A_3) \equiv u_2$ and $s(A_3 I, A_3 A_1) \equiv u_3$. Suppose the quadrances of $\overline{A_1 A_2 A_3}$ are Q_1, Q_2 and Q_3 as usual, and the circumquadrance is K. Then the inquadrance from I to each of the lines $A_1 A_2$, $A_2 A_3$ and $A_1 A_3$ is

$$R = 16 K u_1 u_2 u_3.$$

Proof. Since I lies on a vertex bisector of each of the three vertices of $\overline{A_1 A_2 A_3}$, the quadrance from I to the three lines of that triangle are equal. From the previous theorem $s(I A_1, I A_2) = 1 - u_3$, so the Spread law in the triangle $\overline{A_1 A_2 I}$ gives

$$Q(A_2, I) = \frac{u_1 Q_3}{1 - u_3}.$$

The quadrance from I to the line $A_1 A_2$ is then

$$
\begin{aligned}
R &= u_2 Q(A_2, I) = \frac{u_1 u_2 Q_3}{1 - u_3} \\
&= \frac{4 u_1 u_2 u_3 Q_3}{4 u_3 (1 - u_3)} = \frac{4 Q_3}{s_3} u_1 u_2 u_3 \\
&= 16 K u_1 u_2 u_3
\end{aligned}
$$

by the Extended spread law (page 144). ■

Exercise 12.8 Suppose that $\overline{A_1 A_2 A_3}$ has incenters I_0, I_1, I_2 and I_3, with the respective inquadrances R_0, R_1, R_2 and R_3. If $\mathcal{A}$ is the quadrea of the triangle $\overline{A_1 A_2 A_3}$ then show that

$$R_0 R_1 R_2 R_3 = \left(\frac{\mathcal{A}}{16}\right)^2. \quad \diamond$$

Example 12.2 The following example works in the field of *rational complex numbers*—complex numbers $a + bi$ where a and b are rational numbers. Suppose that $\overline{A_1 A_2 A_3}$ is a triangle with

$$A_1 \equiv [1, 1 + i] \qquad \text{and} \qquad A_2 \equiv [1 - i, -2i]$$

and with incenter $O \equiv [0, 0]$. Then using the proof of the Incenter spread theorem

$$A_3 = \left[-\frac{16}{39} + \frac{20}{117} i, \frac{46}{117} - \frac{10}{39} i \right].$$

The quadrea of $\overline{A_1 A_2 A_3}$ is

$$\mathcal{A} = -\frac{99\,328}{13\,689} + \frac{400\,768}{4563} i$$

and the circumquadrance is

$$K = \frac{25}{64} - \frac{25}{96} i.$$

The spreads u_1, u_2 and u_3 are

$$u_1 = -\frac{32}{195} - \frac{56}{195}i$$

$$u_2 = -\frac{4}{195} + \frac{32}{195}i$$

$$u_3 = \frac{9}{5}.$$

The equations of the three vertex bisectors meeting at I are

$$
\begin{aligned}
h_1 &\equiv A_1 I = \langle 1 + i : -1 : 0 \rangle \\
h_2 &\equiv A_2 I = \langle 2i : 1 - i : 0 \rangle \\
h_3 &\equiv A_3 I = \langle 46 - 30i : 48 - 20i : 0 \rangle .
\end{aligned}
$$

The other vertex bisectors through A_1, A_2 and A_3 respectively are perpendicular to these, so by the Altitude to a line theorem (page 41) they can be determined to be

$$
\begin{aligned}
j_1 &= \langle 1 : 1 + i : -1 - 2i \rangle \\
j_2 &= \langle 1 - i : -2i : 4 + 2i \rangle \\
j_3 &= \langle 72 - 30i : -69 + 45i : 40 - 60i \rangle .
\end{aligned}
$$

The other incenters are

$$
\begin{aligned}
I_1 &= h_1 j_2 = h_1 j_3 = \left[-\frac{1}{3} - i, \frac{2}{3} - \frac{4}{3}i \right] \\
I_2 &= h_2 j_1 = h_2 j_3 = \left[\frac{1}{3} + \frac{2}{3}i, 1 + \frac{1}{3}i \right] \\
I_3 &= h_3 j_1 = h_3 j_2 = \left[-\frac{5}{2} + \frac{1}{2}i, \frac{5}{2} - i \right]
\end{aligned}
$$

and the inquadrances are

$$
\begin{aligned}
R_0 &= \frac{16}{39} - \frac{8}{13}i \\
R_1 &= \frac{688}{351} + \frac{8}{13}i \\
R_2 &= -\frac{92}{351} - \frac{136}{117}i \\
R_3 &= \frac{2287}{156} - \frac{211}{26}i.
\end{aligned}
$$

These values may be used to check some of the formulas of this section. ◇

Isometries

Transformations which preserve quadrance are particularly important for geometry. This chapter studies and classifies these *isometries*, including translations, central reflections and central rotations. Solutions to the equation $q^2 + r^2 = 1$ naturally become involved.

13.1 Translations, rotations, reflections

Definition A transformation σ is an **isometry** precisely when it is both invertible and

$$Q(A_1, A_2) = Q(\sigma(A_1), \sigma(A_2))$$

for any points A_1 and A_2. An isometry that fixes the origin $O \equiv [0,0]$ is an **orthogonality.**

Exercise 13.1 Show that if σ is an isometry, then so is the inverse function σ^{-1}, and that if σ_1 and σ_2 are isometries, then so is the composition $\sigma_1 \circ \sigma_2 = \sigma_1 \sigma_2$. $\diamond$

Exercise 13.2 Show that for any point A the rotation ρ_A in A (page 52) is an isometry. Show that for any non-null line l the reflection σ_l in l (page 52) is an isometry. $\diamond$

Example 13.1 For numbers u and v the transformation $\tau_{u,v}$ defined by

$$\tau_{u,v}([x,y]) \equiv [x+u, y+v]$$

is a **translation**. The inverse of $\tau_{u,v}$ is $\tau_{-u,-v}$, and for any points A_1 and A_2

$$Q(A_1, A_2) = Q(\tau_{u,v}(A_1), \tau_{u,v}(A_2))$$

so $\tau_{u,v}$ is an isometry. If $B \equiv [u,v]$ then $\tau_{u,v}$ is also denoted by τ_B. $\diamond$

Example 13.2 For any numbers q and r satisfying $q^2 + r^2 = 1$, the transformation $\sigma_{q,r}$ defined by

$$\sigma_{q,r}\left([x,y]\right) \equiv [qx + ry, rx - qy]$$

is a **central reflection**. It is an orthogonality, since its inverse is itself, it fixes the origin, and for any two points $A_1 \equiv [x_1, y_1]$ and $A_2 \equiv [x_2, y_2]$

$$
\begin{aligned}
& Q\left(\sigma_{q,r}\left(A_1\right), \sigma_{q,r}\left(A_2\right)\right) \\
=\ & Q\left([qx_1 + ry_1, rx_1 - qy_1], [qx_2 + ry_2, rx_2 - qy_2]\right) \\
=\ & \left(q\left(x_2 - x_1\right) + r\left(y_2 - y_1\right)\right)^2 + \left(r\left(x_2 - x_1\right) - q\left(y_2 - y_1\right)\right)^2 \\
=\ & \left(q^2 + r^2\right)\left(\left(x_2 - x_1\right)^2 + \left(y_2 - y_1\right)^2\right) \\
=\ & Q\left(A_1, A_2\right). \quad \diamond
\end{aligned}
$$

Exercise 13.3 Show that if l is a non-null central line (passing through $O \equiv [0,0]$), then the reflection σ_l in l is a central reflection, and that every central reflection is of the form σ_l for some unique central line l. $\diamond$

Example 13.3 For any numbers q and r satisfying $q^2 + r^2 = 1$, the transformation $\rho_{q,r}$ defined by

$$\rho_{q,r}\left([x,y]\right) \equiv [qx - ry, rx + qy]$$

is a **central rotation**. The inverse of $\rho_{q,r}$ is $\rho_{q,-r}$, and for any two points $A_1 \equiv [x_1, y_1]$ and $A_2 \equiv [x_2, y_2]$

$$
\begin{aligned}
& Q\left(\rho_{q,r}\left(A_1\right), \rho_{q,r}\left(A_2\right)\right) \\
=\ & Q\left([qx_1 - ry_1, rx_1 + qy_1], [qx_2 - ry_2, rx_2 + qy_2]\right) \\
=\ & \left(q\left(x_2 - x_1\right) + r\left(y_1 - y_2\right)\right)^2 + \left(r\left(x_2 - x_1\right) - q\left(y_1 - y_2\right)\right)^2 \\
=\ & \left(q^2 + r^2\right)\left(\left(x_2 - x_1\right)^2 + \left(y_2 - y_1\right)^2\right) \\
=\ & Q\left(A_1, A_2\right)
\end{aligned}
$$

so since $\rho_{q,r}$ fixes the origin, it is an orthogonality. $\diamond$

Exercise 13.4 Show that an isometry cannot be simultaneously both a central rotation and a central reflection. Which of the two is the identity transformation ι? $\diamond$

Exercise 13.5 Show that for numbers q and r satisfying $q^2 + r^2 = 1$, and numbers t and u satisfying $t^2 + u^2 = 1$,

$$\sigma_{t,u}\sigma_{q,r} = \rho_{v,w}$$

where

$$v = qt + ru \qquad \text{and} \qquad w = qu - rt$$

while

$$\rho_{q,r}\rho_{t,u} = \rho_{t,u}\rho_{q,r} = \rho_{l,m}$$

where

$$l = qt - ru \qquad \text{and} \qquad m = qu + rt. \quad \diamond$$

In Chapter 16, the Unit circle theorem describes all ordered pairs $[q, r]$ satisfying $q^2 + r^2 = 1$, and the previous exercise is related to multiplication of complex numbers.

13.2 Classifying isometries

Theorem 91 (Isometries preserve collinearity) Suppose that σ is an isometry. Then A_1, A_2 and A_3 are collinear points precisely when $\sigma(A_1)$, $\sigma(A_2)$ and $\sigma(A_3)$ are collinear points.

Proof. It follows from the Quadrea theorem (page 68) that three points A_1, A_2 and A_3 forming quadrances $Q_1 \equiv Q(A_2, A_3)$, $Q_2 \equiv Q(A_1, A_3)$ and $Q_3 \equiv Q(A_1, A_2)$ are collinear precisely when $\mathcal{A} \equiv A(Q_1, Q_2, Q_3) = 0$. Now since an isometry preserves quadrances, this is equivalent to the condition that $\sigma(A_1)$, $\sigma(A_2)$ and $\sigma(A_3)$ are collinear. $\blacksquare$

Theorem 92 (Specifying isometries) An isometry is completely determined by its action on the points $O \equiv [0, 0]$, $I_1 \equiv [1, 0]$ and $I_2 \equiv [0, 1]$.

Proof. Suppose that σ_1 and σ_2 are both isometries which agree on the three points $O \equiv [0, 0]$, $I_1 \equiv [1, 0]$ and $I_2 \equiv [0, 1]$. Then the isometry $\sigma \equiv \sigma_2^{-1}\sigma_1$ fixes all three points, and it suffices to show that σ must be the identity isometry ι, by showing that σ fixes all other points too.

For a point $A \equiv [x, y]$, suppose that $\sigma(A) \equiv [u, v]$. Then the quadrances from A and $\sigma(A)$ to the points O, I_1 and I_2 must be respectively equal, so that

$$
\begin{align}
x^2 + y^2 &= u^2 + v^2 \tag{13.1}\\
(x - 1)^2 + y^2 &= (u - 1)^2 + v^2 \tag{13.2}\\
x^2 + (y - 1)^2 &= u^2 + (v - 1)^2. \tag{13.3}
\end{align}
$$

Now (13.1) minus (13.2) gives $2x - 1 = 2u - 1$, so that $x = u$, and similarly (13.1) minus (13.3) leads to $y = v$. Thus $\sigma(A) = A$ and so $\sigma = \iota$. $\blacksquare$

Theorem 93 (Orthogonality) An orthogonality is either a central rotation or a central reflection.

Proof. Suppose that μ is an orthogonality with $\mu(I_1) \equiv D_1 \equiv [q, r]$ and $\mu(I_2) \equiv D_2$. Then since $Q(O, I_1) = 1$,

$$
Q(O, D_1) = q^2 + r^2 = 1.
$$

The quadrances in triangle $\overline{OI_1I_2}$ are $Q_1 = Q_2 = 1$ and $Q_3 = 2$ so by Pythagoras' theorem, OI_1 is perpendicular to OI_2. Since the isometry μ preserves quadrances, the quadrances in triangle $\overline{OD_1D_2}$ are then also $Q_1 = Q_2 = 1$ and $Q_3 = 2$, so that OD_1 is perpendicular to OD_2. That means D_2 is a multiple of $[r, -q]$, and since $Q(O, D_2) = 1$ the only two possibilities are

$$D_2 = [r, -q]$$

or

$$D_2 = [-r, q].$$

By the Specifying isometries theorem, this information then determines μ. In the first case μ agrees with the central reflection $\sigma_{q,r}$, and in the second case μ agrees with the central rotation $\rho_{q,r}$. ∎

Theorem 94 (Classification of isometries) An isometry σ can be uniquely expressed as

$$\sigma = \tau\mu$$

where μ is an orthogonality and τ is a translation.

Proof. Suppose that the isometry σ satisfies $\sigma(O) \equiv B$. If $\tau \equiv \tau_B$ then $\tau^{-1}\sigma$ fixes O, so is an orthogonality μ, and $\sigma = \tau\mu$. To show uniqueness, suppose also that $\sigma = \tau'\mu'$ for some translation τ' and some orthogonality μ'. Then

$$B = \sigma(O) = (\tau'\mu')(O) = \tau'(O).$$

Since a translation is determined by its effect on one point, $\tau' = \tau$. But then $\mu' = \tau^{-1}\sigma = \mu$. So the expression for σ is unique. ∎

Exercise 13.6 Show that the rotation ρ_O in the origin $O \equiv [0,0]$ is a central rotation, and that $\rho_O = \rho_{-1,0}$. Show that for any point A, $\rho_A = \tau_B\rho_O$ where

$$B \equiv \rho_A(O). \ \diamond$$

Exercise 13.7 Show that if $l \equiv \langle a : b : c \rangle$ then $\sigma_l = \tau_B\sigma_k$ where

$$B \equiv \left[\frac{-2ac}{a^2 + b^2}, \frac{-2bc}{a^2 + b^2} \right] = \sigma_l(O)$$

and where σ_k is the central reflection in the line $k \equiv \langle a : b : 0 \rangle$, given by

$$\sigma_k([x, y]) = \left[\frac{(b^2 - a^2)x - 2aby}{a^2 + b^2}, \frac{-2abx + (a^2 - b^2)y}{a^2 + b^2} \right]. \ \diamond$$

Regular stars and polygons

This chapter introduces regular stars and polygons, which illustrate cyclical and dihedral symmetry in the plane, and occur often in applications over the decimal numbers. The existence of regular stars of a given order n is a number theoretical issue, analysed here for the cases $n = 3, 5$ and 7. Regular polygons are constructed from regular stars by successive reflections of a point on one of the lines of the star, motivating an unorthodox labelling of vertices. The case of the regular pentagon receives special attention. The lineations Σ_l defined in Chapter 4 play a major role.

14.1 Regular stars

Definition A **regular star of order** n is a list of n distinct mutually non-parallel lines $[l_0, l_1, \cdots, l_{n-1}]$ such that $l_{k+1} = \sum_{l_k} (l_{k-1})$ for all k, with the convention that $l_k \equiv l_{k+n}$ for all k, and the conventions that

$$[l_0, l_1, \cdots, l_{n-2}, l_{n-1}] \equiv [l_1, l_2, \cdots, l_{n-1}, l_0]$$
$$[l_0, l_1, \cdots, l_{n-2}, l_{n-1}] \equiv [l_{n-1}, l_{n-2}, \cdots, l_1, l_0].$$

Any spread s of the form $s(l_i, l_j)$, with l_i and l_j lines in the star, is a **spread** of the star. If $s \equiv s(l_1, l_2)$ then the spreads of the star are all of the form $S_k(s)$ for some k, and so contained in the spread sequence for s.

In particular $S_n(s) = 0$, and from the Cyclic reflection theorem (page 56) $S_n(r) = 0$ for any spread r of the star.

Order seven star

14.2   Order three stars

Theorem 95 (Order three star) A regular star of order three exists precisely when the number 3 is a non-zero square.

Proof. Suppose that a regular star $[l_0, l_1, l_2]$ of order three exists. Then $s(l_0, l_1) = s(l_1, l_2) = s(l_2, l_0) \equiv s$ for some non-zero number s. Since l_0, l_1 and l_2 are distinct concurrent lines, no two can be parallel, so that the Three equal spreads theorem (page 101) shows that

$$0 = s(l_0, l_0) = S_3(s) = s(3 - 4s)^2.$$

Thus $s = 3/4$ is non-zero and by the Spread number theorem (page 76) is a spread number, so that

$$s(1 - s) = 3/16$$

is a square. Thus 3 is both non-zero and a square.

Conversely suppose that $3 \equiv r^2$ for some non-zero number r. Then consider

$$l_0 \equiv \langle 0 : 1 : 0 \rangle \qquad l_1 \equiv \langle r : 1 : 0 \rangle \qquad l_2 \equiv \langle -r : 1 : 0 \rangle.$$

Since

$$s(l_0, l_1) = s(l_0, l_2) = \frac{r^2}{r^2 + 1} = \frac{3}{4} = \frac{(2r)^2}{(r^2 + 1)^2} = s(l_2, l_3)$$

it follows from the Spread reflection theorem (page 95) that $[l_0, l_1, l_2]$ is a regular star of order three. ∎

Example 14.1 In the fields $\mathbb{F}_3, \mathbb{F}_5, \mathbb{F}_7, \mathbb{F}_{17}$ and $\mathbb{F}_{19}$, the number 3 is not a non-zero square, so there are no regular stars of order three. ◇

Example 14.2 In the field $\mathbb{F}_{11}$, $3 = 5^2$, so an example of a regular star of order three is $[l_0, l_1, l_2]$, where

$$l_0 \equiv \langle 0 : 1 : 0 \rangle \qquad l_1 \equiv \langle 5 : 1 : 0 \rangle \qquad l_2 \equiv \langle 6 : 1 : 0 \rangle. \quad ◇$$

Example 14.3 In the field $\mathbb{F}_{13}$, $3 = 4^2$, so an example of a regular star of order three is $[l_0, l_1, l_2]$, where

$$l_0 \equiv \langle 0 : 1 : 0 \rangle \qquad l_1 \equiv \langle 4 : 1 : 0 \rangle \qquad l_2 \equiv \langle 9 : 1 : 0 \rangle. \quad ◇$$

Example 14.4 In the rational number field, 3 is not a square, so regular stars of order three do not exist. However in the decimal number field $3 = \left(\sqrt{3}\right)^2$, so an example of a regular star of order three is $[l_0, l_1, l_2]$, where

$$l_0 \equiv \langle 0 : 1 : 0 \rangle \qquad l_1 \equiv \langle \sqrt{3} : 1 : 0 \rangle \qquad l_2 \equiv \langle -\sqrt{3} : 1 : 0 \rangle. \quad ◇$$

14.3 Order five stars

Theorem 96 (Order five star) A regular star of order five exists precisely when there is a non-zero number r satisfying the conditions i) $r^2 = 5$ and ii) $2(5 - r)$ is a square.

Proof. Suppose that a regular star $[l_0, l_1, l_2, l_3, l_4]$ of order five exists with $s(l_1, l_2) \equiv s \neq 0$. By the Consecutive spreads theorem (page 103)

$$S_5(s) = s(5 - 20s + 16s^2)^2 = 0. \tag{14.1}$$

Thus s is non-zero and satisfies the quadratic equation $5 - 20s + 16s^2 = 0$, so that also $s \neq 1$. Complete the square to obtain

$$(s - 5/8)^2 = 5/64.$$

A solution s exists precisely when 5 is a square, so that $s = (5 + r)/8$ for some number r satisfying $r^2 = 5$. If $r = 0$ then $5 = 0$ so that $s = 0$ which is impossible. Since s is a spread number,

$$s(1 - s) = (5 + r)(3 - r)/64 = (10 - 2r)/64$$

is a square, so that $2(5 - r)$ is a square. Thus r is non-zero and satisfies i) and ii).

Conversely suppose that there is some non-zero number r with the properties that i) $r^2 = 5$ and ii) $2(5 - r) = v^2$ for some number v. Then you may check that

$$l_0 \equiv \langle 0 : 1 : 0 \rangle \qquad l_1 \equiv \langle v : 3 - r : 0 \rangle \qquad l_2 \equiv \langle v(3 - r) : 2 - 2r : 0 \rangle$$
$$l_3 \equiv \langle v(r - 3) : 2 - 2r : 0 \rangle \qquad l_4 \equiv \langle -v : 3 - r : 0 \rangle$$

defines a regular star $[l_0, l_1, l_2, l_3, l_4]$ of order five. ∎

Example 14.5 In the fields $\mathbb{F}_3, \mathbb{F}_5, \mathbb{F}_7, \mathbb{F}_{13}$ and $\mathbb{F}_{17}$ the equation $S_5(s) = 0$ has no non-zero solutions, and so there are no regular stars of order 5. ◇

Example 14.6 In the field $\mathbb{F}_{11}$ the equation $S_5(s) = 0$ has exactly two non-zero solutions $s = 7 = (5 + 7)/8$ and $s = 8 = (5 + 4)/8$. But the spread numbers in $\mathbb{F}_{11}$ are $0, 1, 2, 3, 6, 9$ or 10, so there are no regular stars of order 5. Equivalently the numbers $2(5 - 7) = 7$ and $2(5 - 4) = 2$ are not squares. ◇

Example 14.7 In the field $\mathbb{F}_{19}$ the equation $S_5(s) = 0$ has exactly two non-zero solutions $s = 9 = (5 + 10)/8$ and $s = 16 = (5 + 9)/8$. These are spread numbers, or equivalently the numbers $2(5 - 10) = 9$ and $2(5 - 9) = 11$ are squares. An example of a regular star $[l_0, l_1, l_2, l_3, l_4]$ which has these spreads is

$$l_0 \equiv \langle 0 : 1 : 0 \rangle \qquad l_1 \equiv \langle 2 : 1 : 0 \rangle \qquad l_2 \equiv \langle 5 : 1 : 0 \rangle$$
$$l_3 \equiv \langle -5 : 1 : 0 \rangle \qquad l_4 \equiv \langle -2 : 1 : 0 \rangle \qquad ◇$$

A Go board has dimensions 19×19, the smallest square grid for which five fold symmetry exists in the above sense.

14.4   Order seven stars

The analysis of the previous two sections does not easily continue for higher order stars. However one can still make statements of the following kind.

Theorem 97 (Order seven star) A regular star of order seven exists precisely when there is a non-zero number s for which

$$7 - 56s + 112s^2 - 64s^3 = 0$$

and such that $s(1-s)$ is a square.

Proof. Suppose that a regular star $[l_0, l_1, \cdots, l_6]$ exists with $s(l_0, l_1) \equiv s \neq 0$. By the Consecutive spreads theorem

$$S_7(s) = s\left(7 - 56s + 112s^2 - 64s^3\right)^2 = 0. \tag{14.2}$$

Thus s is non-zero, satisfies the cubic equation $7 - 56s + 112s^2 - 64s^3 = 0$, and because it is a spread number, satisfies the condition that $s(1-s)$ is a square.

Conversely suppose that s is a non-zero spread number satisfying (14.2). There are two lines l_0 and l_1 with spread $s(l_0, l_1) = s$, and suppose that they intersect at the point P. Using the rule $l_{k+1} = \Sigma_{l_k}(l_{k-1})$ the reflection sequence

$$\cdots l_{-1}, l_0, l_1, l_2, \cdots$$

may be obtained, and since $S_7(s) = 0$ you know that $l_7 = l_0$, since it is both parallel to l_1 and also passes through P. Thus $l_{n+7} = l_n$ for any n. If any two of the lines $l_0, l_1, \cdots, l_6$ are the same, then the reflection sequence satisfies $l_{n+k} = l_n$ for any n for some positive integer $1 \leq k < 7$. But then since k and 7 are relatively prime, it follows that $l_0 = l_1$, which is impossible. Thus $[l_0, l_1, \cdots, l_6]$ is a regular star of order seven. ∎

Example 14.8 In the fields $\mathbb{F}_3, \mathbb{F}_5, \mathbb{F}_7, \mathbb{F}_{11}, \mathbb{F}_{17}, \mathbb{F}_{19}$ and $\mathbb{F}_{23}$ the equation $S_7(s) = s\left(7 - 56s + 112s^2 - 64s^3\right)^2 = 0$ has no non-zero solutions, and so there are no regular stars of order 7. In the field $\mathbb{F}_{13}$ the equation $S_7(s) = 0$ has exactly three non-zero solutions $s = 2$, $s = 5$ and $s = 11$. But the spread numbers in $\mathbb{F}_{13}$ are $0, 1, 4, 6, 7, 8$ or 10, so there are no regular stars of order 7. ◇

Example 14.9 In the field $\mathbb{F}_{29}$ the equation $S_7(s) = 0$ has exactly three non-zero solutions $s = 6$, $s = 7$ and $s = 25$. These are spread numbers, and the regular star $[l_0, l_1, \cdots, l_6]$ where

$$
\begin{array}{llll}
l_0 \equiv \langle 0 : 1 : 0 \rangle & l_1 \equiv \langle 15 : 1 : 0 \rangle & l_2 \equiv \langle 11 : 1 : 0 \rangle & l_3 \equiv \langle 20 : 1 : 0 \rangle \\
l_4 \equiv \langle 9 : 1 : 0 \rangle & l_5 \equiv \langle 18 : 1 : 0 \rangle & l_6 \equiv \langle 14 : 1 : 0 \rangle &
\end{array}
$$

has spreads $0, 6, 25$ and 7. ◇

Example 14.10 In the rational number field (14.2) has no solutions, so there are no regular stars of order seven. In the decimal number field regular stars of order seven exist, as the equation $S_7(s) = 0$ has non-zero solutions

$$\gamma_1 \approx 0.188\,255\,099\ldots \qquad \gamma_2 \approx 0.611\,260\,467\ldots \qquad \gamma_3 \approx 0.950\,484\,434\ldots. \quad \diamond$$

14.5 Regular polygons

Suppose that $[l_0, l_1, \cdots, l_{n-1}]$ is a regular star of order n with common intersection P. Adopt the convention that $l_{k+n} \equiv l_k$ for any integer k, so that $\cdots l_{-1}, l_0, l_1, \cdots$ is a reflection sequence of lines. Then by the Cyclic reflection theorem (page 56), for any integers k and l

$$\Sigma_{l_k}(l_j) = l_{2k-j}.$$

The Reflection theorem (page 55) implies that

$$\sigma_{l_{2k-j}} = \sigma_{l_k} \sigma_{l_j} \sigma_{l_k}.$$

In particular

$$\sigma_{l_2} = \sigma_{l_1} \sigma_{l_0} \sigma_{l_1} \qquad \sigma_{l_3} = \sigma_{l_2} \sigma_{l_1} \sigma_{l_2}$$

and so on. From this and the fact that $\sigma_l^{-1} = \sigma_l$ for all l, it follows that

$$\sigma_{l_2} \sigma_{l_0} = \sigma_{l_2} \sigma_{l_1} \sigma_{l_2} \sigma_{l_1} = \sigma_{l_3} \sigma_{l_1}$$

and so on.

Exercise 14.1 Extend the argument to show that for any integers j, k and m

$$\sigma_{l_j} \sigma_{l_k} = \sigma_{l_{j+m}} \sigma_{l_{k+m}}. \quad \diamond$$

Choose a point A_0 on l_0 distinct from P. Define the sequence of points

$$A_0, A_2 \equiv \sigma_{l_1}(A_0), A_4 \equiv \sigma_{l_3}(A_2), A_6 \equiv \sigma_{l_5}(A_4), \cdots$$

and so on, so that A_{2k} lies on l_{2k} by induction. Using the above relations you find that

$$
\begin{aligned}
A_4 &= \sigma_{l_3} \sigma_{l_1}(A_0) = \sigma_{l_2} \sigma_{l_0}(A_0) = \sigma_{l_2}(A_0) \\
A_6 &= \sigma_{l_5} \sigma_{l_2}(A_0) = \sigma_{l_3} \sigma_{l_0}(A_0) = \sigma_{l_3}(A_0) \\
A_8 &= \sigma_{l_7} \sigma_{l_3}(A_0) = \sigma_{l_4} \sigma_{l_0}(A_0) = \sigma_{l_4}(A_0)
\end{aligned}
$$

and so on. Thus for any positive integer k,

$$A_{2k} = \sigma_{l_k}(A_0).$$

In particular

$$A_{2n} = \sigma_{l_n}(A_0) = \sigma_{l_0}(A_0) = A_0.$$

The n-gon $\overline{A_0 A_2 \cdots A_{2(n-1)}}$ constructed this way is called **regular**. Note that

$$Q\left(P, A_0\right) = Q\left(P, A_2\right) = \cdots = Q\left(P, A_{2(n-1)}\right).$$

In the case of n odd, the points $A_0, A_2, \cdots, A_{2(n-1)}$ are all distinct because they lie on distinct lines.

In the case of $n = 2m$ even, the points A_k and A_{k+n} lie on the same line l_k, and $A_{k+n} = \sigma_{l_{k+m}}\left(A_k\right) \neq A_k$ since $\sigma_{l_{k+m}}$ acts on the points lying on l_k as the rotation in P, which fixes only P. Thus in this case the points $A_0, A_2, \cdots, A_{2(n-1)}$ are also distinct.

Example 14.11 If $[l_0, l_1, l_2, l_3, l_4]$ is a regular star of order five, then for any point A_0 on l_0 distinct from the common intersection P of the lines, one obtains by this construction a regular 5-gon, or **pentagon**, $\overline{A_0 A_2 A_4 A_6 A_8}$ as shown in Figure 14.1.

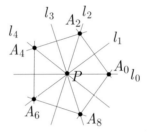

Figure 14.1: Regular pentagon ◇

Example 14.12 If $[l_0, l_1, l_2, l_3, l_4, l_5]$ is a regular star of order six, then for any point A_0 on l_0 distinct from the common intersection P of the lines, one obtains by this construction a regular 6-gon, or **hexagon**, $\overline{A_0 A_2 A_4 A_6 A_8 A_{10}}$ as shown in Figure 14.2.

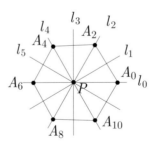

Figure 14.2: Regular hexagon ◇

If $\overline{A_0 A_2 \cdots A_{2(n-1)}}$ is a regular n-gon of order n constructed from a regular star $[l_0, l_1, \cdots, l_{n-1}]$ of order n, then a triangle of three successive points such as $\overline{A_0 A_2 A_4}$, $\overline{A_2 A_4 A_6}, \cdots, \overline{A_{2(n-1)} A_0 A_2}$ is a **corner triangle** of the n-gon.

Theorem 98 (Polygon triangle) Suppose that $\overline{A_0 A_2 \cdots A_{2(n-1)}}$ is a regular n-gon constructed from a regular star $[l_0, l_1, \cdots, l_{n-1}]$ of order n with common intersection point P. Suppose that $s \equiv s(l_0, l_1) = s(l_1, l_2) = \cdots$ and that $\overline{Q(P, A_{2k})} \equiv Q$ for all k. Then the quadrances and spreads of the corner triangle $\overline{A_0 A_2 A_4}$ are

$$R \equiv Q(A_0, A_2) = Q(A_2, A_4) = 4sQ$$
$$D \equiv Q(A_0, A_4) = 16s(1-s)Q$$

and

$$s(A_0 A_4, A_0 A_2) = s(A_4 A_0, A_4 A_2) = s$$
$$s(A_2 A_0, A_2 A_4) = 4s(1-s).$$

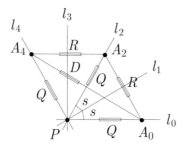

Figure 14.3: Polygon triangle theorem

Proof. Since $s(l_0, l_1) = s(l_1, l_2) \equiv s$, the Isosceles reflection theorem (page 124) shows that

$$R \equiv Q(A_0, A_2) = Q(A_2, A_4) = 4sQ.$$

Similarly since

$$s(l_0, l_2) = s(l_2, l_4) = S_2(s) = 4s(1-s)$$

it follows that

$$D \equiv Q(A_0, A_4) = 4 \times 4s(1-s)Q = 16s(1-s)Q.$$

Now in $\overline{A_0 A_2 A_4}$ use the Isosceles triangle theorem (page 122) to get

$$s(A_0 A_4, A_0 A_2) = s(A_4 A_0, A_4 A_2) = 1 - D/(4R).$$
$$= 1 - (1 - s) = s.$$

Then use the Spread law to see that

$$s(A_2 A_0, A_2 A_4) = 4s(1-s). \quad \blacksquare$$

Exercise 14.2 Extend this theorem to show that if a regular n-gon $\overline{A_0 A_2 \cdots A_{2(n-1)}}$ is constructed from a regular star $[l_0, l_1, \cdots, l_{n-1}]$ of order n with common intersection P and with $s \equiv s(l_0, l_1) = s(l_1, l_2) = \cdots$ as above, and that $Q(P, A_k) \equiv Q$ for all k, then

$$Q(A_0, A_{2k}) = 4 S_k(s) Q$$

for all $k = 0, 1, \cdots, n - 1$. This gives a geometric interpretation of $S_k(s)$. ◇

Exercise 14.3 Show that in the decimal number system the non-trivial zeroes of

$$S_5(s) = s \left(5 - 20s + 16s^2\right)^2 = 0$$

are

$$\alpha \equiv \left(5 - \sqrt{5}\right)/8 \approx 0.345\,491\ldots \qquad \text{and} \qquad \beta \equiv \left(5 + \sqrt{5}\right)/8 \approx 0.904\,508\ldots.$$

With notation as in Figure 14.4, show that if $Q(A, B) \equiv R$ is the common quadrance of the sides, then

$$Q(P, A) = (1 - \alpha) R/\beta = R/4\alpha \qquad Q(P, M) = (1 - \alpha) R/4\alpha$$
$$Q(B, F) = (1 - \alpha) R \qquad\qquad Q(B, E) = 4(1 - \alpha) R = \beta R/\alpha.$$

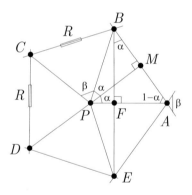

Figure 14.4: Spreads in a pentagon ◇

Exercise 14.4 Using the notation of the previous exercise, show that the proportion $\beta : \alpha$ is equal to both $s(PA, PB) : s(PB, PE)$ and $Q(B, E) : Q(A, B)$. ◇

Exercise 14.5 (Harder) Show that in $\mathbb{F}_{19}$ the five points

$$A_0 \equiv [2, -4] \qquad A_2 \equiv [1, 0] \qquad A_4 \equiv [2, 4] \qquad A_6 \equiv [7, -3] \qquad A_8 \equiv [7, 3]$$

form a regular pentagon $\overline{A_0 A_2 A_4 A_6 A_8}$ with center $O \equiv [0, 0]$. Show that the intersections of the diagonals of this pentagon yield five new points, also forming a regular pentagon, and that by repeating this operation a total of eighteen times, the original pentagon is recovered. ◇

Conics

After points and lines and combinations of them, the next natural objects of study in geometry are *conics*, given by quadratic equations. In the setting of universal geometry, there are interesting families of conics which can be defined metrically, such as *circles, ribbons, parabolas, quadrolas* and *grammolas*. This raises perhaps the first serious problem of metrical algebraic geometry: How to classify conics? No answer is given here. Much remains to be discovered about these intriguing curves.

15.1 Centers of conics

Definition A **conic** $q \equiv \langle d : e : f : a : b : c \rangle$ is a 6-proportion, enclosed in pointed brackets, such that at least one of d, e or f is non-zero.

The conic $q \equiv \langle d : e : f : a : b : c \rangle$ will sometimes also be written in the form

$$
q = \left\langle \begin{array}{ccc} d & : & e & : & f \\ & a & : & b \\ & & c \end{array} \right\rangle.
$$

Definition A point $X \equiv [x, y]$ **lies on** the conic $q \equiv \langle d : e : f : a : b : c \rangle$, or equivalently q **passes through** X, precisely when

$$
dx^2 + exy + fy^2 + ax + by + c = 0.
$$

This is an **equation** of the conic q, as is any equivalent equation derived from it using the usual rules for manipulating equations. A conic q is **standard** precisely when it passes through the origin $O \equiv [0,0]$. A conic q is **empty** if no point lies on q.

In studying conics, looking for symmetry is useful. Recall from page 52 that if $C \equiv [u, v]$, then the rotation in C is defined by $\rho_C\left([x, y]\right) \equiv [2u - x, 2v - y]$.

Definition A point $C \equiv [u, v]$ is a **center** of the conic $q \equiv \langle d : e : f : a : b : c \rangle$ precisely when
$$dx^2 + exy + fy^2 + ax + by + c$$
is unchanged by the substitutions $x \to 2u - x$ and $y \to 2v - y$.

Example 15.1 The point $C \equiv [1, 2]$ is a center for the conic $\langle 1 : 2 : -1 : -6 : 2 : 1 \rangle$ since

$$(2 - x)^2 + 2\,(2 - x)\,(4 - y) - (4 - y)^2 - 6\,(2 - x) + 2\,(4 - y) + 1$$
$$= \; x^2 + 2xy - y^2 - 6x + 2y + 1. \quad \diamond$$

Theorem 99 (Conic center) The conic $q \equiv \langle d : e : f : a : b : c \rangle$ has a unique center C precisely when $e^2 - 4df \neq 0$, in which case

$$C = \left[\frac{2af - be}{e^2 - 4df}, \frac{2bd - ae}{e^2 - 4df}\right].$$

If $e^2 - 4df = 0$ and $e : 2f : b = 2d : e : a$, then there is more than one center. If $e^2 - 4df = 0$ and $e : 2f : b \neq 2d : e : a$, then there is no center.

Proof. The condition for $[u, v]$ to be a center of $q \equiv \langle d : e : f : a : b : c \rangle$ is

$$d\,(2u - x)^2 + e\,(2u - x)\,(2v - y) + f\,(2v - y)^2 + a\,(2u - x) + b\,(2v - y) + c$$
$$= \; dx^2 + exy + fy^2 + ax + by + c$$

which simplifies to

$$x\,(2du + ev + a) + y\,(eu + 2fv + b) - (2du + ev + a)\,u - (eu + 2fv + b)\,v = 0.$$

This is satisfied precisely when the coefficients of x and y are zero, that is when

$$eu + 2fv + b = 2du + ev + a = 0.$$

By page 30 this pair of linear equations in u and v has a unique solution precisely when $e^2 - 4df \neq 0$, in which case

$$u = \frac{2af - be}{e^2 - 4df}$$
$$v = \frac{2bd - ae}{e^2 - 4df}.$$

If $e^2 - 4df = 0$ then there is more than one solution precisely when $e : 2f : b = 2d : e : a$, and no solution otherwise. ∎

Exercise 15.1 Find all centers of the conics with equations $x^2 + 2xy + y^2 = 0$ and $x^2 + 2xy + y^2 + x = 0$. ◇

Exercise 15.2 Show that if C_1 and C_2 are distinct centers for a conic q, then every point lying on C_1C_2 is a center for q. ◇

Definition A conic q is **centered** precisely when it has a center, and is a **central conic** precisely when it has $O \equiv [0,0]$ as a center.

15.2 Circles and ribbons

Definition A **circle** c is a conic whose equation in $X \equiv [x,y]$ has the form

$$Q(X,C) = K$$

for some fixed point C and some fixed number K.

It will be seen below that the point C and the number K are determined by the circle c. The point C is the unique center of c, and the number K is the **quadrance** of c. A circle c is **central** precisely when its center is $O \equiv [0,0]$. A circle c is **null** precisely when its quadrance is $K \equiv 0$.

Example 15.2 In the field $\mathbb{F}_{11}$, Figure 15.1 shows the eleven central circles, in particular the circles of quadrance one (circles) and quadrance two (gray squares).

5	6	8	①	7	4	3	4	7	①	8	6
4	8	10	3	9	6	5	6	9	3	10	8
3	①	3	7	2	10	9	10	2	7	3	①
2	7	9	2	8	5	4	5	8	2	9	7
1	4	6	10	5	2	①	2	5	10	6	4
0	3	5	9	4	①	0	①	4	9	5	3
-1	4	6	10	5	2	①	2	5	10	6	4
-2	7	9	2	8	5	4	5	8	2	9	7
-3	①	3	7	2	10	9	10	2	7	3	①
-4	8	10	3	9	6	5	6	9	3	10	8
-5	6	8	①	7	4	3	4	7	①	8	6
	-5	-4	-3	-2	-1	0	1	2	3	4	5

Figure 15.1: Central circles in $\mathbb{F}_{11}$

The number in any position is the quadrance of the circle on which it lies. Each of the ten non-null circles has exactly 12 points lying on it, and the null circle has only one point lying on it. Figure 15.2 is a view of the central circle of quadrance one on a larger scale.

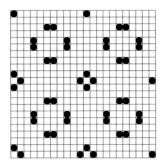

Figure 15.2: Circle of quadrance one in $\mathbb{F}_{11}$ ◇

Exercise 15.3 In the field $\mathbb{F}_{13}$, Figure 15.3 shows the thirteen central circles, in particular the circles of quadrance one (circles) and quadrance two (gray boxes), as well as the central null circle (black squares). Each of the twelve non-null circles has exactly 12 points lying on it, while the null circle has 25 points lying on it.

	-6	-5	-4	-3	-2	-1	0	1	2	3	4	5	6
6	7	9	0	6	1	11	10	11	1	6	0	9	7
5	9	11	2	8	3	0	12	0	3	8	2	11	9
4	0	2	6	12	7	4	3	4	7	12	6	2	0
3	6	8	12	5	0	10	9	10	0	5	12	8	6
2	1	3	7	0	8	5	4	5	8	0	7	3	1
1	11	0	4	10	5	2	1	2	5	10	4	0	11
0	10	12	3	9	4	1	0	1	4	9	3	12	10
-1	11	0	4	10	5	2	1	2	5	10	4	0	11
-2	1	3	7	0	8	5	4	5	8	0	7	3	1
-3	6	8	12	5	0	10	9	10	0	5	12	8	6
-4	0	2	6	12	7	4	3	4	7	12	6	2	0
-5	9	11	2	8	3	0	12	0	3	8	2	11	9
-6	7	9	0	6	1	11	10	11	1	6	0	9	7

Figure 15.3: Central circles in $\mathbb{F}_{13}$

Figure 15.4 shows on the left a larger view of the central circle of quadrance one, and on the right a larger view of the central null circle.

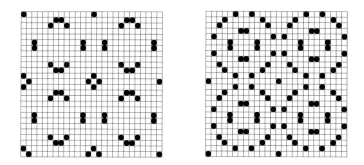

Figure 15.4: Circles of quadrance one and zero in $\mathbb{F}_{13}$ ◇

Theorem 100 (Circle uniqueness) The center and quadrance of a circle c are unique.

Proof. Suppose that $C \equiv [u, v]$ is a fixed point and K a number. With $X \equiv [x, y]$, the equation

$$Q(X, C) = K$$

is

$$(x - u)^2 + (y - v)^2 = K$$

which defines the circle

$$c \equiv \langle 1 : 0 : 1 : -2u : -2v : u^2 + v^2 - K \rangle.$$

With the proportion scaled so that the first and third entries are 1, the coordinates u and v of the center C are immediate from the fourth and fifth entries, and then the quadrance K is determined from the last entry. ∎

Exercise 15.4 Show that $q \equiv \langle d : e : f : a : b : c \rangle$ is a circle precisely when $e = 0$ and $d = f \neq 0$. ◇

Exercise 15.5 Show that in the field $\mathbb{F}_{13}$ every point lying on the unique central null circle c lies either on the line $\langle 2 : 3 : 0 \rangle$ or the line $\langle 3 : 2 : 0 \rangle$, and conversely that every point lying on one of these lines also lies on c. Generalize. ◇

Exercise 15.6 Recall from page 67 that $Q(X, l)$ denotes the quadrance from the point X to the line l. A **ribbon** r is a conic whose equation in $X \equiv [x, y]$ has the form

$$Q(X, l) = K$$

for some fixed non-null line l and some fixed number K. Show that l and K are unique, and that every point lying on l is a center for r. ◇

15.3 Parabolas

Definition A **parabola** p is a conic whose equation in $X \equiv [x, y]$ has the form

$$Q(X, F) = Q(X, l)$$

for some fixed point F and some fixed non-null line l not passing through F.

It will be seen below that the point F and the line l are determined by p. The point F is the **focus** and the line l the **directrix** of p.

Example 15.3 If $a \neq 0$ then the parabola p with focus $F \equiv [a, 0]$ and directrix $l \equiv \langle 1 : 0 : a \rangle$ has equation

$$(x - a)^2 + y^2 = (x + a)^2$$

or $y^2 = 4ax$. Thus $p = \langle 0 : 0 : 1 : -4a : 0 : 0 \rangle$. ⋄

Example 15.4 In the field $\mathbb{F}_{11}$ two views of the parabola p with equation

$$y^2 = 4x$$

are pictured in Figure 15.5 (squares), along with the focus $F \equiv [1, 0]$ (dot) and the directrix $l \equiv \langle 1 : 0 : 1 \rangle$ (gray boxes). Note that the parabola still deserves its name.

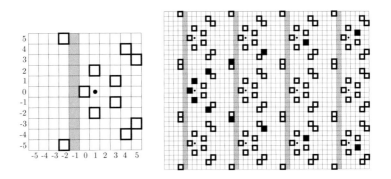

Figure 15.5: Parabola $y^2 = 4x$ in $\mathbb{F}_{11}$: two views

Exercise 15.7 Show that a parabola p does not have a center. In particular a parabola cannot be a circle. ⋄

Exercise 15.8 Show that a parabola has a unique **axis**, namely a line l for which the reflection σ_l preserves the equation of the conic. ⋄

Exercise 15.9 Show that there is a unique point lying on both a parabola and its axis, called the **vertex**. ⋄

Theorem 101 (Parabola uniqueness) The focus and directrix of a parabola p are unique.

Proof. If $F \equiv [u, v]$ and $l \equiv \langle a : b : c \rangle$ are a corresponding focus and directrix for p then using the Quadrance to a line theorem (page 67) the conic has equation

$$(x - u)^2 + (y - v)^2 = \frac{(ax + by + c)^2}{a^2 + b^2}.$$

After expansion this gives

$$p = \left\langle \begin{array}{c} b^2 : -2ab : a^2 \\ -2ac - 2\left(a^2 + b^2\right) u : -2bc - 2\left(a^2 + b^2\right) v \\ \left(a^2 + b^2\right)\left(u^2 + v^2\right) - c^2 \end{array} \right\rangle.$$

Let's see how to recover the point F and the line l from this proportion. Since $\langle a : b : c \rangle$ is a line at least one of a and b is non-zero, and the proportion p determines which is non-zero. Suppose that $a \neq 0$, so that without loss of generality $a = 1$ and $p = \langle D : E : 1 : A : B : C \rangle$, with D, E, F, A, B and C now determined uniquely.

The number b can be recovered from $-2b = E$, and then there are three equations for u, v and c, namely

$$-2c - 2\left(1 + b^2\right) u = A \quad (15.1)$$
$$-2bc - 2\left(1 + b^2\right) v = B \quad (15.2)$$
$$\left(1 + b^2\right)\left(u^2 + v^2\right) - c^2 = C. \quad (15.3)$$

Use (15.1) and (15.2) to solve for u and v in terms of c

$$u = \frac{-2c - A}{2\left(1 + b^2\right)}$$
$$v = \frac{-2bc - B}{2\left(1 + b^2\right)}$$

so that (15.3) becomes

$$\left((2c + A)^2 + (2bc + B)^2\right) - 4\left(1 + b^2\right) c^2 = 4\left(1 + b^2\right) C.$$

Upon expansion however this becomes linear in c, namely

$$A^2 + B^2 + 4\left(A + Bb\right) c = 4\left(1 + b^2\right) C$$

giving a unique value of c provided that $4\left(A + Bb\right) = 4A - 2BE \neq 0$. Replace A, B and E with the respective values above and simplify to see that this condition is equivalent to

$$\left(1 + b^2\right)\left(u + bv + c\right) \neq 0.$$

But $1 + b^2 \neq 0$ because l is non-null, and $u + bv + c \neq 0$ since F does not lie on l, so there is a unique value of c, and hence also of u and v. ∎

15.4 Quadrolas

Definition A **quadrola** q is a conic whose equation in $X \equiv [x, y]$ has the form

$$A\left(Q\left(X, F_1\right), Q\left(X, F_2\right), K\right) = 0 \tag{15.4}$$

for some distinct fixed points F_1 and F_2, and some fixed non-zero number K, such that $Q\left(F_1, F_2\right)$ is neither 0 nor K.

Recall that $A\left(x_1, x_2, x_3\right) \equiv \left(x_1 + x_2 + x_3\right)^2 - 2\left(x_1^2 + x_2^2 + x_3^2\right)$ is Archimedes' function.

The points F_1 and F_2 are **foci**, and the number K the associated **quadrance** of the quadrola.

Exercise 15.10 (Harder) Show that if -1 is not a square then the foci and quadrance of a quadrola are unique. $\diamond$

Exercise 15.11 Show that the equation (15.4) is of degree two in x and y, so that a quadrola is indeed a conic. $\diamond$

Example 15.5 If $a \neq 0$ then the quadrola q with foci $F_1 \equiv [a, 0]$ and $F_2 \equiv [-a, 0]$ and quadrance K has equation

$$4\left(K - 4a^2\right) x^2 + 4Ky^2 = K\left(K - 4a^2\right).$$

Note that $Q\left(F_1, F_2\right) = 4a^2$. In the decimal number field if $4a^2 < K$ then this is an ellipse, if $0 < K < 4a^2$ then this is a hyperbola, and if $K < 0$ then this is an 'empty ellipse'. For a general field, if $-1 = i^2$ then q also has foci $G_1 \equiv [0, ia]$ and $G_2 \equiv [0, -ia]$ with associated quadrance $L \equiv K - 4a^2$. $\diamond$

Example 15.6 In $\mathbb{F}_{11}$ suppose that $F_1 \equiv [1, 0]$, $F_2 \equiv [-1, 0]$ and $K \equiv 1$. Then two views of the quadrola $q \equiv \langle 7 : 0 : 5 : 0 : 0 : 1 \rangle$ (large squares) are shown in Figure 15.6.

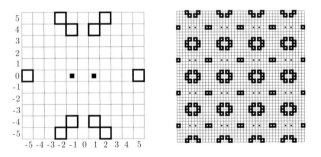

Figure 15.6: Quadrola $7x^2 + 5y^2 + 1 = 0$ in $\mathbb{F}_{11}$: two views

Exercise 15.12 Show that a quadrola is a centered conic. $\diamond$

Exercise 15.13 (Harder) Show that a quadrola has two axes (see Exercise 15.8). $\diamond$

15.5 Grammolas

Definition A **grammola** g is a conic whose equation in $X \equiv [x, y]$ has the form

$$Q(X, l_1) + Q(X, l_2) = K$$

for some fixed non-null lines l_1 and l_2 which are neither parallel nor perpendicular, and some non-zero number K.

Then l_1 and l_2 are the **diagonal lines,** and K is the **quadrance** of the grammola g.

Exercise 15.14 (Harder) Show that the diagonal lines and quadrance of a grammola are unique. ◇

Example 15.7 Suppose that $l_1 \equiv \langle a : -1 : 0 \rangle$ and $l_2 \equiv \langle a : 1 : 0 \rangle$ with $a^2 \neq \pm 1$, and let g be the grammola with diagonal lines l_1 and l_2 and quadrance $K \neq 0$. By the Quadrance to a line theorem (page 67) the equation for g is

$$\frac{(ax - y)^2}{a^2 + 1} + \frac{(ax + y)^2}{a^2 + 1} = K.$$

This simplifies to

$$2a^2 x^2 + 2y^2 = K(a^2 + 1). ◇$$

Example 15.8 In the decimal number field the grammola g with equation $2x^2 + 8y^2 = 5$ (the case $a \equiv 1/2$ and $K \equiv 1$ of the previous example) is shown in Figure 15.7 along with the diagonal lines with equations $x - 2y = 0$ and $x + 2y = 0$. Note that the diagonal lines intersect the grammola, which is in this case an ellipse, at the distinguished points $\left[\pm \frac{\sqrt{5}}{2}, \pm \frac{\sqrt{5}}{4} \right]$.

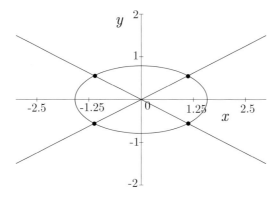

Figure 15.7: Grammola $2x^2 + 8y^2 = 5$ ◇

Example 15.9 In the field $\mathbb{F}_{11}$ the grammola g with equation $2x^2 + 8y^2 = 5$ is shown in Figure 15.8 (large squares) along with its diagonal lines $l_1 \equiv \langle 1 : -2 : 0 \rangle$ and $l_2 \equiv \langle 1 : 2 : 0 \rangle$ (small squares). Note that the diagonal lines also pass through the four points $[\pm 2, \pm 1]$ lying on the grammola.

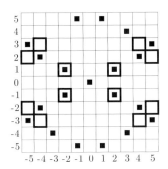

Figure 15.8: Grammola $2x^2 + 8y^2 = 5$ in $\mathbb{F}_{11}$ ◇

Exercise 15.15 Show that a grammola is a centered conic. ◇

Exercise 15.16 Show that in $\mathbb{F}_{11}$ the grammola $2x^2 + 8y^2 = 5$ is not a quadrola. ◇

Exercise 15.17 Give an example of a quadrola which is not a grammola. ◇

Exercise 15.18 (Harder) Show that a grammola with diagonal lines l_1 and l_2 has two axes precisely when the vertex $\overline{l_1 l_2}$ is square, in which case the axes are bisectors of $\overline{l_1 l_2}$. ◇

15.6   Intersections with lines

Definition A line l **intersects** a conic q at a point A precisely when A lies on both l and q. A line which intersects a conic q at two distinct points is a **chord** of the conic.

Theorem 102 (Conic line intersection) If a line l intersects a conic q in three or more distinct points, then every point lying on l lies on q.

Proof. This is a consequence of the fact that a quadratic equation has at most two zeroes in a field. ■

16

Geometry of circles

This chapter investigates basic properties of circles, particularly the useful Subtended spread theorem and some of its consequences, and shows also how to parametrize points lying on circles. This includes both the unit circle and the projective circle. An exercise shows how to multiply complex numbers in rational polar form.

16.1 Diameters and chords

Definition A line which intersects a circle c and passes through the center C of c is a **diameter** of the circle.

Definition For a triangle $\overline{A_1A_2A_3}$ with circumcenter C and circumquadrance K, the circle c with center C and quadrance K is the **circumcircle** of $A_1A_2A_3$.

Theorem 103 (Right diameter) Suppose that the line A_1A_2 of the triangle $\overline{A_1A_2A_3}$ is a diameter of the circumcircle c. Then $\overline{A_1A_2A_3}$ has a right vertex at A_3.

Proof. This is a consequence of the Right midpoint theorem (page 126), since if C is the circumcenter, $Q(A_1,C) = Q(A_2,C) = Q(A_3,C)$, implying that A_3 is a right vertex. ∎

Exercise 16.1 Show that a diameter of a non-null circle is a chord of the circle. ◇

Exercise 16.2 Show that the vertex formed by two distinct diameters of a fixed non-null circle is always a square vertex. ◇

Theorem 104 (Circle chord) A chord of a non-null circle is a non-null line.

Proof. Suppose that the non-null circle c has center $C \equiv [u, v]$ and quadrance $K \neq 0$, and that the distinct points $A_1 \equiv [x_1, y_1]$ and $A_2 \equiv [x_1 + a, y_1 + b]$ are both points of intersection of c and a chord l of c. Then

$$
\begin{aligned}
(x_1 - u)^2 + (y_1 - v)^2 &= K \\
(x_1 + a - u)^2 + (y_1 + b - v)^2 &= K.
\end{aligned}
$$

Take the difference between these two equations to get

$$2a(u - x_1) + 2b(v - y_1) - a^2 + b^2.$$

Now by the Null line theorem (page 60), $l = A_1 A_2$ is a null line precisely when $Q(A_1, A_2) = a^2 + b^2 = 0$. In this case $b = ia \neq 0$ for some number i satisfying $i^2 = -1$, so that

$$(u - x_1) + i(v - y_1) = 0.$$

But then

$$(x_1 - u)^2 + (y_1 - v)^2 = 0 = K$$

which contradicts the fact that c is non-null. Thus a chord l of a non-null circle is necessarily a non-null line.   ∎

Exercise 16.3 Show that a line l intersects a non-null circle c in at most two points.
◇

16.2   Spreads in a circle

The next result follows from the Extended spread law (page 144), and is fundamental when dealing with circles. The classical version over the decimal numbers must distinguish between two separate cases, depending on which 'side' of the chord the third point is on, and must also be careful about the relative positions of the triangle and the center of the circle. The universal version here is more robust.

Theorem 105 (Subtended spread) Suppose that A_1 and A_2 are two distinct points lying on a non-null circle c with center C, and define the spread $s \equiv s(CA_1, CA_2)$. Suppose that A_3 is any other point lying on c, with $s_3 \equiv s(A_3 A_1, A_3 A_2)$. Then s_3 is independent of the position of A_3, and furthermore

$$s = S_2(s_3) \equiv 4s_3(1 - s_3).$$

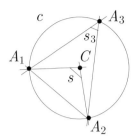

Figure 16.1: Subtended spreads theorem

Proof. Suppose that the quadrance of c is $K \neq 0$. From the previous exercise, A_1, A_2 and A_3 are non-collinear. By the Extended spread law

$$\frac{s_3}{Q_3} = \frac{1}{4K} \tag{16.1}$$

where $Q_3 \equiv Q(A_1, A_2) \neq 0$ by the Circle chord theorem combined with the Null line theorem (page 60). Thus the spread s_3 is constant independent of the position of A_3 on the circle c.

Combine (16.1) with the Isosceles triangle theorem (page 122) in $\overline{A_1 A_2 C}$ to get

$$\begin{aligned} s &= \frac{Q_3}{K}\left(1 - \frac{Q_3}{4K}\right) \\ &= 4s_3(1 - s_3) \equiv S_2(s_3). \quad \blacksquare \end{aligned}$$

Definition The spread s_3 determined by the side $\overline{A_1 A_2}$ on the circle c is the spread **subtended** by $\overline{A_1 A_2}$.

Theorem 106 (Equal products) Suppose that A_1, A_2, A_3 and A_4 are distinct points lying on a circle c such that $A_1 A_4$ and $A_2 A_3$ intersect at a point B. Then

$$Q(A_1, B) Q(B, A_4) = Q(A_2, B) Q(B, A_3).$$

Proof. From the Subtended spread theorem,

$$\begin{aligned} s(A_2 A_1, A_2 A_3) &= s(A_4 A_1, A_4 A_3) \equiv s_1 \\ s(A_1 A_2, A_1 A_4) &= s(A_3 A_2, A_3 A_4) \equiv s_2. \end{aligned}$$

By collinearity

$$s\left(A_2 A_1, A_2 A_3\right) = s\left(A_2 A_1, A_2 B\right) = s_1$$
$$s\left(A_4 A_1, A_4 A_3\right) = s\left(A_4 B, A_4 A_3\right) = s_1$$
$$s\left(A_1 A_2, A_1 A_4\right) = s\left(A_1 A_2, A_1 B\right) = s_2$$
$$s\left(A_3 A_2, A_3 A_4\right) = s\left(A_3 B, A_3 A_4\right) = s_2.$$

Thus the Spread law in the triangles $\overline{A_1 A_2 B}$ and $\overline{B A_4 A_3}$ gives

$$\frac{s_1}{s_2} = \frac{Q\left(A_1, B\right)}{Q\left(A_2, B\right)} = \frac{Q\left(B, A_3\right)}{Q\left(B, A_4\right)}$$

so that

$$Q\left(A_1, B\right) Q\left(B, A_4\right) = Q\left(A_2, B\right) Q\left(B, A_3\right). \quad \blacksquare$$

Note that in the rational or decimal number field, the theorem refers to both of the diagrams in Figure 16.2.

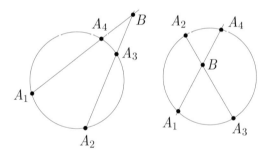

Figure 16.2: Equal products theorem

Exercise 16.4 (Van Schouten's theorem) Suppose that $\overline{A_1 A_2 A_3}$ is an equilateral triangle with circumcircle c, and that B is any point on c. Show that

$$\{Q\left(A_1, B\right), Q\left(A_2, B\right), Q\left(A_3, B\right)\}$$

is a quad triple. ◇

Exercise 16.5 (Brahmagupta's theorem) Suppose that the quadrilateral $\overline{ABCD}$ has points lying on a non-null circle c, with perpendicular diagonals AC and BD intersecting at P. Show that the altitude from P to AD passes through the midpoint M of $\overline{BC}$. ◇

Exercise 16.6 Suppose that A and B are distinct points lying on a diameter of a circle c with center C, and that $Q\left(A, C\right) = Q\left(B, C\right)$. Show that for any point X lying on c, the quantity $Q\left(A, X\right) + Q\left(B, X\right)$ is constant independent of X. ◇

16.3 Parametrizing circles

Definition The **projective circle** c_P is the circle with center $C \equiv [0, 1/2]$ and quadrance $K \equiv 1/4$. The **unit circle** c_U is the circle with center $O \equiv [0, 0]$ and quadrance $K \equiv 1$.

The equation of c_P is

$$x^2 + \left(y - \frac{1}{2}\right)^2 = \frac{1}{4}$$

and the four points $[0, 0]$, $[0, 1]$ and $[\pm 1/2, 1/2]$ lie on c_P.

The equation of c_U is

$$x^2 + y^2 = 1$$

and the four points $[\pm 1, 0]$ and $[0, \pm 1]$ lie on c_U. Recall by Section 13.1 that points lying on c_U parametrize central rotations as well as central reflections.

Theorem 107 (Projective circle) For any number λ satisfying $\lambda^2 \neq -1$, the point

$$\left[\frac{\lambda}{1 + \lambda^2}, \frac{1}{1 + \lambda^2}\right]$$

lies on c_P. Apart from $[0, 0]$ every point lying on c_P is of this form.

Proof. It is easy to check that for any number λ satisfying $\lambda^2 \neq -1$, the point

$$\left[\frac{\lambda}{1 + \lambda^2}, \frac{1}{1 + \lambda^2}\right]$$

lies on c_P. If $A \equiv [x, y]$ is any point on c_P other than $[0, 0]$, then $y \neq 0$, so let $\lambda \equiv x/y$. Then $x = \lambda y$, and because A lies on c_P

$$(\lambda y)^2 + \left(y - \frac{1}{2}\right)^2 = \frac{1}{4}.$$

This simplifies to the quadratic

$$y\left(y + y\lambda^2 - 1\right) = 0$$

so that $\lambda^2 \neq -1$ and $y = 1/\left(1 + \lambda^2\right)$. Thus

$$A = \left[\frac{\lambda}{1 + \lambda^2}, \frac{1}{1 + \lambda^2}\right]$$

has the required form. ∎

Exercise 16.7 Show that lines passing through $O \equiv [0,0]$ and points lying on the projective circle c_P are in one to one correspondence. ◇

Theorem 108 (Unit circle) For any number λ satisfying $\lambda^2 \neq -1$, the point

$$\left[\frac{1-\lambda^2}{1+\lambda^2} , \frac{2\lambda}{1+\lambda^2} \right]$$

lies on c_U. Apart from $[-1,0]$ every point lying on c_U is of this form.

Proof. The point $[x,y]$ lies on c_P precisely when

$$x^2 + \left(y - \frac{1}{2} \right)^2 - \frac{1}{4} = x^2 + y^2 - y = 0.$$

The point $[2y - 1, 2x]$ lies on c_U precisely when

$$(2y - 1)^2 + (2x)^2 - 1 = 4 \left(y^2 - y + x^2 \right) = 0.$$

Thus $[x,y]$ lies on c_P precisely when $[2y - 1, 2x]$ lies on c_U. The parametrization of the previous theorem then gives the parametrization

$$\left[\frac{2}{1+\lambda^2} - 1 , \frac{2\lambda}{1+\lambda^2} \right] = \left[\frac{1-\lambda^2}{1+\lambda^2} , \frac{2\lambda}{1+\lambda^2} \right]$$

of the points on c_U, excluding $[-1,0]$. ∎

Exercise 16.8 (Rational polar form of complex numbers) Identify $[x,y]$ with the complex number $z = x + iy$. Then show that every complex number z lying on the unit circle with equation $x^2 + y^2 = 1$, except for $z = -1$, can be written as

$$z = \frac{(1+i\lambda)^2}{1+\lambda^2}$$

for a unique decimal number λ, and conversely any such number lies on the unit circle. Show that $i\lambda$ is the intersection of the imaginary axis and the line passing through z and -1. If (r, λ) denotes the complex number $r(1+i\lambda)^2 / (1+\lambda^2)$ then show that

$$(r_1, \lambda_1)(r_2, \lambda_2) = \left(r_1 r_2, \frac{\lambda_1 + \lambda_2}{1 - \lambda_1 \lambda_2} \right).$$

Explain why the formula of Exercise 9.2 (page 116) makes its appearance here. ◇

Quadrilaterals

This chapter discusses some basic facts about cyclic quadrilaterals, Ptolemy's theorem, Brahmagupta's formula, and the Four point relation, essentially due to Euler.

17.1 Cyclic quadrilaterals

Definition A quadrilateral $\overline{A_1 A_2 A_3 A_4}$ is **cyclic** precisely when all the points A_i lie on a circle c.

Theorem 109 (Cyclic quadrilateral) The quadrilateral $\overline{A_1 A_2 A_3 A_4}$ with $A_1 \equiv [x_1, y_1]$, $A_2 \equiv [x_2, y_2]$, $A_3 \equiv [x_3, y_3]$ and $A_4 \equiv [x_4, y_4]$ is cyclic precisely when

$$\left[\left(x_1^2 + y_1^2 \right) x_2 y_3 \right]_4^- = 0.$$

Proof. (Using a computer) The condition that $\overline{A_1 A_2 A_3 A_4}$ be cyclic is

$$Q(C, A_1) = Q(A_4, C)$$

where C is the circumcenter of $\overline{A_1 A_2 A_3}$ as given in the Circumcenter theorem (page 143). Expand this and rearrange to obtain the stated formula. ∎

Suppose that $\overline{A_1 A_2 A_3 A_4}$ is a cyclic quadrilateral with all points A_i lying on the circle c of quadrance K. By the Subtended spread theorem (page 178), the spread subtended by the side $\overline{A_i A_j}$ from any point A on c is independent of A, and will be denoted by r_{ij}, so that for example $r_{12} \equiv s(A_3 A_1, A_3 A_2) = s(A_4 A_1, A_4 A_2)$.

The spreads r_{12}, r_{23}, r_{34} and r_{14} are the **subtended spreads** of the cyclic quadrilateral, and the spreads r_{13} and r_{24} are the **diagonal subtended spreads**.

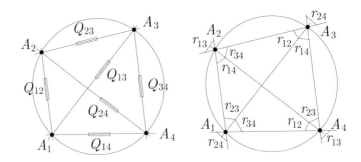

Figure 17.1: Quadrances and subtended spreads in a cyclic quadrilateral

Quadrances, diagonal quadrances, subtended spreads and diagonal subtended spreads of a quadrilateral are shown in Figure 17.1. The diagonal subtended spreads coincide with the usual spreads of $\overline{A_1 A_2 A_3 A_4}$, and if the circle c has quadrance K then by the Extended spread law

$$Q_{ij} = Q\left(A_i, A_j\right) = 4K r_{ij}$$

for all $i \neq j$. It is therefore useful to consider the subtended spreads r_{ij} as basic measurements in a cyclic quadrilateral, since they are independent of scaling.

Theorem 110 (Cyclic quadrilateral spreads) The subtended spreads r_{12}, r_{23}, r_{34} and r_{14} of a cyclic quadrilateral satisfy the Quadruple spread formula (page 99)

$$R\left(r_{12}, r_{23}, r_{34}, r_{14}\right) = 0.$$

Furthermore

$$r_{13} = \frac{\left(r_{12} - r_{23}\right)^2 - \left(r_{14} - r_{34}\right)^2}{2\left(r_{12} + r_{23} - r_{14} - r_{34} - 2r_{12}r_{23} + 2r_{14}r_{34}\right)}$$

$$r_{24} = \frac{\left(r_{12} - r_{14}\right)^2 - \left(r_{23} - r_{34}\right)^2}{2\left(r_{12} + r_{14} - r_{23} - r_{34} - 2r_{12}r_{14} + 2r_{23}r_{34}\right)}$$

provided that the denominators are not zero.

Proof. Both $\{r_{12}, r_{23}, r_{13}\}$ and $\{r_{14}, r_{34}, r_{13}\}$ are spread triples, since these are the spreads of lines meeting at A_2 and A_4 respectively. Since r_{13} is common to both, the Two spread triples theorem (page 98) shows that $R\left(r_{12}, r_{23}, r_{34}, r_{14}\right) = 0$, and that r_{13} can be expressed as stated. The argument with r_{24} is similar, using the two spread triples $\{r_{12}, r_{14}, r_{24}\}$ and $\{r_{23}, r_{34}, r_{24}\}$. ∎

A cyclic quadrilateral with subtended spreads r_{12}, r_{23}, r_{34} and r_{14} is **solvable** precisely when the denominators in the above theorem are both nonzero.

17.2 Circumquadrance formula

Define the **circumquadrance** K of a cyclic quadrilateral $\overline{A_1 A_2 A_3 A_4}$ to be the quadrance of the circle on which the points lie. This is also the circumquadrance of any three of the points of the quadrilateral. The next theorem gives a generally quadratic formula for K in terms of the quadrances.

Theorem 111 (Quadrilateral circumquadrance) If a cyclic quadrilateral $\overline{A_1 A_2 A_3 A_4}$ lying on a circle c has quadrances Q_{12}, Q_{23}, Q_{34} and Q_{14}, then the quadrance K of the circle c satisfies the equation

$$pK^2 - 2qK + r = 0$$

where

$$p = Q(Q_{12}, Q_{23}, Q_{34}, Q_{14})$$

$$
\begin{aligned}
q &= (Q_{12}Q_{14} - Q_{23}Q_{34})(Q_{23}Q_{14} - Q_{12}Q_{34})(Q_{12} + Q_{23} - Q_{34} - Q_{14}) \\
&+ (Q_{12}Q_{14} - Q_{23}Q_{34})(Q_{34}Q_{14} - Q_{12}Q_{23})(Q_{12} - Q_{23} + Q_{34} - Q_{14}) \\
&+ (Q_{12}Q_{23} - Q_{34}Q_{14})(Q_{23}Q_{14} - Q_{12}Q_{34})(Q_{12} - Q_{23} - Q_{34} + Q_{14})
\end{aligned}
$$

and

$$r = (Q_{12}Q_{14} - Q_{23}Q_{34})(Q_{23}Q_{14} - Q_{12}Q_{34})(Q_{12}Q_{23} - Q_{34}Q_{14}).$$

Proof. (Using a computer) Note that p is the Quadruple quad function (page 70) applied to Q_{12}, Q_{23}, Q_{34} and Q_{14}. By the Cyclic quadrilateral spreads theorem, the four subtended spreads r_{12}, r_{23}, r_{34} and r_{14} of $\overline{A_1 A_2 A_3 A_4}$ satisfy the Quadruple spread formula

$$R(r_{12}, r_{23}, r_{34}, r_{14}) = 0$$

where R is the Quadruple spread function.

Now when the relations

$$r_{ij} = Q_{ij}/4K$$

are substituted, this becomes an equation involving K and the quadrances Q_{12}, Q_{23}, Q_{34} and Q_{14}. After cancellation of a factor of $256K^6$, this has the form

$$pK^2 - 2qK + r = 0$$

with coefficients p, q and r that are polynomial expressions in Q_{12}, Q_{23}, Q_{34} and Q_{14}. These coefficients can be rearranged to take the stated forms. ∎

Exercise 17.1 (Using a computer) Show that in the notation of the above theorem

$$
\begin{aligned}
(2q)^2 - 4pr \;=\; & 4Q_{12}Q_{23}Q_{34}Q_{14} \left(Q_{12} + Q_{23} - Q_{34} - Q_{14} \right)^2 \\
& \times \left(Q_{12} - Q_{23} + Q_{34} - Q_{14} \right)^2 \left(Q_{12} - Q_{23} - Q_{34} + Q_{14} \right)^2 . \quad \diamond
\end{aligned}
$$

Example 17.1 In the field $\mathbb{F}_{11}$ consider the existence of a cyclic quadrilateral with quadrances

$$Q_{12} \equiv 5 \qquad Q_{23} \equiv 3 \qquad Q_{34} \equiv 6 \qquad Q_{14} \equiv 6.$$

The constants p, q and r can be evaluated to be $3, 0$ and 10 respectively, so the equation for the circumquadrance K of the quadrilateral is

$$3K^2 + 10 = 0$$

with solutions $K = 2$ and 9. On the central circle with quadrance $K \equiv 2$, the quadrilateral $\overline{A_1 A_2 A_3 A_4}$ has the above quadrances, where

$$A_1 \equiv [2,3] \qquad A_2 \equiv [9,3] \qquad A_3 \equiv [1,10] \qquad A_4 \equiv [8,9].$$

On the central circle with quadrance $K \equiv 9$, the quadrilateral $\overline{B_1 B_2 B_3 B_4}$ also has the above quadrances, where

$$B_1 \equiv [4,2] \qquad B_2 \equiv [3,0] \qquad B_3 \equiv [8,0] \qquad B_4 \equiv [9,7].$$

Both examples are shown in Figure 17.2.

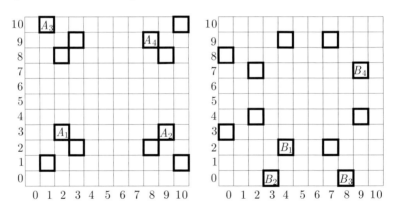

Figure 17.2: Cyclic quadrilaterals on circles of quadrance 2 and 9

For the quadrilateral $\overline{A_1 A_2 A_3 A_4}$ the lines are $l_{12} = \langle 0 : 7 : 1 \rangle$, $l_{23} = \langle 7 : 8 : 1 \rangle$, $l_{34} = \langle 2 : 3 : 1 \rangle$ and $l_{14} = \langle 1 : 10 : 1 \rangle$ while the diagonal lines are $l_{13} = \langle 8 : 9 : 1 \rangle$ and $l_{24} = \langle 8 : 5 : 1 \rangle$. The spreads of the quadrilateral $\overline{A_1 A_2 A_3 A_4}$ are $s_1 = 6$, $s_2 = 9$, $s_3 = 6$ and $s_4 = 9$. The subtended spreads are $r_{12} = 2$, $r_{23} = 10$, $r_{34} = 9$ and $r_{14} = 9$, with diagonal subtended spreads $r_{13} = 9$ and $r_{24} = 6$. You may verify that r_{12}, r_{23}, r_{34} and r_{14} satisfy the Quadruple spread formula (page 99), and that r_{13} and r_{24} may be determined from them as in that theorem. The quadrea of $\overline{A_1 A_2 A_3 A_4}$ is $\mathcal{A} = 4$.

The quadrilateral $\overline{B_1 B_2 B_3 B_4}$ may be similarly analyzed. Its quadrea is $\mathcal{A} = 9$. $\diamond$

17.3 Cyclic quadrilateral quadrea

Theorem 112 (Cyclic quadrilateral quadrea) Suppose a solvable cyclic quadrilateral $\overline{A_1 A_2 A_3 A_4}$ has quadrances Q_{12}, Q_{23}, Q_{34} and Q_{14} with

$$Q(Q_{12}, Q_{23}, Q_{34}, Q_{14})(Q_{12}Q_{14} - Q_{23}Q_{34})(Q_{23}Q_{14} - Q_{12}Q_{34})(Q_{12}Q_{23} - Q_{34}Q_{14}) \neq 0.$$

Then its quadrea $\mathcal{A}$ satisfies the quadratic equation

$$\mathcal{A}^2 - 2m\mathcal{A} + p = 0$$

where

$$
\begin{aligned}
m &= (Q_{12} + Q_{23} + Q_{34} + Q_{14})^2 - 2(Q_{12}^2 + Q_{23}^2 + Q_{34}^2 + Q_{14}^2) \\
p &= Q(Q_{12}, Q_{23}, Q_{34}, Q_{14}).
\end{aligned}
$$

Proof. (Using a computer) The following proof involves some seemingly miraculous computations requiring a computer. It would be preferable to have a simpler and more direct argument.

Suppose the circumquadrance of the cyclic quadrilateral $\overline{A_1 A_2 A_3 A_4}$ is K. From the Quadrilateral circumquadrance theorem (page 185) you know that K satisfies the equation

$$pK^2 - 2qK + r = 0 \tag{17.1}$$

where p, q and r are known functions of the quadrances Q_{12}, Q_{23}, Q_{34} and Q_{14}, with $p = Q(Q_{12}, Q_{23}, Q_{34}, Q_{14}) \neq 0$ and $r \neq 0$ by assumption. Thus $K \neq 0$. Apply the Cyclic quadrilateral spreads theorem and the relation $Q_{ij} = 4Kr_{ij}$ to obtain

$$
\begin{aligned}
Q_{13} &= 2K\frac{(Q_{12} - Q_{23})^2 - (Q_{14} - Q_{34})^2}{(4K(Q_{12} + Q_{23} - Q_{14} - Q_{34}) - 2Q_{12}Q_{23} + 2Q_{14}Q_{34})} \\
Q_{24} &= 2K\frac{(Q_{12} - Q_{14})^2 - (Q_{23} - Q_{34})^2}{(4K(Q_{12} + Q_{14} - Q_{23} - Q_{34}) - 2Q_{12}Q_{14} + 2Q_{23}Q_{34})}.
\end{aligned}
$$

Use Bretschneider's formula (page 118) to write the quadrea $\mathcal{A}$ of the quadrilateral $\overline{A_1 A_2 A_3 A_4}$ as

$$\mathcal{A} = 4Q_{13}Q_{24} - (Q_{12} + Q_{34} - Q_{23} - Q_{14})^2.$$

Replace Q_{13} and Q_{24} and simplify, to get an expression $\mathcal{A} = f(K)/g(K)$ where f and g are polynomials in K generally of degrees one and two respectively, with coefficients that depend on Q_{12}, Q_{23}, Q_{34} and Q_{14}. Use the expression (17.1) to replace K^2 in $g(K)$ with the linear expression $(2qK - r)/p$ in K. After simplification this gives

$$\mathcal{A} = \frac{aK + b}{cK + d}$$

with a, b, c and d polynomials in Q_{12}, Q_{23}, Q_{34} and Q_{14}. Equivalently

$$K = \frac{\mathcal{A}d - b}{a - \mathcal{A}c}.$$

Substitute this into (17.1) to get a quadratic equation of the form

$$w_1 w_2 \left(\mathcal{A}^2 - 2m\mathcal{A} + p \right) = 0$$

in $\mathcal{A}$, where m and p are as in the statement of the theorem and where

$$
\begin{aligned}
w_1 &= Q\left(Q_{12}, Q_{23}, Q_{34}, Q_{14}\right)\left(Q_{14}Q_{34} - Q_{12}Q_{23}\right)^2 \left(Q_{23}Q_{34} - Q_{12}Q_{14}\right)^2 \\
w_2 &= \left(Q_{23} - Q_{14} - Q_{12} + Q_{34}\right)^2 \left(Q_{14} - Q_{12} - Q_{23} + Q_{34}\right)^2 \left(Q_{12} - Q_{14} - Q_{23} + Q_{34}\right)^4.
\end{aligned}
$$

Now $w_2 \neq 0$, for otherwise one of Q_{13} and Q_{24} would be zero, contradicting the Circle chord theorem (page 178). So if $w_1 \neq 0$ then the theorem follows. ∎

Given quadrances Q_{12}, Q_{23}, Q_{34} and Q_{14} satisfying $w_1 \neq 0$, there are in general then two possible quadreas $\mathcal{A}_1$ and $\mathcal{A}_2$ for a cyclic quadrilateral with these as its quadrances. By properties of the zeroes of a quadratic equation,

$$
\begin{aligned}
\left(\mathcal{A}_1 + \mathcal{A}_2\right)/2 &= \left(Q_{12} + Q_{23} + Q_{34} + Q_{14}\right)^2 - 2\left(Q_{12}^2 + Q_{23}^2 + Q_{34}^2 + Q_{14}^2\right) \\
\mathcal{A}_1 \mathcal{A}_2 &= Q\left(Q_{12}, Q_{23}, Q_{34}, Q_{14}\right).
\end{aligned}
$$

In the first equation you see again the expression of Descartes discussed on page 71. The second equation is a rational form of *Brahmagupta's formula*. It shows that the quantity $Q\left(Q_{12}, Q_{23}, Q_{34}, Q_{14}\right)$ appearing in Brahmagupta's identity (page 72) is the product of the two quadreas of the cyclic quadrilaterals with the given quadrances.

Example 17.2 In Example 17.1 over $\mathbb{F}_{11}$ the cyclic quadrilateral $\overline{A_1 A_2 A_3 A_4}$ had quadrances $Q_{12} \equiv 5$, $Q_{23} \equiv 3$, $Q_{34} \equiv 6$ and $Q_{14} \equiv 6$. So then $m = 1$ and $p = 3$ and the quadrea $\mathcal{A}$ satisfies $\mathcal{A}^2 - 2\mathcal{A} + 3 = 0$, with zeroes 4 and 9 as obtained there. ◇

Theorem 113 (Cyclic signed area) The oriented cyclic quadrilateral $\overrightarrow{A_1 A_2 A_3 A_4}$ with points

$$A_i = \left[2\lambda_i / \left(1 + \lambda_i^2\right), \left(1 - \lambda_i^2\right) / \left(1 + \lambda_i^2\right)\right]$$

$i = 1, 2, 3$ and 4, lying on the unit circle, has signed area $a\left(\overrightarrow{A_1 A_2 A_3 A_4}\right)$ equal to

$$\frac{2\left(\lambda_1 - \lambda_3\right)\left(\lambda_2 - \lambda_4\right)\left(\lambda_1 + \lambda_3 - \lambda_2 - \lambda_4 + \lambda_1\lambda_2\lambda_3 + \lambda_1\lambda_3\lambda_4 - \lambda_2\lambda_3\lambda_4 - \lambda_1\lambda_2\lambda_4\right)}{\left(1 + \lambda_1^2\right)\left(1 + \lambda_2^2\right)\left(1 + \lambda_3^2\right)\left(1 + \lambda_4^2\right)}.$$

Proof. (Using a computer) A direct calculation. ∎

Exercise 17.2 Show that if $\lambda_3 = \lambda_4$, for example, then the signed area of the previous theorem reduces to that of the oriented triangle $\overrightarrow{A_1 A_2 A_3}$, namely

$$a\left(\overrightarrow{A_1 A_2 A_3}\right) = \frac{2(\lambda_1 - \lambda_2)(\lambda_2 - \lambda_3)(\lambda_1 - \lambda_3)}{(1 + \lambda_1^2)(1 + \lambda_2^2)(1 + \lambda_3^2)}. \quad \diamond$$

Example 17.3 In the decimal number field, suppose that a quadrilateral $\overline{A_1 A_2 A_3 A_4}$ has side lengths

$$|A_1, A_2| \equiv 5 \qquad |A_2, A_3| \equiv 8 \qquad |A_3, A_4| \equiv 2 \qquad |A_1, A_4| \equiv 10$$

so that the associated quadrances are $Q_{12} = 25$, $Q_{23} = 64$, $Q_{34} = 4$ and $Q_{14} = 10$. Then using the notation of the Quadrilateral circumquadrance theorem and the Cyclic quadrilateral quadrea theorem, the polynomial expressions p, q, r and m take on the values

$$p = 19\,490\,625 \qquad\qquad q = 582\,390\,000$$
$$r = 16\,964\,640\,000 \qquad\qquad m = 7775.$$

Thus the circumquadrance K of $\overline{A_1 A_2 A_3 A_4}$ satisfies the quadratic equation

$$\begin{aligned}
0 &= 19\,490\,625 K^2 - 1164\,780\,000 K + 16\,964\,640\,000 \\
&= 50\,625\,(7K - 176)\,(55K - 1904)
\end{aligned}$$

so that

$$K = 176/7 \qquad \text{or} \qquad K = 1904/55.$$

The corresponding radii of the circumcircles are the square roots of these quantities, approximately

$$5.014\,265 \qquad \text{or} \qquad 5.883\,721.$$

The quadrea $\mathcal{A}$ of $\overline{A_1 A_2 A_3 A_4}$ satisfies the quadratic equation

$$\mathcal{A}^2 - 15\,550\mathcal{A} + 19\,490\,625 = (\mathcal{A} - 14\,175)(\mathcal{A} - 1375) = 0$$

so that

$$\mathcal{A} = 14\,175 \qquad \text{or} \qquad \mathcal{A} = 1375.$$

The corresponding signed areas are one quarter the square roots of these quantities, approximately

$$\pm 29.764\,702 \qquad \text{or} \qquad \pm 9.270\,248.$$

These two situations are realized in Figure 17.3, drawn to scale in appropriate units.

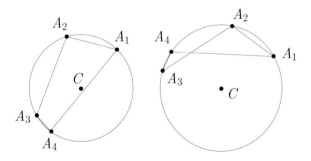

Figure 17.3: Two cyclic quadrilaterals $\diamond$

17.4 Ptolemy's theorem

Ptolemy was one of the great astronomers of antiquity, and his classic text *The Almagest* was for many centuries to astronomy what Euclid's *The Elements* was to geometry.

Theorem 114 (Ptolemy's theorem) Suppose that $\overline{A_1 A_2 A_3 A_4}$ is a solvable cyclic quadrilateral with subtended spreads r_{ij} for $i, j = 1, 2, 3$ and 4. Then

$$\{r_{12} r_{34}, r_{14} r_{23}, r_{13} r_{24}\}$$

is a quad triple.

Proof. (Using a computer) Since $\overline{A_1 A_2 A_3 A_4}$ is solvable, the Cyclic quadrilateral spreads theorem (page 184) gives expressions for r_{13} and r_{24} in terms of r_{12}, r_{23}, r_{34} and r_{14}. Use Archimedes' function A and some pleasant factoring to get

$$A\left(r_{12} r_{34}, r_{14} r_{23}, r_{13} r_{24}\right) = \frac{1}{16} \frac{R\left(r_{12}, r_{23}, r_{34}, r_{14}\right)}{\left(r_{12} + r_{23} - r_{14} - r_{34} - 2r_{12} r_{23} + 2r_{14} r_{34}\right)^2}$$
$$\times \frac{B\left(r_{12}, r_{23}, r_{34}, r_{14}\right)}{\left(r_{12} + r_{14} - r_{23} - r_{34} - 2r_{12} r_{14} + 2r_{23} r_{34}\right)^2}$$

where R is the Quadruple spread function (page 99) and where

$$B\left(a, b, c, d\right) \equiv 4\left(a + c - b - d\right)$$
$$\times \left(\left(a - c\right)^2 \left(b + d\right)\left(b + d - 1\right) - \left(b - d\right)^2 \left(a + c\right)\left(a + c - 1\right)\right)$$
$$- R\left(a, b, c, d\right).$$

The same theorem asserts that the subtended spreads r_{12}, r_{23}, r_{34} and r_{14} satisfy the Quadruple spread formula, so that

$$R\left(r_{12}, r_{23}, r_{34}, r_{14}\right) = 0.$$

Thus

$$A\left(r_{12} r_{34}, r_{14} r_{23}, r_{13} r_{24}\right) = 0$$

and $\{r_{12} r_{34}, r_{14} r_{23}, r_{13} r_{24}\}$ is a quad triple. ∎

Example 17.4 In $\mathbb{F}_{11}$ the quadrilateral $\overline{A_1 A_2 A_3 A_4}$ of Example 17.1 has subtended spreads $r_{12} = 2$, $r_{23} = 10$, $r_{34} = 9$ and $r_{14} = 9$, and diagonal subtended spreads $r_{13} = 9$ and $r_{24} = 6$. Thus Ptolemy's theorem states that $\{2 \times 9, 9 \times 10, 9 \times 6\} = \{7, 2, 10\}$ is a quad triple, which is true since $\left(7 + 2 - 10\right)^2 = 1 = 4 \times 7 \times 2$. ◇

17.5 Four point relation

The Triple quad formula concerned three points on a line, and the associated three quadrances. Here is a generalization to *four* points in the plane, forming *six* quadrances. This formula goes back essentially to Euler, who was interested in the volume of a tetrahedron as a function of its six side lengths. The treatment here borrows from [Dorrie].

Definition The **Euler function** E is

$$E(Q_1, Q_2, Q_3, P_1, P_2, P_3) \equiv \begin{vmatrix} 2P_1 & P_1 + P_2 - Q_3 & P_1 + P_3 - Q_2 \\ P_1 + P_2 - Q_3 & 2P_2 & P_2 + P_3 - Q_1 \\ P_1 + P_3 - Q_2 & P_2 + P_3 - Q_1 & 2P_3 \end{vmatrix}.$$

Theorem 115 (Four point relation) Suppose that the triangle $\overline{A_1 A_2 A_3}$ has quadrances Q_1, Q_2 and Q_3, and that B is any point with quadrances $P_1 \equiv Q(A_1, B)$, $P_2 \equiv Q(A_2, B)$ and $P_3 \equiv Q(A_3, B)$. Then

$$E(Q_1, Q_2, Q_3, P_1, P_2, P_3) = 0.$$

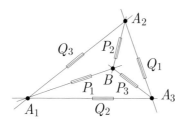

Figure 17.4: Four point relation

Proof. Suppose that $B \equiv [x_0, y_0]$ and that

$$\begin{aligned} A_1 &\equiv [x_0 + x_1, y_0 + y_1] \\ A_2 &\equiv [x_0 + x_2, y_0 + y_2] \\ A_3 &\equiv [x_0 + x_3, y_0 + y_3]. \end{aligned}$$

So

$$P_1 = x_1^2 + y_1^2 \qquad \text{and} \qquad Q_1 = (x_3 - x_2)^2 + (y_3 - y_2)^2$$

and similarly for the other indices.

Thus

$$P_1 + P_2 - Q_3 \quad = \quad x_1^2 + y_1^2 + x_2^2 + y_2^2 - (x_1 - x_2)^2 - (y_1 - y_2)^2$$
$$= \quad 2\,(x_1 x_2 + y_1 y_2)\,.$$

After removing a factor of two, the required determinantal equation is then

$$\begin{vmatrix} x_1^2 + y_1^2 & x_1 x_2 + y_1 y_2 & x_1 x_3 + y_1 y_3 \\ x_1 x_2 + y_1 y_2 & x_2^2 + y_2^2 & x_2 x_3 + y_2 y_3 \\ x_1 x_3 + y_1 y_3 & x_2 x_3 + y_2 y_3 & x_3^2 + y_3^2 \end{vmatrix} = 0.$$

This can be verified directly. Alternatively the matrix in the determinant above is the product of the matrices

$$\begin{pmatrix} 0 & x_1 & y_1 \\ 0 & x_2 & y_2 \\ 0 & x_3 & y_3 \end{pmatrix} \begin{pmatrix} 0 & 0 & 0 \\ x_1 & x_2 & x_3 \\ y_1 & y_2 & y_3 \end{pmatrix}$$

and so the determinant is 0. ∎

Exercise 17.3 Show that

$$E\,(Q_1, Q_2, Q_3, P_1, P_2, P_3)$$
$$= 2\left(\begin{array}{c} 4P_1 P_2 P_3 + (P_2 + P_1 - Q_3)\,(P_2 + P_3 - Q_1)\,(P_1 + P_3 - Q_2) \\ -P_1\,(P_2 + P_3 - Q_1)^2 - P_2\,(P_1 + P_3 - Q_2)^2 - P_3\,(P_2 + P_1 - Q_3)^2 \end{array} \right). \quad \diamond$$

Exercise 17.4 Show that

$$E\,(Q_1, Q_2, Q_3, P_1, P_2, P_3) = \begin{vmatrix} 0 & P_1 & P_2 & P_3 & 1 \\ P_1 & 0 & Q_3 & Q_2 & 1 \\ P_2 & Q_3 & 0 & Q_1 & 1 \\ P_3 & Q_2 & Q_1 & 0 & 1 \\ 1 & 1 & 1 & 1 & 0 \end{vmatrix}. \quad \diamond$$

Exercise 17.5 Show that as a quadratic equation in P_3, the Four point relation can be written in terms of Archimedes' function A as

$$\left(P_3 - P_1 - P_2 + Q_3 - Q_1 - Q_2 + \frac{(Q_1 - Q_2)\,(P_2 - P_1)}{Q_3} \right)^2$$
$$= \frac{A\,(Q_1, Q_2, Q_3)\,A\,(P_1, P_2, Q_3)}{4 Q_3^2}. \quad \diamond$$

Exercise 17.6 Use the Four point relation to re-derive the formula $K = Q_1 Q_2 Q_3 / \mathcal{A}$ (page 145) for the circumquadrance of a triangle with quadrea $\mathcal{A}$ and quadrances Q_1, Q_2 and Q_3. $\diamond$

Euler line and nine point circle

This chapter establishes universal analogues of the classical Euler line and nine point circle. The proofs illustrate two quite different approaches—the traditional synthetic one using a sequence of deductions, and the more modern computational one using algebraic manipulation of coordinates.

18.1   Euler line

Theorem 116 (Euler line) If the characteristic is not three, then the centroid G, circumcenter C and orthocenter O of a triangle $\overline{A_1 A_2 A_3}$ are collinear.

Proof. If $A_1 \equiv [x_1, y_1]$, $A_2 \equiv [x_2, y_2]$ and $A_3 \equiv [x_3, y_3]$ then from Exercise 3.16, the Circumcenter theorem (page 143) and the Orthocenter theorem (page 147), the centroid G, circumcenter C and orthocenter O of $\overline{A_1 A_2 A_3}$ are given by the expressions

$$
G = \left[\frac{x_1 + x_2 + x_3}{3}, \frac{y_1 + y_2 + y_3}{3} \right]
$$

$$
C = \left[\frac{[x_1^2 y_2]_3^- + [y_1^2 y_2]_3^-}{2[x_1 y_2]_3^-}, \frac{[x_1 x_2^2]_3^- - [x_1^2 x_2]_3^-}{2[x_1 y_2]_3^-} \right]
$$

$$
O = \left[\frac{[x_1 x_2 y_2]_3^- - [y_1^2 y_2]_3^-}{[x_1 y_2]_3^-}, \frac{[x_1 y_1 y_2]_3^- + [x_1^2 x_2]_3^-}{[x_1 y_2]_3^-} \right].
$$

Now use Exercise 2.7 (page 29) to deduce that $(2/3)\,C + (1/3)\,O = G$. The Affine combination theorem (page 46) shows that either all three points coincide, or G lies on OC. $\blacksquare$

Exercise 18.1 Show that the three points G, C and O coincide precisely when $\overline{A_1 A_2 A_3}$ is equilateral. $\diamond$

If $\overline{A_1 A_2 A_3}$ is not equilateral, then the line $e \equiv CO$ is the **Euler line** of the triangle.

18.2   Nine point circle

If M_1, M_2 and M_3 are the midpoints of the sides of the triangle $\overline{A_1 A_2 A_3}$, then $\overline{M_1 M_2 M_3}$ is also a triangle, and the circumcircle n and circumcenter N of $\overline{M_1 M_2 M_3}$ are respectively the **nine point circle** and the **nine point center** of the triangle $\overline{A_1 A_2 A_3}$.

Figure 18.1 shows the reason for the terminology, since in the decimal number field the nine point circle also passes through the feet F_1, F_2 and F_3 of the altitudes of $\overline{A_1 A_2 A_3}$, as well as the midpoints P_1, P_2 and P_3 of the respective sides $\overline{A_1 O}, \overline{A_2 O}$ and $\overline{A_3 O}$. Also shown in this Figure is the Euler line e.

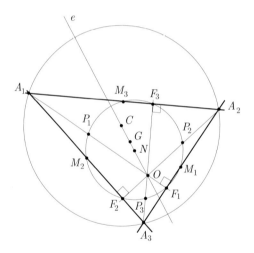

Figure 18.1: Nine point circle and Euler line

Exercise 18.2 (Using a computer) Suppose the triangle $\overline{A_1 A_2 A_3}$ has circumcenter C, orthocenter O and midpoints of the sides M_1, M_2 and M_3. If $A_1 \equiv [x_1, y_1]$, $A_2 \equiv [x_2, y_2]$ and $A_3 \equiv [x_3, y_3]$, then show that the circumcenter N of $\overline{M_1 M_2 M_3}$ is the point

$$N = \left[\frac{[x_1^2 y_2]_3^- + 2[x_1 x_2 y_2]_3^- - [y_1^2 y_2]_3^-}{4[x_1 y_2]_3^-}, \frac{[x_1^2 x_2]_3^- + 2[x_1 y_1 y_2]_3^- - [x_1^2 y_2]_3^-}{4[x_1 y_2]_3^-} \right].$$

Deduce that N is the midpoint of $\overline{OC}$, and hence lies on the Euler line e. $\diamond$

Theorem 117 (Nine point circle) The nine point circle n of a non-null triangle $\overline{A_1A_2A_3}$ passes through the midpoints M_1, M_2 and M_3 of the sides, the feet F_1, F_2 and F_3 of the altitudes, and the midpoints P_1, P_2 and P_3 of the respective sides $\overline{A_1O}, \overline{A_2O}$ and $\overline{A_3O}$, where O is the orthocenter.

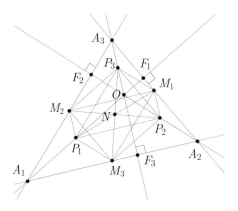

Figure 18.2: Nine point circle theorem

Proof. By Thales' theorem (page 48) applied to both $\overline{A_1A_2A_3}$ and $\overline{A_1A_2O}$, the sides $\overline{M_1M_2}$ and $\overline{P_1P_2}$ are both parallel to A_1A_2, and both have quadrance equal to $Q_3/4$. The same argument, applied to both $\overline{A_1A_3O}$ and $\overline{A_2A_3O}$, shows that the sides $\overline{M_2P_1}$ and $\overline{M_1P_2}$ are both parallel to A_3O, and have quadrance equal to $Q(A_3, O)/4$.

Hence $\overline{P_1P_2M_1M_2}$ is a rectangle. Similarly $\overline{P_1P_3M_1M_3}$ and $\overline{P_2P_3M_2M_3}$ are rectangles. These three rectangles have the property that any two share a common diagonal side. Thus the centers of these rectangles coincide at a point N. By Exercise 5.4, the Parallelogram center theorem (page 49) and the Midpoint theorem (page 60), the quadrance from N to any of the points M_i or P_j are equal, for $i, j = 1, 2$ and 3. Thus these six points lie on a circle n centered at N, which is the circumcircle of $\overline{M_1M_2M_3}$.

Since M_3P_3 is a diagonal of the circle n and $s(F_3M_3, F_3P_3) = 1$, the Right midpoint theorem (page 126) shows that F_3 also lies on n. Thus by symmetry the three feet F_1, F_2 and F_3 all lie on n. ∎

Example 18.1 In the field $\mathbb{F}_{17}$ the triangle $\overline{A_1A_2A_3}$ with points

$$A_1 \equiv [2, 3] \qquad A_2 \equiv [10, 5] \qquad A_3 \equiv [6, 12]$$

has lines $l_1 = \langle 2 : 6 : 1 \rangle$, $l_2 = \langle 7 : 12 : 1 \rangle$ and $l_3 = \langle 12 : 3 : 1 \rangle$, with l_3 a null line. The circumcenter is $C = [5, 8]$, the orthocenter is $O = [8, 4]$, and the centroid is $G = [6, 1]$. The midpoints of the sides are $M_1 = [8, 0]$, $M_2 = [4, 16]$ and $M_3 = [6, 4]$. The nine point circle n has center $N = [15, 6]$ and quadrance zero, so is a null circle.

The Euler line is $\langle 3 : 15 : 1 \rangle$. The feet of the altitudes are $F_1 = [0, 14]$ and $F_2 = [13, 15]$, but there is no foot F_3, as the altitude to the null line l_3 does not intersect it. The midpoints of the sides $\overline{A_1 O}$, $\overline{A_2 O}$ and $\overline{A_3 O}$ are $P_1 = [5, 12]$, $P_2 = [9, 13]$ and $P_3 = [7, 8]$.

This is all shown in Figure 18.3, where the midpoints M_1, M_2 and M_3, the feet F_1 and F_2, and the midpoints P_1, P_2 and P_3 all lie on the nine point circle n (circles), and O, N, G and C all lie on the Euler line (black boxes). Note that N also lies on the nine-point circle, so the circle still deserves its name!

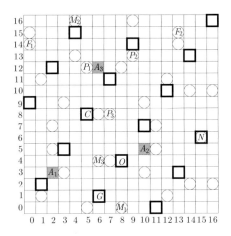

Figure 18.3: Nine point circle in $\mathbb{F}_{17}$ ◇

Exercise 18.3 (Eight point circle) Show that if a quadrilateral $\overline{A_1 A_2 A_3 A_4}$ has perpendicular diagonals then the midpoints M_{12}, M_{23}, M_{34} and M_{14} of the sides and the feet F_{12}, F_{23}, F_{34} and F_{14} of the altitudes from the respective midpoints to the opposite sides all lie on a circle. See Figure 18.4.

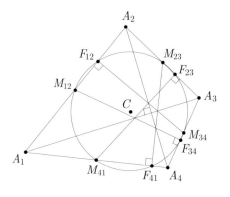

Figure 18.4: Eight point circle ◇

Tangent lines and tangent conics

The notion of a *tangent line* to a conic (or indeed to any algebraic curve) does not require derivations, derivatives or indeed any calculus, and applies to general fields. Generalizing leads to the idea of a *tangent conic*. In this way classical properties of conics can be extended to universal geometry, and then applied to metrical algebraic geometry. For example, since conics come in different types, you may classify points on curves according to the geometric properties of the tangent conic. Tangent conics to the folium of Descartes and the lemniscate of Bernoulli are studied.

In this chapter the translational structure of the plane becomes important, particularly the isometries τ_B defined in Chapter 13. Some calculations require a computer.

19.1 Translates and Taylor conics

Recall from Chapter 15 that the conic $q \equiv \langle d : e : f : a : b : c \rangle$ is standard precisely when it passes through the origin $O \equiv [0,0]$, or equivalently when $c = 0$. The standard conic $q \equiv \langle d : e : f : a : b : 0 \rangle$ is **singular** precisely when $a = b = 0$.

Definition If $q \equiv \langle d : e : f : a : b : 0 \rangle$ is a non-singular standard conic, then the line $T^{(1)}q \equiv \langle a : b : 0 \rangle$ is the **tangent line to q at O**.

The idea is now to generalize this notion to points lying on arbitrary conics. Recall from Chapter 13 that the translate of $X \equiv [x, y]$ by $B \equiv [u, v]$ is the point

$$\tau_B([x, y]) \equiv [x + u, y + v].$$

Theorem 118 (Translate of a conic) Suppose that $B \equiv [u, v]$. Then the point $X \equiv [x, y]$ lies on the conic $q \equiv \langle d : e : f : a : b : c \rangle$ precisely when the translate $\tau_B([x, y])$ lies on the conic $q_1 \equiv \langle d_1 : e_1 : f_1 : a_1 : b_1 : c_1 \rangle$, where

$$d_1 \equiv d \qquad e_1 \equiv e \qquad f_1 \equiv f$$

and

$$a_1 \equiv a - 2du - ev \qquad b_1 \equiv b - 2fv - eu$$
$$c_1 \equiv du^2 + euv + fv^2 - au - bv + c.$$

Proof. The coefficients of q_1 are chosen so that the following polynomial identity holds

$$d(x - u)^2 + e(x - u)(y - v) + f(y - v)^2 + a(x - u) + b(y - v) + c$$
$$= d_1 x^2 + e_1 xy + f_1 y^2 + a_1 x + b_1 y + c_1.$$

Then $\tau_B([x, y]) \equiv [x + u, y + v]$ lies on q_1 precisely when $[x, y]$ lies on q. ∎

Definition The conic $q_1 \equiv \tau_B(q)$ defined in this theorem is the **translate of q by B**.

Example 19.1 The circle $c \equiv \langle 1 : 0 : 1 : 0 : 0 : -1 \rangle$ has equation

$$x^2 + y^2 - 1 = 0.$$

If $B \equiv [2, 3]$, then the point $[x, y]$ lies on c precisely when $\tau_B([x, y]) = [x + 2, y + 3]$ lies on the circle $\tau_B(c)$ with equation

$$(x - 2)^2 + (y - 3)^2 - 1 = 0.$$

Expand to see that $\tau_B(c) = \langle 1 : 0 : 1 : -4 : 6 : 12 \rangle$. ◇

Example 19.2 The conic $q \equiv \langle 1 : -2 : -1 : 1 : 0 : -5 \rangle$ has equation

$$x^2 - 2xy - y^2 + x - 5 = 0 \tag{19.1}$$

and $A \equiv [3, 1]$ lies on q. Then $\tau_A^{-1}(q)$ is a standard conic, and its equation is obtained by replacing in (19.1) each x by $x + 3$, and each y by $y + 1$. This simplifies to

$$x^2 - 2xy - y^2 + 5x - 8y = 0$$

so that $\tau_A^{-1}(q) = \langle 1 : -2 : -1 : 5 : -8 : 0 \rangle$. ◇

Definition If the point A lies on the conic q then the standard conic $\tau_A^{-1}(q)$ is the **Taylor conic of q at A**. It is also denoted by q_A.

19.2 Tangent lines

Suppose that q is a conic passing through the point $A \equiv [x_0, y_0]$. Suppose that

$$q_A \equiv \left\langle \begin{array}{ccccc} d_0 & : & e_0 & : & f_0 \\ & a_0 & : & b_0 & \\ & & 0 & & \end{array} \right\rangle$$

is the Taylor conic of q at A. The point A is a **non-singular point of** q precisely when at least one of a_0 and b_0 are non-zero. In this case the line

$$l \equiv T^{(1)}q_A \equiv \langle a_0 : b_0 : 0 \rangle$$

is the tangent line to q_A at O. The translate $\tau_A(l)$ is then the **tangent line to** q **at** A, and is denoted $T_A^{(1)}q$. Thus

$$T_A^{(1)}q = \tau_A\left(T^{(1)}q_A\right) = \tau_A\left(T^{(1)}\tau_A^{-1}(q)\right).$$

So to find the tangent line to a conic q at some non-singular point A lying on it, first translate q by applying τ_A^{-1}, then take the linear part, and then translate this line back by applying τ_A. This ensures that the tangent line passes through A.

Example 19.3 From Example 19.2, the conic $q \equiv \langle 1 : -2 : -1 : 1 : 0 : -5 \rangle$ passes through $A \equiv [3, 1]$ and

$$q_A = \langle 1 : -2 : -1 : 5 : -8 : 0 \rangle.$$

Thus A is a non-singular point of q (since one of 5 and -8 is non-zero). The tangent line to q_A at O is $T^{(1)}q_A = \langle 5 : -8 : 0 \rangle$. The tangent line to q at A thus has equation $5(x-3) - 8(y-1) = 0$, so it is $T_A^{(1)}q = \langle 5 : -8 : -7 \rangle$. The conic q and the tangent line to q at A are illustrated in the decimal number field in Figure 19.1.

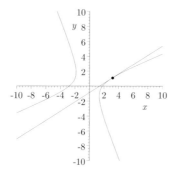

Figure 19.1: Tangent line to a conic ◇

Theorem 119 (Tangent to a conic) Suppose the point $A \equiv [x_0, y_0]$ is a non-singular point lying on the conic $q \equiv \langle d : e : f : a : b : c \rangle$. Then the tangent line to q at A is

$$T_A^{(1)} q = \langle a + 2dx_0 + ey_0 : b + ex_0 + 2fy_0 : ax_0 + by_0 + 2c \rangle .$$

Proof. Since q has equation $0 = dx^2 + exy + fy^2 + ax + by + c$, the equation for q_A is

$$
\begin{aligned}
0 &= d\left(x + x_0\right)^2 + e\left(x + x_0\right)\left(y + y_0\right) + f\left(y + y_0\right)^2 \\
&\quad + a\left(x + x_0\right) + b\left(y + y_0\right) + c \\
&= dx^2 + exy + fy^2 + \left(a + 2dx_0 + ey_0\right) x + \left(b + 2fy_0 + ex_0\right) y.
\end{aligned}
$$

By assumption at least one of the coefficients of x or y is non-zero, so the tangent line $T^{(1)} q_A$ has equation

$$0 = \left(a + 2dx_0 + ey_0\right) x + \left(b + 2fy_0 + ex_0\right) y.$$

The equation of the tangent line $T_A^{(1)} q$ is then

$$
\begin{aligned}
0 &= \left(a + 2dx_0 + ey_0\right)\left(x - x_0\right) + \left(b + ex_0 + 2fy_0\right)\left(y - y_0\right) \\
&= \left(a + ey_0 + 2dx_0\right) x + \left(b + ex_0 + 2fy_0\right) y + ax_0 + by_0 + 2c
\end{aligned}
$$

where the constant term is simplified by the fact that $[x_0, y_0]$ lies on q. ∎

Example 19.4 The tangent line to the parabola $p \equiv \langle 0 : 0 : 1 : -4 : 0 : 0 \rangle$ with equation $y^2 = 4x$ at the point $\left[y_0^2, 2y_0\right]$ is

$$\left\langle -4 : 4y_0 : -4y_0^2 \right\rangle = \left\langle 1 : -y_0 : y_0^2 \right\rangle .$$

All points lying on p are non-singular. ◇

Theorem 120 (Tangent to a circle) Every point A lying on a non-null circle c is non-singular. If C is the center of c then the tangent line to c at A is the altitude from A to AC, and is a non-null line.

Proof. Suppose that $A \equiv [x_0, y_0]$ lies on the circle c. If $C \equiv [x_1, y_1]$ is the center of c, then the equation for c is

$$\left(x - x_1\right)^2 + \left(y - y_1\right)^2 = \left(x_0 - x_1\right)^2 + \left(y_0 - y_1\right)^2$$

which yields

$$c = \left\langle 1 : 0 : 1 : -2x_1 : -2y_1 : 2y_0y_1 + 2x_0x_1 - x_0^2 - y_0^2 \right\rangle .$$

By the previous Tangent to a conic theorem

$$
\begin{aligned}
T_A^{(1)}c &= \left\langle -2x_1 + 2x_0 : -2y_1 + 2y_0 : -2x_1 x_0 + -2y_1 y_0 + 2\left(2y_0 y_1 + 2x_0 x_1 - x_0^2 - y_0^2\right) \right\rangle \\
&= \left\langle x_1 - x_0 : y_1 - y_0 : x_0^2 + y_0^2 - x_1 x_0 - y_1 y_0 \right\rangle.
\end{aligned}
$$

This is a non-null line since $(x_0 - x_1)^2 + (y_0 - y_1)^2$ is the quadrance of c, which is non-zero. The Line through two points theorem (page 38) gives

$$
AC = \left\langle y_1 - y_0 : x_0 - x_1 : x_1 y_0 - x_0 y_1 \right\rangle
$$

which is indeed perpendicular to $T_A^{(1)}c$. Thus $T_A^{(1)}c$ is the altitude from A to AC. ■

Theorem 121 (Parabola reflection) Suppose k is the tangent line to a parabola p at a point A lying on it. Then

$$
s(k, m) = s(k, n)
$$

where $m \equiv AF$ with F the focus of p and n is the altitude from A to the directrix l.

Proof. (Using a computer) If $F \equiv [x_1, y_1]$ and $l \equiv \langle a : b : c \rangle$ are the focus and directrix of a parabola p, then the equation for p is $w(x, y) = 0$ where

$$
\begin{aligned}
w(x, y) &= b^2 x^2 - 2abxy + a^2 y^2 - \left(2ac + 2\left(a^2 + b^2\right) x_1\right) x \\
&\quad - \left(2bc + 2\left(a^2 + b^2\right) y_1\right) y + \left(a^2 + b^2\right)\left(x_1^2 + y_1^2\right) - c^2.
\end{aligned}
$$

Suppose that $A \equiv [x_0, y_0]$ is a point lying on the parabola. Then by the Tangent to a conic theorem, the tangent line to p at A is

$$
k \equiv \left\langle \begin{array}{c} b^2 x_0 - aby_0 - \left(a^2 + b^2\right) x_1 - ac : -abx_0 + a^2 y_0 - \left(a^2 + b^2\right) y_1 - bc \\ -x_0 \left(ac + \left(a^2 + b^2\right) x_1\right) - y_0 \left(bc + \left(a^2 + b^2\right) y_1\right) - c^2 + \left(a^2 + b^2\right)\left(x_1^2 + y_1^2\right) \end{array} \right\rangle.
$$

The Line through two points theorem (page 38) gives

$$
m \equiv AF = \left\langle y_1 - y_0 : x_0 - x_1 : x_1 y_0 - x_0 y_1 \right\rangle.
$$

The Altitude to a line theorem (page 41) shows the altitude from A to l to be

$$
n \equiv \left\langle -b : a : bx_0 - ay_0 \right\rangle.
$$

Having the equations of the three lines k, m and n, use the definition of the spread to obtain an expression for $s(k, m) - s(k, n)$ in terms of x_0 and y_0. Using a computer, this difference in spreads can be shown to be a rational function of x_0 and y_0, with $w(x_0, y_0)$ as a factor. Since A lies on p, this difference is then zero. ■

Exercise 19.1 Check this argument more directly for the parabola p with equation $y^2 = 4ax$. ◇

Exercise 19.2 Show that for the parabola p with equation $y^2 = 4x$ the tangents to p at any two distinct points A_1 and A_2 lying on p intersect, say at a point B. Show further that if F is the focus of p then

$$(Q(A_1, B))^2 : (Q(A_2, B))^2 = Q(A_1, F) : Q(A_2, F).$$

The situation is illustrated over $\mathbb{F}_{11}$ in Figure 19.2, where $F \equiv [1, 0]$, $A_1 \equiv [1, 2]$, $A_2 \equiv [4, -4]$ and $B \equiv [-2, -1]$. Then both sides of the above equation are $5 : 1$.

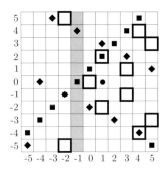

Figure 19.2: Two tangents to $y^2 = 4x$ in $\mathbb{Z}_{11}$ ◇

Exercise 19.3 (Quadrola reflection–Harder) Show that the tangent line to a quadrola q at a point A lying on it makes equal spreads with the lines AF_1 and AF_2, where F_1 and F_2 are a pair of foci of q. ◇

19.3   Higher order curves and tangents

The notation and definitions for conics and their tangents generalize to higher order curves.

A **cubic curve** q is a proportion of the form $\langle g : h : i : j : d : e : f : a : b : c \rangle$ representing the equation $z(x, y) = 0$ where

$$z(x, y) \equiv gx^3 + hx^2 y + ixy^2 + jy^3 + dx^2 + exy + fy^2 + ax + by + c$$

and where i is just another coefficient and does not have its usual special meaning. If $A \equiv [x_0, y_0]$ lies on the curve q, meaning that $z(x_0, y_0) = 0$, then the polynomial $w(x, y)$ obtained by replacing x by $x + x_0$ and y by $y + y_0$ in $z(x, y)$ has no constant term. Then

$$w(x, y) = g_1 x^3 + h_1 x^2 y + i_1 xy^2 + j_1 y^3 + d_1 x^2 + e_1 xy + f_1 y^2 + a_1 x + b_1 y = 0$$

is the equation of the **Taylor curve** q_A to q at A. Then A is **non-singular**, or more accurately **first order non-singular**, precisely when at least one of a_1 or b_1 is non-zero. In this case the line $T_A^{(1)} q = \tau_A(\langle a_1 : b_1 : 0 \rangle)$ is the **tangent line** to q at A.

Furthermore A is **second order non-singular** precisely when at least one of d_1, e_1, f_1 is non-zero. In this case $T_A^{(2)} q = \tau_A \left(\langle d_1 : e_1 : f_1 : a_1 : b_1 : 0 \rangle \right)$ is the **tangent conic to** q **at** A.

Note that the two notions of non-singular are completely independent. The tangent line $T_A^{(1)} q$ is also tangent to the tangent conic $T_A^{(2)} q$ at A.

Two cubic curves q_1 and q_2 **intersect at** A precisely when A lies on them both. In this case they are **tangent at** A precisely when A is a non-singular point of both and $T_A^{(1)} q_1 = T_A^{(1)} q_2$. The two curves are **second order tangent at** A precisely when A is a second order non-singular point of both and $T_A^{(2)} q_1 = T_A^{(2)} q_2$.

These concepts generalize to higher degree curves and higher order tangents. The next two sections apply this kind of analysis using tangent conics to two famous curves, and suggest further questions arising from these notions.

19.4   Folium of Descartes

Suppose the field is not of characteristic three. The folium of Descartes q is a cubic curve with equation

$$x^3 + y^3 + 3xy = 0 \tag{19.2}$$

Example 19.5 In the decimal number field the curve is shown in Figure 19.3.

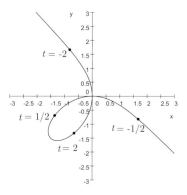

Figure 19.3: Folium of Descartes

By setting $y = tx$ and substituting, (19.2) becomes

$$x^2 \left(x + t^3 x + 3t \right) = 0.$$

Thus either $x = 0$, in which case $y = 0$, or $[x, y]$ has the form

$$\left[-\frac{3t}{1 + t^3}, -\frac{3t^2}{1 + t^3} \right]. \tag{19.3}$$

Conversely, for every t for which $t^3 \neq -1$, the point (19.3) lies on the folium, giving a parametrization of the curve, including the point $[0,0]$ when $t = 0$.

Example 19.6 In the field $\mathbb{F}_{13}$, Figure 19.4 shows the folium q with the various values of the parameter t. There are only 10 points, since $t = 4, 10$ and 12 satisfy $t^3 = -1$ and so do not contribute.

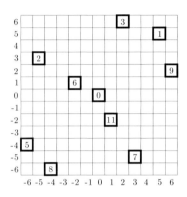

Figure 19.4: The folium of Descartes in $\mathbb{F}_{13}$ ◇

Fix a point A lying on the folium q corresponding to a value t. Translate by τ_A^{-1} to get a standard cubic q_1 with equation

$$0 = \left(x - \frac{3t}{1+t^3} \right)^3 + \left(y - \frac{3t^2}{1+t^3} \right)^3 + 3 \left(x - \frac{3t}{1+t^3} \right) \left(y - \frac{3t^2}{1+t^3} \right)$$

or

$$
\begin{aligned}
0 = {} & x^3 + y^3 - \frac{9t}{1+t^3} x^2 + 3xy - \frac{9t^2}{1+t^3} y^2 \\
& - \frac{9\left(t^3 - 2\right) t^2}{(t+1)^2 \left(t^2 - t + 1\right)^2} x + \frac{9\left(2t^3 - 1\right) t}{(t+1)^2 \left(t^2 - t + 1\right)^2} y.
\end{aligned}
\tag{19.4}
$$

Then A is singular precisely when $t = 0$, since this is the only value for which both coefficients of x and y are zero, since the field is not of characteristic three.

Suppose that $t \neq 0$. To find the tangent line $T_A^{(1)} q$ to q at A, take the linear terms of q_1 and translate back using τ_A to get

$$-\frac{9\left(t^3 - 2\right) t^2}{(t+1)^2 \left(t^2 - t + 1\right)^2} \left(x + \frac{3t}{1+t^3} \right) + \frac{9\left(2t^3 - 1\right) t}{(t+1)^2 \left(t^2 - t + 1\right)^2} \left(y + \frac{3t^2}{1+t^3} \right) = 0.$$

Simplify this equation for $T_A^{(1)} q$ to get

$$t \left(2 - t^3\right) x + \left(2t^3 - 1\right) y + 3t^2 = 0.
\tag{19.5}$$

Returning to (19.4), the existence of the quadratic term $3xy$ ensures that every point A lying on q is second order non-singular, even when $t = 0$. To find the tangent conic $T_A^{(2)}q$ to q at A, take the terms of degree two or less in q_1 and translate back using τ_A to get

$$
\begin{aligned}
0 = {} & -\frac{9t}{1+t^3}\left(x+\frac{3t}{1+t^3}\right)^2 + 3\left(x+\frac{3t}{1+t^3}\right)\left(y+\frac{3t^2}{1+t^3}\right) - \frac{9t^2}{1+t^3}\left(y+\frac{3t^2}{1+t^3}\right)^2 \\
& -\frac{9\left(t^3-2\right)t^2}{\left(t+1\right)^2\left(t^2-t+1\right)^2}\left(x+\frac{3t}{1+t^3}\right) + \frac{9\left(2t^3-1\right)t}{\left(t+1\right)^2\left(t^2-t+1\right)^2}\left(y+\frac{3t^2}{1+t^3}\right).
\end{aligned}
$$

After simplification you get for $T_A^{(2)}q$ the equation

$$
0 = 3t\left(1+t^3\right)x^2 - \left(1+t^3\right)^2 xy + 3t^2\left(1+t^3\right)y^2 + 9t^2 x + 9t^4 y + 9t^3. \tag{19.6}
$$

When $t = 0$ this conic is a *pair of lines*, with equation $xy = 0$.

Example 19.7 In the field $\mathbb{F}_{13}$, Figure 19.5 shows the point $A \equiv [1, -2]$, which corresponds to the parameter $t = 11$ and lies on the folium q (large open squares). Using (19.5) the tangent line to q at A (gray boxes) has equation $2x + 3y + 4 = 0$. Using (19.6) the tangent conic to q at A (small black squares) has equation $3x^2 + 3xy + 7y^2 + 10x + y + 6 = 0$. Notice that the tangent line intersects the folium at two points, and the tangent conic intersects the folium at four points.

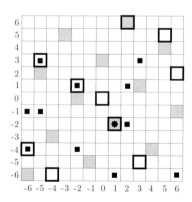

Figure 19.5: Tangent line and tangent conic at $[1, -2]$ ◇

Example 19.8 (Using some linear algebra) In the decimal number field, to determine whether the tangent conic is an ellipse, parabola or hyperbola in the usual decimal number sense, consider the associated quadratic form to (19.6). After removing the factor $1 + t^3$, this has matrix

$$
M \equiv \begin{bmatrix} 3t & -\left(1+t^3\right)/2 \\ -\left(1+t^3\right)/2 & 3t^2 \end{bmatrix}.
$$

Then $\det M = (-1/4)\left(t^6 - 34t^3 + 1\right)$. The quadratic equation $x^2 - 34x + 1 = 0$ has solutions $x = 17 \pm 12\sqrt{2}$ which are reciprocals. Thus when $t = \sqrt[3]{17 \pm 12\sqrt{2}}$ the tangent conic is a parabola, while for t between $\sqrt[3]{17 - 12\sqrt{2}} \approx 0.308\ldots$ and $\sqrt[3]{17 + 12\sqrt{2}} \approx 3.238\ldots$ the tangent conic is an ellipse, and otherwise a hyperbola.

The graphs of tangent lines and tangent conics to the folium of Descartes are shown below, illustrating cases where the tangent conic is elliptic, hyperbolic and parabolic.

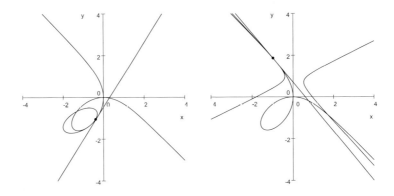

Figure 19.6: Elliptic and hyperbolic tangent conics at $t = 2$ and $t = -2$

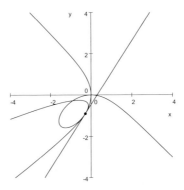

Figure 19.7: Parabolic tangent conic at $t = \sqrt[3]{17 + 12\sqrt{2}}$ ◇

Exercise 19.4 (Harder) Suppose that A and B are distinct points on the folium q corresponding respectively to the parameters t and u. Show that the tangent conic $T_A^{(2)} q$ to q at A passes through B if $(tu)^3 = 1$.

In the special case when $u = t^{-1}$, show that the spread between the tangent line $T_A^{(1)} q$ at A and the tangent line to the tangent conic $T_B^{(2)} q$ at A equals the spread between the tangent line $T_B^{(1)} q$ at B and the tangent line to the tangent conic $T_A^{(2)} q$ at B. ◇

19.5 Lemniscate of Bernoulli

A **Cassini oval** is a particular form of quartic curve, whose equation in $P \equiv [x, y]$ is

$$Q\left(P, F_1\right) Q\left(P, F_2\right) = K$$

for some distinct points F_1 and F_2 and a non-zero number K. A particular case is the **lemniscate of Bernoulli** b, where $F_1 \equiv [a, 0]$, $F_2 \equiv [-a, 0]$ and $K \equiv a^4$, giving the equation

$$\left(x^2 + y^2\right)^2 = 2a^2\left(x^2 - y^2\right).$$

This equation is **even**, in the sense that it involves only $x^2 \equiv X$ and $y^2 \equiv Y$. Setting $a^2 \equiv A$, it becomes the associated equation in X and Y

$$(X + Y)^2 = 2A\left(X - Y\right).$$

To find a parametrization of this associated equation, suppose that $Y = tX$, so that

$$X^2\left(1 + t\right)^2 = 2AX\left(1 - t\right).$$

If $X = 0$ then the choices for Y are $Y = 0$ and $Y = -2A$. Otherwise $[X, Y]$ is of the form

$$\left[\frac{2A\left(1 - t\right)}{\left(1 + t\right)^2}, \frac{2At\left(1 - t\right)}{\left(1 + t\right)^2}\right]$$

where $t \neq -1$.

Suppose $B = [x_0, y_0]$ is a point on the lemniscate b, so that the equation for the Taylor curve b_B is

$$\left(\left(x + x_0\right)^2 + \left(y + y_0\right)^2\right)^2 = 2A\left(\left(x + x_0\right)^2 - \left(y + y_0\right)^2\right)$$

which expands to

$$
\begin{aligned}
0 = \quad & x^4 + 2x^2y^2 + y^4 + 4x_0x^3 + 4y_0x^2y + 4x_0xy^2 + 4y_0y^3 \\
& + 2\left(3x_0^2 + y_0^2 - A\right)x^2 + 8x_0y_0xy + 2\left(x_0^2 + 3y_0^2 + A\right)y^2 \\
& + 4x_0\left(x_0^2 + y_0^2 - A\right)x + 4y_0\left(x_0^2 + y_0^2 + A\right)y.
\end{aligned}
$$

Take linear terms to get the equation of the tangent line $T^{(1)}b_B$

$$0 = x_0\left(x_0^2 + y_0^2 - A\right)x + y_0\left(y_0^2 + x_0^2 + A\right)y$$

and translate back to get the equation of the tangent line $T_B^{(1)}b$ to b at B

$$0 = x_0\left(x_0^2 + y_0^2 - A\right)x + y_0\left(y_0^2 + x_0^2 + A\right)y - A\left(x_0^2 - y_0^2\right).$$

The equation of the tangent conic $T^{(2)}b_B$ is

$$
\begin{aligned}
0 \;=\; & \left(3x_0^2 + y_0^2 - A\right) x^2 + 4x_0 y_0 xy + \left(x_0^2 + 3y_0^2 + A\right) y^2 \\
& + 2x_0 \left(x_0^2 + y_0^2 - A\right) x + 2y_0 \left(x_0^2 + y_0^2 + A\right) y.
\end{aligned}
$$

Translate back to get the equation of the tangent conic $T_B^{(2)}b$ to b at B

$$
\begin{aligned}
0 \;=\; & \left(3x_0^2 + y_0^2 - A\right) x^2 + 4x_0 y_0 xy + \left(x_0^2 + 3y_0^2 + A\right) y^2 \\
& - 4x_0 \left(y_0^2 + x_0^2\right) x - 4y_0 \left(y_0^2 + x_0^2\right) y + 3A \left(x_0^2 - y_0^2\right).
\end{aligned}
$$

Note that

$$
\left(4x_0 y_0\right)^2 - 4\left(3x_0^2 + y_0^2 - A\right)\left(x_0^2 + 3y_0^2 + A\right) = 4\left(-8Ax_0^2 + 8Ay_0^2 + A^2\right)
$$

which is zero precisely when

$$
x_0^2 - y_0^2 = A/8.
$$

This equation defines the **discriminant conic** of the lemniscate. By the Conic center theorem (page 168) the tangent conic $T_B^{(2)}b$ is central unless B lies on the intersection of the lemniscate and this discriminant conic. The discriminant conic is a quadrola.

Exercise 19.5 Show that the lemniscate and the discriminant conic are **inverses** of each other: this means that along any line passing through the origin O, the products of the quadrances from O to the lemniscate and to the discriminant conic are constant.
◇

Lemniscate in the rational number field

Example 19.9 Over the rational number field, suppose that $a \equiv 1$, so that the lemniscate b has equation

$$
\left(x^2 + y^2\right)^2 = 2\left(x^2 - y^2\right).
$$

In Figure 19.8 both the lemniscate and the discriminant conic $x^2 - y^2 = 1/8$, which in this case is a usual hyperbola, are shown. The two curves intersect at the points $\left[\pm\sqrt{5}/4, \pm\sqrt{3}/4\right]$.

The tangent line and tangent conic at the point $\left[\sqrt{5}/4, \sqrt{3}/4\right] \approx [0.559\ldots, 0.433\ldots]$ are also shown. The latter is the parabola

$$
\left\langle 1 : 2\sqrt{15} : 15 : -4\sqrt{5} : -4\sqrt{3} : 3 \right\rangle.
$$

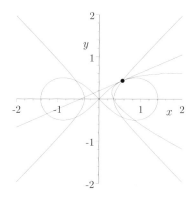

Figure 19.8: Parabolic tangent conic

The tangent line and tangent conic at the points $[0.4, 0.347\ldots]$ and $[0.7, 0.345\,041\ldots]$ are shown in Figures 19.9 and 19.10 respectively.

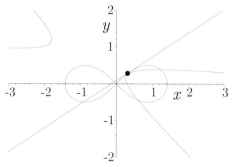

Figure 19.9: Hyperbolic tangent conic

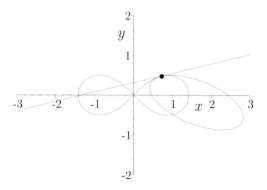

Figure 19.10: Elliptical tangent conic ⋄

Lemniscate in $\mathbb{F}_{11}$

Example 19.10 In the field $\mathbb{F}_{11}$, Figure 19.11 shows two views of the lemniscate (gray squares) with equation $\left(x^2 + y^2\right)^2 = 2\left(x^2 - y^2\right)$, and the discriminant conic (diamonds) with equation $x^2 - y^2 = 7$. These curves intersect at the points $[\pm 1, \pm 4]$.

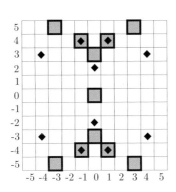 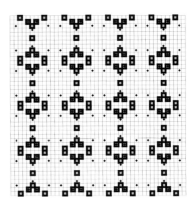

Figure 19.11: Lemniscate and discriminant conic: two views

The left diagram in Figure 19.12 shows the tangent line $\langle 4 : 7 : 1 \rangle$ (small circles) and tangent conic $\langle 3 : 10 : 1 : 7 : 6 : 9 \rangle$ (small black squares) to the lemniscate (gray squares) at the point $[1, 4]$. The tangent conic is a parabola, with directrix $\langle 10 : 5 : 1 \rangle$ (stars) and focus $[9, 9] = [-2, -2]$ (large circle).

The right diagram in Figure 19.12 shows the tangent line (small circles) and tangent conic $\langle 4 : 0 : 3 : 0 : 1 : 3 \rangle$ (small black squares) to the lemniscate (gray squares) at the point $[0, 3]$. The tangent conic in this case is a grammola, with diagonal lines $\langle 3 : 2 : 4 \rangle$ and $\langle 1 : 3 : 6 \rangle$, and quadrance $K \equiv 9$.

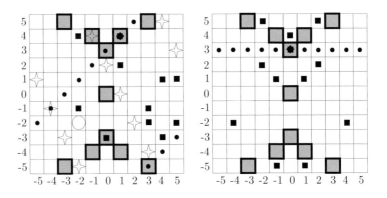

Figure 19.12: Tangent conics at $[1, 4]$ and $[0, 3]$ ⋄

Part IV

Applications

20

Triangle spread rules

This chapter introduces concepts for working over the rational and decimal number fields. It shows how to practically construct a spread ruler, how to define rays and sectors, and gives the important *Triangle spread rules* that augment rational trigonometry in these particular fields, and which are particularly useful for practical applications. The arguments and definitions are generally informal.

20.1 Spread ruler

The **spread ruler** shown in Figure 20.1 allows you to measure spreads between two lines in a similar way that a protractor measures angles between two rays.

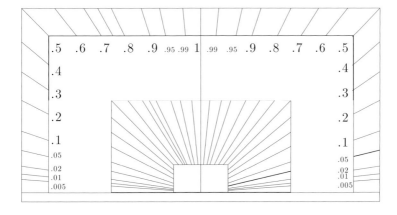

Figure 20.1: Spread ruler

Making a spread ruler is perhaps more straightforward than making a protractor. Consider the right triangle $\overline{OAB}$ with spread s at O, with $Q\left(O,A\right) \equiv 1$ and $Q\left(A,B\right) \equiv Q$. Then by Pythagoras' theorem and the Spread ratio theorem (page 77)

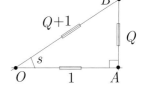

$$s = \frac{Q}{Q+1}$$

so that

$$Q = \frac{s}{1-s}.$$

It follows that if $O \equiv [0,0]$ and $A \equiv [1,0]$, then the position of B, given s, is

$$B = \left[1, \sqrt{s/\left(1-s\right)}\right].$$

Exercise 20.1 Show how to use the symmetry between s and $1-s$ to restrict necessary values of s to the range $[0, 1/2]$. ◇

Here are some approximate values for the construction of a spread ruler.

s	0.05	0.1	0.2	0.25	0.3	0.4	0.5
$\sqrt{s/\left(1-s\right)}$	0.230	0.333	0.5	0.577	0.655	0.816	1.0

20.2   Line segments, rays and sectors

The definitions of this section hold for the decimal or rational number fields, and rely on properties of positive numbers. For these fields, the terms *side* and **line segment** will be used interchangeably. The point A **lies on** the line segment $\overline{A_1 A_2}$ precisely when

$$A = \lambda_1 A_1 + \lambda_2 A_2$$

for some numbers $\lambda_1, \lambda_2 \geq 0$ satisfying $\lambda_1 + \lambda_2 = 1$. Such a point A is **interior** to the line segment precisely when $\lambda_1, \lambda_2 > 0$. The notion 'A lies on $\overline{A_1 A_2}$' is more general than 'A is an element of $\overline{A_1 A_2}$', since $\overline{A_1 A_2} \equiv \{A_1, A_2\}$ has only two elements.

Two line segments $\overline{A_1 A_2}$ and $\overline{B_1 B_2}$ **overlap** precisely when there is a point which is interior to both, and are **adjacent** precisely when there is no point which is interior to both and exactly one point which is an element of both.

Suppose that three collinear points A_1, A_2 and A_3 form quadrances $Q_1 \equiv Q\left(A_2, A_3\right)$, $Q_2 \equiv Q\left(A_1, A_3\right)$ and $Q_3 \equiv Q\left(A_1, A_2\right)$. Then $\{Q_1, Q_2, Q_3\}$ is a quad triple, so that given Q_1 and Q_2, the third quadrance Q_3 is obtained from the triple quad formula

$$\left(Q_3 - Q_1 - Q_2\right)^2 = 4Q_1 Q_2.$$

For a general field this is as much as one can say. However over the decimal or rational number fields one knows that quadrances are always positive, so that the solutions are

$$Q_3 = Q_1 + Q_2 \pm 2\sqrt{Q_1 Q_2}.$$

Then you can determine, in terms of the relative positions of $\overline{A_1 A_3}$ and $\overline{A_2 A_3}$, just which of these two possibilities occurs.

Collinear quadrance rules Suppose that $Q_1 \equiv Q(A_2, A_3)$, $Q_2 \equiv Q(A_1, A_3)$ and $Q_3 \equiv Q(A_1, A_2)$ are the quadrances formed by three collinear points A_1, A_2 and A_3. Then

1. If $\overline{A_1 A_3}$ and $\overline{A_2 A_3}$ are adjacent then $Q_3 = Q_1 + Q_2 + 2\sqrt{Q_1 Q_2}$

2. If $\overline{A_1 A_3}$ and $\overline{A_2 A_3}$ are overlapping then $Q_3 = Q_1 + Q_2 - 2\sqrt{Q_1 Q_2}$.

A **ray** $\overrightarrow{A_1 A_2}$, also written $\overleftarrow{A_2 A_1}$, is an ordered pair $[A_1, A_2]$ of distinct points, with the convention that

$$\overrightarrow{A_1 A_2} = \overrightarrow{A_1 A_3}$$

precisely when

$$A_3 = \lambda_1 A_1 + \lambda_2 A_2$$

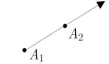

for some numbers λ_1 and λ_2 satisfying $\lambda_1 + \lambda_2 = 1$ and $\lambda_2 \geq 0$.
This notion treats A_2 and A_3 symmetrically. The point A_1 is the **base point** of the ray $\overrightarrow{A_1 A_2}$. A point B **lies on** the ray $\overrightarrow{A_1 A_2}$ precisely when

$$B = \lambda_1 A_1 + \lambda_2 A_2$$

with $\lambda_1 + \lambda_2 = 1$ and $\lambda_2 \geq 0$. Two rays $\overrightarrow{A_1 A_2}$ and $\overrightarrow{B_1 B_2}$ are **parallel** precisely when $A_1 A_2$ is parallel to $B_1 B_2$.

A **sector** $\alpha \equiv \overleftrightarrow{A_2 A_1 A_3}$ is a set $\left\{ \overleftarrow{A_2 A_1}, \overrightarrow{A_1 A_3} \right\}$ of non-parallel rays with a common base point A_1. The point B **lies on** the sector $\overleftrightarrow{A_2 A_1 A_3}$ precisely when

$$B = \lambda_2 A_2 + \lambda_1 A_1 + \lambda_3 A_3$$

with $\lambda_1 + \lambda_2 + \lambda_3 = 1$ and $\lambda_2, \lambda_3 \geq 0$. Figure 20.2 shows (some of) the points B lying on $\alpha = \overleftrightarrow{A_2 A_1 A_3}$.

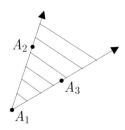

Figure 20.2: The sector $\overleftrightarrow{A_2 A_1 A_3} = \left\{ \overleftarrow{A_2 A_1}, \overrightarrow{A_1 A_3} \right\}$

A sector $\alpha \equiv \overleftrightarrow{A_2 A_1 A_3}$ determines two rays $\overrightarrow{A_1 A_2}$ and $\overrightarrow{A_1 A_3}$, together with two lines $A_1 A_2$ and $A_1 A_3$. The **spread** $s(\alpha)$ **of the sector** α is the spread between these two lines, so that

$$s(\alpha) = s\left(\overleftrightarrow{A_2 A_1 A_3}\right) \equiv s(A_1 A_2, A_1 A_3).$$

20.3   Acute and obtuse sectors

The sector $\alpha \equiv \overleftrightarrow{A_2 A_1 A_3}$ is **acute type**, abbreviated as **(ac)**, precisely when

$$Q(A_1, A_2) + Q(A_1, A_3) \geq Q(A_2, A_3)$$

and **obtuse type**, abbreviated as **(ob)**, precisely when

$$Q(A_1, A_2) + Q(A_1, A_3) \leq Q(A_2, A_3).$$

The sector α is a **right sector** precisely when $s(\alpha) = 1$. By Pythagoras' theorem, a sector is a right sector precisely when it is both acute and obtuse.

Exercise 20.2 Show that these definitions are indeed well-defined. $\diamond$

A general sector determines both a spread and a type. These two pieces of information can be usefully recorded together when referring to sectors. Figure 20.3 shows two sectors, the left with an (acute) spread of $s = 0.625$ (ac) and the right with an (obtuse) spread of 0.845 (ob).

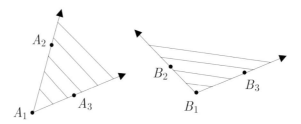

Figure 20.3: Acute and obtuse sectors

If three mutually non-parallel rays $\overrightarrow{A_0 A_1}$, $\overrightarrow{A_0 A_2}$ and $\overrightarrow{A_0 A_3}$ have the common base point A_0, then there are two possible relations between the two sectors $\beta_3 \equiv \overleftrightarrow{A_1 A_0 A_2}$ and $\beta_1 \equiv \overleftrightarrow{A_2 A_0 A_3}$. They **overlap** precisely when there is a point B which lies on both sectors but not on any of the rays $\overrightarrow{A_0 A_1}$, $\overrightarrow{A_0 A_2}$ or $\overrightarrow{A_0 A_3}$. They are **adjacent** precisely when the only points which lie on both sectors lie on the ray $\overrightarrow{A_0 A_2}$. These two situations are respectively shown in Figure 20.4.

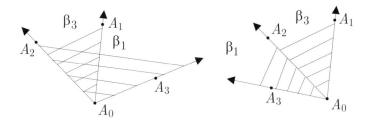

Figure 20.4: Overlapping and adjacent sectors

If $\beta_2 \equiv \overleftrightarrow{A_3 A_0 A_1}$ then the three sectors β_1, β_2 and β_3 may have the property that one of them overlaps with each of the other two, while those other two are adjacent, as in either of the diagrams in Figure 20.4. Another possibility is that any two of them are adjacent, as in Figure 20.5.

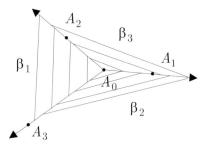

Figure 20.5: Three adjacent sectors

A triangle $\overline{A_1 A_2 A_3}$ gives rise to three distinguished sectors, namely $\alpha_1 \equiv \overleftrightarrow{A_2 A_1 A_3}$, $\alpha_2 \equiv \overleftrightarrow{A_3 A_2 A_1}$ and $\alpha_3 \equiv \overleftrightarrow{A_1 A_3 A_2}$. The spreads of these sectors are then the usual spreads of the triangle. If the spreads of the three sectors are $s_1 \equiv s(\alpha_1)$, $s_2 \equiv s(\alpha_2)$ and $s_3 \equiv s(\alpha_3)$ then the Triple spread formula asserts that $\{s_1, s_2, s_3\}$ is a spread triple, so that

$$(s_3 - (s_1 + s_2 - 2s_1 s_2))^2 = 4 s_1 s_2 (1 - s_1)(1 - s_2). \tag{20.1}$$

When viewed as a quadratic equation in s_3 in the decimal number field, the two solutions can be labelled the **little spread** $r_l = r_l(s_1, s_2)$ and the **big spread** $r_b \equiv r_b(s_1, s_2)$ where

$$
\begin{aligned}
r_l(s_1, s_2) &= s_1 + s_2 - 2s_1 s_2 - 2\sqrt{s_1 s_2 (1 - s_1)(1 - s_2)} \\
r_b(s_1, s_2) &= s_1 + s_2 - 2s_1 s_2 + 2\sqrt{s_1 s_2 (1 - s_1)(1 - s_2)}.
\end{aligned}
$$

20.4   Acute and obtuse triangles

The point B **lies on** the triangle $\overline{A_1 A_2 A_3}$ precisely when

$$B = \lambda_1 A_1 + \lambda_2 A_2 + \lambda_3 A_3$$

for some numbers $\lambda_1, \lambda_2, \lambda_3 \geq 0$ satisfying $\lambda_1 + \lambda_2 + \lambda_3 = 1$. Such a point B is **interior** to the triangle if $\lambda_1, \lambda_2, \lambda_3 > 0$.

A triangle $\overline{A_1 A_2 A_3}$ is **acute** if all three of its sectors are acute. Otherwise it is **obtuse**. If the quadrances of the triangle are Q_1, Q_2 and Q_3 as usual, then the sector with base point A_1 (or just the **sector at** A_1) is acute precisely when $Q_2 + Q_3 \geq Q_1$, and similarly for the other sectors. So the triangle is acute precisely when

$$Q_1 + Q_2 \geq Q_3 \qquad Q_2 + Q_3 \geq Q_1 \qquad Q_3 + Q_1 \geq Q_2. \qquad (20.2)$$

Observe that if the corresponding spreads of the triangle are s_1, s_2 and s_3, then by the Spread law and the fact that all the quadrances and spreads are positive, the sector at A_3 is acute, or alternatively the spread of the sector $s\left(\overleftarrow{A_1 A_3 A_2}\right)$ is acute, precisely when either

$$Q_1 + Q_2 \geq Q_3 \qquad \text{or} \qquad s_1 + s_2 \geq s_3.$$

Exercise 20.3 Show that if a triangle $\overline{A_1 A_2 A_3}$ has spreads s_1, s_2 and s_3, then any two of the following inequalities implies the third, and implies the triangle is acute.

$$s_1 \geq |s_2 - s_3| \qquad s_2 \geq |s_3 - s_1| \qquad s_3 \geq |s_1 - s_2|. \quad \diamond$$

Exercise 20.4 Show that a triangle can have at most one obtuse sector. $\diamond$

Problem 2 Show that $\overline{A_1 A_2 A_3}$ is acute precisely when the circumcenter C lies on the triangle.

Solution. Suppose that the quadrances of $\overline{A_1 A_2 A_3}$ are Q_1, Q_2 and Q_3 as usual, and that the quadrea is $\mathcal{A}$. The Affine circumcenter theorem (page 146) shows that C is the affine combination

$$C = \gamma_1 A_1 + \gamma_2 A_2 + \gamma_3 A_3$$

where

$$\begin{aligned}
\gamma_1 &\equiv Q_1 \left(Q_2 + Q_3 - Q_1 \right) / \mathcal{A} \\
\gamma_2 &\equiv Q_2 \left(Q_1 + Q_3 - Q_2 \right) / \mathcal{A} \\
\gamma_3 &\equiv Q_3 \left(Q_1 + Q_2 - Q_3 \right) / \mathcal{A}.
\end{aligned}$$

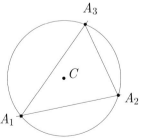

So C is in the interior of $\overline{A_1 A_2 A_3}$ precisely when the three inequalities for acuteness are satisfied. ∎

20.5 Triangle spread rules

The following rules apply to the rational and decimal number fields, and those closely related to them. They provide an important guide to dealing with acute and obtuse sectors in practical applications of rational trigonometry.

Triangle spread rules Suppose that s_1, s_2 and s_3 are the respective spreads of the three sectors $\alpha_1 \equiv \overleftrightarrow{A_2 A_1 A_3}$, $\alpha_2 \equiv \overleftrightarrow{A_3 A_2 A_1}$ and $\alpha_3 \equiv \overleftrightarrow{A_1 A_3 A_2}$ of a triangle $\overline{A_1 A_2 A_3}$. Then

1. The spread s_3 is equal to $r_b (s_1, s_2)$ precisely when s_1 and s_2 are both acute

2. The spread s_3 is obtuse precisely when s_1 and s_2 are acute and $s_1 + s_2 \leq 1$.

This is summarized in the following table, which gives the value of s_3, depending on s_1 and s_2.

s_3	s_1 (ac) s_2 (ac)	s_1 (ac) s_2 (ob)
$s_1 + s_2 \leq 1$	$r_b (s_1, s_2)$ (ob)	$r_l (s_1, s_2)$ (ac)
$s_1 + s_2 \geq 1$	$r_b (s_1, s_2)$ (ac)	$r_l (s_1, s_2)$ (ac)

Problem 3 Demonstrate the validity of these rules.

Solution (Rule 1). Recall that the Triple spread formula, as a quadratic equation in s_3, has normal form

$$(s_3 - (s_1 + s_2 - 2s_1 s_2))^2 = 4s_1 s_2 (1 - s_1) (1 - s_2).$$

Suppose that

$$s_3 = r_l (s_1, s_2) = s_1 + s_2 - 2s_1 s_2 - 2\sqrt{s_1 s_2 (1 - s_1) (1 - s_2)}. \tag{20.3}$$

If s_1 is acute then $s_3 + s_2 \geq s_1$, so that

$$s_2 - s_1 s_2 \geq \sqrt{s_1 s_2 (1 - s_1) (1 - s_2)}.$$

Use the fact that any spread s satisfies $0 \leq s \leq 1$ to see that both sides are positive, so the inequality is maintained when both sides are squared. Thus

$$s_2 (1 - s_1) \geq s_1 (1 - s_2)$$

which is equivalent to

$$s_2 \geq s_1.$$

Similarly if s_2 is acute then

$$s_1 \geq s_2.$$

Thus if both s_1 and s_2 are acute then $s_1 = s_2 \equiv s$, in which case by (20.3)

$$s_3 = 2s - 2s^2 - 2s(1 - s) = 0.$$

This is impossible, so you may conclude that if s_1 and s_2 are acute, then

$$s_3 = s_1 + s_2 - 2s_1 s_2 + 2\sqrt{s_1 s_2 (1 - s_1)(1 - s_2)} = r_b(s_1, s_2).$$

Conversely if $s_3 = r_b(s_1, s_2)$ then

$$s_3 + s_2 = s_1 + 2s_2(1 - s_1) + 2\sqrt{s_1 s_2 (1 - s_1)(1 - s_2)} \geq s_1$$

so s_1 is acute, and similarly s_2 is acute. ∎

Solution (Rule 2).   Recall from Exercise 7.2 (page 90) that the Triple spread formula $S(s_1, s_2, s_3) = 0$ can be rewritten as the equation

$$
\begin{aligned}
& s_3 (s_3 - (s_1 + s_2))(1 - (s_1 + s_2)) \\
= {}& ((s_1 + s_2 - s_3) s_3 + (s_3 - s_1 + s_2)(s_3 - s_2 + s_1))(1 - s_3).
\end{aligned}
\qquad (20.4)
$$

Now s_1 and s_2 are acute precisely when

$$s_3 - s_1 + s_2 \geq 0 \qquad \text{and} \qquad s_3 - s_2 + s_1 \geq 0$$

respectively, while s_3 is obtuse precisely when

$$s_3 - (s_1 + s_2) \geq 0.$$

Any spread s of a triangle satisfies $0 < s \leq 1$. So if s_1 and s_2 are acute and $s_1 + s_2 \leq 1$, then s_3 must be obtuse, since otherwise the right hand side of (20.4) is strictly positive while the left hand side is negative.

Conversely suppose s_3 is obtuse. Then s_1 and s_2 are acute by Exercise 20.4. If $s_1 + s_2 > 1$ then the left hand side of (20.4) is strictly negative, so that

$$((s_1 + s_2 - s_3) s_3 + (s_3 - s_1 + s_2)(s_3 - s_2 + s_1)) = s_3 s_1 + s_3 s_2 + 2s_1 s_2 - s_1^2 - s_2^2 < 0.$$

But then

$$s_3 (s_1 + s_2) < (s_1 - s_2)^2$$

which is impossible since

$$s_3 (s_1 + s_2) \geq (s_1 + s_2)^2 > (s_1 - s_2)^2.$$

Thus $s_1 + s_2 \leq 1$. ∎

Two dimensional problems

This chapter gives some geometrical applications in the decimal number plane.

21.1 Harmonic relation

Problem 4 Distinct points A_1, A_2 and A_3 lie on a line l, with B_1, B_2 and B_3 points on the respective altitudes from A_1, A_2 and A_3 to l, such that B_1, B_2 and A_3 are collinear, as are A_1, B_2 and B_3, as in Figure 21.1. Define $Q_1 \equiv Q(A_1, B_1)$, $Q_2 \equiv Q(A_2, B_2)$ and $Q_3 \equiv Q(A_3, B_3)$. Show that $\{1/Q_1, 1/Q_2, 1/Q_3\}$ is a quad triple.

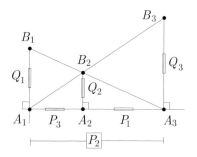

Figure 21.1: Harmonic configuration

Solution. Define $P_1 \equiv Q(A_2, A_3)$, $P_2 \equiv Q(A_1, A_3)$ and $P_3 \equiv Q(A_1, A_2)$. Then by the Twist ratio theorem (page 78)

$$t\left(A_3A_2, A_3B_2\right) \;=\; \frac{Q_2}{P_1} = \frac{Q_1}{P_2} \tag{21.1}$$

$$t\left(A_1A_2, A_1B_2\right) \;=\; \frac{Q_2}{P_3} = \frac{Q_3}{P_2}. \tag{21.2}$$

By the Triple quad formula $\{P_1, P_2, P_3\}$ forms a quad triple, so that

$$\left(P_1 + P_3 - P_2\right)^2 = 4P_1P_3.$$

Divide both sides by P_2^2 and substitute using (21.1) and (21.2) to get

$$\left(\frac{Q_2}{Q_1} + \frac{Q_2}{Q_3} - 1\right)^2 = 4\frac{Q_2^2}{Q_1Q_3}$$

or

$$\left(\frac{1}{Q_1} + \frac{1}{Q_3} - \frac{1}{Q_2}\right)^2 = 4\frac{1}{Q_1}\frac{1}{Q_3}.$$

This is the statement that $\{1/Q_1, 1/Q_2, 1/Q_3\}$ is a quad triple. ∎

21.2 Overlapping triangles

Problem 5 Two triangles $\overline{ABC}$ and $\overline{ABD}$ share a side $\overline{AB}$ as shown in Figure 21.2, with quadrances as indicated. What are the quadrances $Q\left(A, E\right)$, $Q\left(B, E\right)$, $Q\left(C, E\right)$ and $Q\left(D, E\right)$?

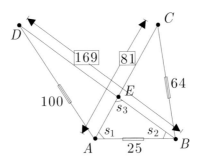

Figure 21.2: Overlapping triangles

Solution. Introduce the spreads s_1, s_2 and s_3 of the sectors of $\overline{ABE}$ as shown. Use the Cross law in $\overline{ABC}$, together with the fact that $81 + 25 > 64$, to get

$$s_1 = 1 - \frac{\left(81 + 25 - 64\right)^2}{4 \times 25 \times 81} = \frac{176}{225} \;(\text{ac}).$$

Similarly in $\overline{ABD}$, since $169 + 25 > 100$,

$$s_2 = 1 - \frac{(169 + 25 - 100)^2}{4 \times 169 \times 25} = \frac{2016}{4225} \text{ (ac)}.$$

Now use the Triple spread formula in $\overline{ABE}$ to obtain the quadratic equation

$$s_3^2 - \frac{975\,136}{950\,625} s_3 + \frac{215\,296}{2313\,441} = 0. \tag{21.3}$$

Since s_1 and s_2 are acute, and

$$s_1 + s_2 = \frac{176}{225} + \frac{2016}{4225} = \frac{47\,888}{38\,025} > 1$$

the Triangle spread rules (page 219) show that the correct solution to (21.3) is

$$\begin{aligned} s_3 &= r_b(s_1, s_2) \text{ (ac)} \\ &= \frac{487\,568}{950\,625} + \frac{10\,528}{316\,875}\sqrt{154} \text{ (ac)}. \end{aligned}$$

Then the Spread law in $\overline{ABE}$ gives

$$\frac{176/225}{Q(B, E)} = \frac{2016/4225}{Q(A, E)} = \frac{1}{25}\left(\frac{487\,568}{950\,625} + \frac{10\,528}{316\,875}\sqrt{154}\right).$$

This yields the values

$$Q(A, E) = \frac{34\,556\,382}{525\,625} - \frac{2238\,516}{525\,625}\sqrt{154}$$

$$Q(B, E) = \frac{56\,649\,307}{525\,625} - \frac{3669\,666}{525\,625}\sqrt{154}.$$

Now the Collinear quadrance rules show that since $\overline{AC}$ and $\overline{AE}$ are overlapping,

$$\begin{aligned} Q(C, E) &= Q(A, C) + Q(A, E) - 2\sqrt{Q(A, C)\,Q(A, E)} \\ &= \frac{111\,662\,307}{525\,625} - \frac{7758\,666}{525\,625}\sqrt{154} \end{aligned}$$

and similarly

$$\begin{aligned} Q(D, E) &= Q(B, D) + Q(B, E) - 2\sqrt{Q(B, D)\,Q(B, E)} \\ &= \frac{18\,789\,082}{525\,625} + \frac{1476\,384}{525\,625}\sqrt{154}. \end{aligned}$$

Note, perhaps surprisingly, that the square roots involved work out pleasantly, meaning that all expressions of the form

$$\sqrt{a + b\sqrt{154}}$$

which occur turn out to be expressible in the simpler form $c + d\sqrt{154}$, with c and d rational numbers. ∎

21.3 Eyeball theorem

This result is described in [Gutierrez].

Problem 6 Suppose that two circles have centers C_1 and C_2, respective quadrances K_1 and K_2, and that tangents from each center to the other circle are drawn, intersecting the two circles in points A, B and E, F respectively, as in Figure 21.3. Show that

$$Q(A, B) = Q(E, F).$$

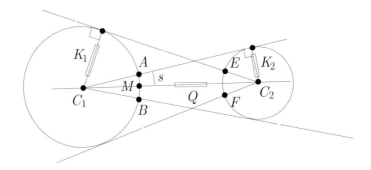

Figure 21.3: Eyeball theorem

Solution. Suppose that $Q(C_1, C_2) \equiv Q$ and define the spread $s \equiv s(C_1A, C_1C_2)$. Then use the Spread ratio theorem (page 77) to find that

$$s = \frac{K_2}{Q}.$$

Let M denote the midpoint of the side $\overline{AB}$, so that in the right triangle $\overline{AMC_1}$

$$s = \frac{Q(A, M)}{K_1}.$$

From this

$$Q(A, M) = \frac{K_1 K_2}{Q}$$

so that by the Midpoint theorem (page 60)

$$Q(A, B) = \frac{4K_1 K_2}{Q}.$$

This is symmetric in K_1 and K_2, so it also equals $Q(E, F)$. ∎

21.4 Quadrilateral problem

Problem 7 A quadrilateral $\overline{A_1 A_2 A_3 A_4}$ has quadrances $Q_{12} \equiv 65$, $Q_{34} \equiv 26$, and $Q_{14} \equiv 49$, and diagonal quadrances $Q_{13} \equiv 61$ and $Q_{24} \equiv 100$ as in Figure 21.4. Find $Q \equiv Q_{23}$.

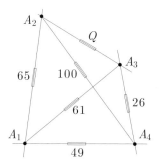

Figure 21.4: A quadrilateral problem

Solution 1: (Using Euler's function). The Four point relation (page 191) states that

$$E\left(100, 65, 49, 61, 26, Q\right) = 0.$$

This becomes the quadratic equation

$$\left(Q - 114\right)^2 = \left(80\right)^2$$

with solutions 34 and 194. But $65 + 49 > 100$ so $\overleftrightarrow{A_2 A_1 A_4}$ is acute, and then so is $\overleftrightarrow{A_2 A_1 A_3}$. Thus $65 + 61 > Q$, so that $Q = 34$. ■

Solution 2: (Using spreads and the Triangle spread rules). Let the intersection of the diagonal lines $A_1 A_3$ and $A_2 A_4$ be C. From the Cross law and the definitions of acute and obtuse,

$$s\left(\overleftrightarrow{A_4 A_1 A_3}\right) = 1 - \frac{\left(49 + 61 - 26\right)^2}{4 \times 49 \times 61} = \frac{25}{61} \ \text{(ac)}.$$

Similarly

$$s\left(\overleftrightarrow{A_2 A_1 A_4}\right) = 64/65 \ \text{(ac)} \qquad s\left(\overleftrightarrow{A_1 A_4 A_2}\right) = 16/25 \ \text{(ac)}$$
$$s\left(\overleftrightarrow{A_1 A_4 A_3}\right) = 25/26 \ \text{(ac)} \qquad s\left(\overleftrightarrow{A_1 A_2 A_4}\right) = 784/1625 \ \text{(ac)}.$$

This yields Figure 21.5, also showing the unknown spreads

$$x \equiv s\left(\overleftrightarrow{A_2 A_1 A_3}\right) \qquad \text{and} \qquad z \equiv s\left(\overleftrightarrow{A_1 C A_4}\right).$$

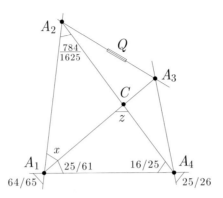

Figure 21.5: Spreads known and unknown

Then the Triple spread formula applied to the spread triple $\{25/61, 16/25, z\}$ gives the quadratic equation

$$\left(z - \frac{801}{1525}\right)^2 = \left(\frac{144}{305}\right)^2.$$

Now

$$25/61 + 16/25 = \frac{1601}{1525} > 1$$

so use the Triangle spread rules in $\overline{A_1 A_4 C}$ to see that

$$z = \frac{801}{1525} + \frac{144}{305} = \frac{1521}{1525} \text{ (ac)}.$$

Although you could now similarly solve for x using the Triple spread formula in $\overline{A_1 A_2 C}$, another approach is to apply the Two spread triples theorem (page 98). Since $\{x, 1521/1525, 784/1625\}$ and $\{x, 25/61, 64/65\}$ are both spread triples, and the sector $\overleftrightarrow{A_1 C A_2}$ is obtuse,

$$x = \frac{\left(\frac{1521}{1525} - \frac{784}{1625}\right)^2 - \left(\frac{25}{61} - \frac{64}{65}\right)^2}{2 \times \left(\frac{1521}{1525} + \frac{784}{1625} - \frac{25}{61} - \frac{64}{65} - 2 \times \frac{1521}{1525} \times \frac{784}{1625} + 2 \times \frac{25}{61} \times \frac{64}{65}\right)}$$

$$= \frac{1849}{3965} \text{ (ac)}.$$

Now use the Cross law in $\overline{A_1 A_2 A_3}$,

$$(Q - 65 - 61)^2 = 4 \times 61 \times 65 \times \left(1 - \frac{1849}{3965}\right)$$

to obtain

$$(Q - 126)^2 = (92)^2.$$

Since x is acute, $65 + 61 \geq Q$, so the solution must be

$$Q = 126 - 92 = 34. \quad \blacksquare$$

Three dimensional problems

This chapter illustrates applications of rational trigonometry and universal geometry to practical problems involving three-dimensional space over the decimal numbers. Giving a careful and reasonably complete introduction to three-dimensional geometry is not easy, which is one of the reasons why no-one has done it yet. Instead, the usual physical arguments and description by pictures will be adopted, which is of course logically unsatisfying.

22.1 Planes

The notions of parallel and perpendicular lines extend to three-dimensional space. Rather briefly, a **plane** Π is given by a linear equation in the coordinates $[x, y, z]$ of space, with the plane passing through the non-collinear points A, B and C denoted ABC. We'll assume that for the decimal number field most of the results of two dimensional geometry developed thus far hold in any plane in three-dimensional space.

Two planes are **parallel** if they do not intersect. A line n is **perpendicular** to a plane Π if it is perpendicular to every line lying on Π. In such a case n is a **normal** to Π. Any two lines perpendicular to a plane Π are themselves parallel.

Define the **spread** $S(\Pi_1, \Pi_2)$ between the planes Π_1 and Π_2 to be the spread $s(n_1, n_2)$ between respective normals n_1 and n_2. Two planes Π_1 and Π_2 are **perpendicular** precisely when $S(\Pi_1, \Pi_2) = 1$; this is equivalent to the condition that one of the planes contains (or passes through) a normal to the other.

The spread between a line l and a plane Π intersecting at a point A is defined to be the spread between l and the line m formed by intersecting Π with the plane through l and the normal n to Π at A.

22.2 Boxes

A *box* is assumed to be **rectangular**, meaning that any two of its faces which meet are perpendicular.

Problem 8 The horizontal sides of a box have quadrances 3 and 4, while the vertical side has quadrance 5. Find the quadrances of the long diagonals, the spread that they make with the base, and the possible spreads between two long diagonals.

Solution. Label the vertices of the box as shown, with

$$Q(A,B) = 3 \qquad Q(B,C) = 4 \qquad Q(C,G) = 5.$$

Then by Pythagoras' theorem

$$Q(A,C) = Q(A,B) + Q(B,C) = 3 + 4 = 7$$

and so also

$$Q(A,G) = Q(A,C) + Q(C,G) = 7 + 5 = 12.$$

Thus the quadrance of the long diagonal side $\overline{AG}$ is 12 and by symmetry the other long diagonal sides $\overline{BH}$, $\overline{DF}$ and $\overline{CE}$ also have quadrance 12. The spread that any of these long diagonals makes with the base (the plane containing A, B, C and D) is

$$s(AC, AG) = \frac{Q(C,G)}{Q(A,G)} = \frac{5}{12}.$$

If P is the center of the box then the quadrance from P to any vertex is one quarter the quadrance of a long diagonal side, hence 3. The spread between the two diagonals AG and BH, which intersect at P, is then equal to the spread $s(PA, PB)$ in the equilateral triangle $\overline{APB}$ with equal quadrances 3, which by the Equilateral triangle theorem (page 125) is 3/4.

The spread between the two diagonals AG and DF is the spread $s(PA, PD)$ in the isosceles triangle $\overline{DPA}$ with quadrances $3, 3$ and 4. By the Isosceles triangle theorem (page 122) this is

$$s(PA, PD) = \frac{4}{3}\left(1 - \frac{4}{4 \times 3}\right) = \frac{8}{9}.$$

Similarly

$$s(PA, PE) = \frac{5}{3}\left(1 - \frac{5}{4 \times 3}\right) = \frac{35}{36}.$$

The three possibilities for spreads between diagonals are 3/4, 8/9 and 35/36. ∎

Exercise 22.1 Show more generally that if the quadrances of a box are P, Q and R then the three spreads formed by pairs of long diagonals are

$$\frac{4P(Q+R)}{(P+Q+R)^2}$$
$$\frac{4Q(R+P)}{(P+Q+R)^2}$$
$$\frac{4R(P+Q)}{(P+Q+R)^2}. \quad \diamond$$

Exercise 22.2 Show that in Problem 8 the spread between the plane ABP and the line PF is $20/27$. $\diamond$

Problem 9 The top V of a flagpole subtends a spread of 0.12 at a point A which is a distance of 70 due south, and a spread of 0.19 at a point B which is due west of the flagpole. Calculate the distance $|A, B|$ from A to B.

Solution. This problem is given in terms of distance, so first convert the information into rational trigonometry. If the base of the flagpole is C then $Q(A, C) = (70)^2 = 4900$. In the right triangle $\overline{ACV}$ the spread at A is 0.12, so the spread at V is $1 - 0.12 = 0.88$, and the Spread law gives

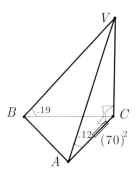

$$Q(C, V) = \frac{0.12}{0.88} \times Q(A, C) = \frac{3}{22} \times 4900 = \frac{7350}{11}.$$

In the right triangle $\overline{BCV}$ the spread at B is 0.19, so the spread at V is $1 - 0.19 = 0.81$, and the Spread law gives

$$\begin{aligned} Q(C, B) &= \frac{0.81}{0.19} \times Q(C, V) \\ &= \frac{81}{19} \times \frac{7350}{11} = \frac{595\,350}{209}. \end{aligned}$$

Use Pythagoras' theorem to get

$$Q(A, B) = 4900 + \frac{595\,350}{209} = \frac{1\,619\,450}{209}.$$

So far no approximations have been introduced. To calculate the distance from A to B, take the square root of the quadrance, to get

$$|A, B| = \frac{35\sqrt{276\,298}}{209}$$

which is approximately 88.02. ■

22.3 Pyramids

A *pyramid* consists of a rectangular base with an apex directly above the center of the base.

Problem 10 A square $\overline{ABCD}$ with quadrance 10 is the base of a pyramid. The quadrance from the center P of the base to the apex V, directly above it, is 18. Find the spread $s(VA, VC)$, and the spread between the planes ABV and BCV.

Solution. The triangle $\overline{AVC}$ is isosceles with P the midpoint of the side $\overline{AC}$, and VP bisects the vertex at V. In the right triangle $\overline{ABC}$, use Pythagoras' theorem to see that $Q(A, C) = 20$, so that

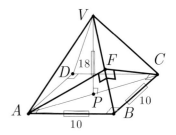

$$Q(A, P) = Q(A, C)/4 = 5.$$

Use Pythagoras' theorem in the right triangle $\overline{APV}$ to see that $Q(A, V) = 23$, so that

$$s(VA, VP) = 5/23.$$

By symmetry $s(VC, VP) = 5/23$, so now use the Equal spreads theorem (page 94) to get

$$s(VA, VC) = 4 \times \frac{5}{23} \times \left(1 - \frac{5}{23}\right) = \frac{360}{529}.$$

To determine the spread between the planes ABV and BCV, find the foot F of the altitude from A to VB, which by symmetry is also the foot of the altitude from C to VB. Then the plane AFC is perpendicular to VB, so that the spread S between the planes ABV and BCV is equal to the spread r between the lines AF and FC. The isosceles triangle $\overline{ABV}$ has quadrances $23, 23$ and 10, so by the Isosceles triangle theorem (page 122)

$$s(VA, VB) = \frac{10}{23}\left(1 - \frac{10}{4 \times 23}\right) = \frac{205}{(23)^2}$$

and thus

$$Q(A, F) = Q(A, V)\, s(VA, VF) = 205/23.$$

Similarly

$$Q(C, F) = 205/23.$$

So in the isosceles triangle $\overline{AFC}$

$$r = s(FA, FC) = \frac{20}{205/23}\left(1 - \frac{20}{4 \times (205/23)}\right) = \frac{1656}{1681} = S. \quad \blacksquare$$

22.4 Wedges

A *wedge* is formed by two intersecting planes, often with one of the planes horizontal.

Problem 11 Suppose an inclined plane has a spread of S with the horizontal plane. An insect climbing up the plane walks on a straight line which makes a spread of r with the line of greatest slope. At what spread to the horizontal does the insect climb on this path?

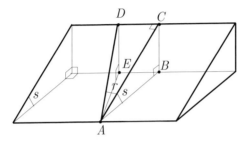

Figure 22.1: Path on a wedge

Solution. Denote by AC a line making the maximum possible spread $s \equiv S$ with the horizontal, and AD the path of the insect, as in Figure 22.1. The spread between AC and AD is r, and you need to find the spread $s\left(AE, AD\right)$. There are no units in the problem, so assume that $Q\left(B,C\right) = Q\left(E,D\right) = 1$. From the right triangle $\overline{ABC}$

$$Q\left(A,C\right) = \frac{Q\left(B,C\right)}{s} = \frac{1}{s}.$$

From the right triangle $\overline{ACD}$, with right vertex at C,

$$Q\left(A,D\right) = \frac{Q\left(A,C\right)}{1-r} = \frac{1}{s\left(1-r\right)}.$$

Thus the right triangle $\overline{ADE}$ gives

$$s\left(AE, AD\right) = \frac{Q\left(D,E\right)}{Q\left(A,D\right)} = s\left(1-r\right) = S\left(1-r\right). \quad \blacksquare$$

22.5   Three dimensional Pythagoras' theorem

Problem 12 Suppose that three points B_1, B_2 and B_3 in space are distinct from a point C and that the three lines CB_1, CB_2 and CB_3 are mutually perpendicular. Let $\mathcal{A}$ be the quadrea of the triangle $\overline{B_1 B_2 B_3}$, and $\mathcal{A}_1, \mathcal{A}_2$ and $\mathcal{A}_3$ the quadreas of the triangles $\overline{CB_2 B_3}, \overline{CB_1 B_3}$ and $\overline{CB_1 B_2}$ respectively. Show that

$$\mathcal{A} = \mathcal{A}_1 + \mathcal{A}_2 + \mathcal{A}_3.$$

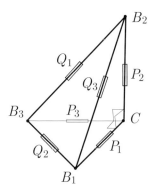

Figure 22.2: Three-dimensional Pythagoras

Solution. Let Q_1, Q_2 and Q_3 denote the quadrances of the triangle $\overline{B_1 B_2 B_3}$, with $P_1 = Q(B_1, C)$, $P_2 = Q(B_2, C)$ and $P_3 = Q(B_1, C)$. Since the triangles $\overline{CB_2 B_3}, \overline{CB_1 B_3}$ and $\overline{CB_1 B_2}$ are right triangles,

$$Q_1 = P_2 + P_3 \qquad Q_2 = P_1 + P_3 \qquad Q_3 = P_1 + P_2.$$

The quadrea $\mathcal{A}$ of $\overline{B_1 B_2 B_3}$ is

$$\begin{aligned}
\mathcal{A} &= 4 Q_1 Q_2 - (Q_1 + Q_2 - Q_3)^2 \\
&= 4 (P_2 + P_3)(P_1 + P_3) - 4 P_3^2 \\
&= 4 (P_2 P_3 + P_1 P_3 + P_1 P_2).
\end{aligned}$$

But by the Right quadrea theorem (page 68)

$$\mathcal{A}_1 = 4 P_2 P_3 \qquad \mathcal{A}_2 = 4 P_1 P_3 \qquad \mathcal{A}_3 = 4 P_1 P_2.$$

Thus $\mathcal{A} = \mathcal{A}_1 + \mathcal{A}_2 + \mathcal{A}_3.$ ∎

Exercise 22.3 Show that any triangle $\overline{B_1 B_2 B_3}$ forming part of such a right tetrahedron is acute, and given such a triangle there are in general exactly two such tetrahedra. ◇

22.6 Pagoda and seven-fold symmetry

Problem 13 A retired engineer decides to build the roof of a pagoda with a base of a regular 7-gon, with the quadrance of each side 2, and the apex V above the center C of the regular 7-gon at a quadrance of 1 from the base. The roof then consists of seven identical isosceles triangles. What should the quadrances and spreads of these triangles be?

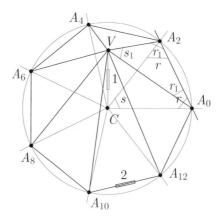

Figure 22.3: A seven-sided pagoda

Solution. Suppose the regular 7-gon is $\overline{A_0 A_2 A_4 A_6 A_8 A_{10} A_{12}}$ as in Figure 22.3. The lines $A_0 C, A_2 C, \cdots, A_{12} C$ form a regular star of order seven, so the spread $s \equiv s \left(\overleftrightarrow{A_0 C A_2} \right)$ must satisfy

$$S_7 (s) = s \left(7 - 56s + 112s^2 - 64s^3 \right)^2 = 0.$$

Of the three approximate solutions,

$$0.188\,255 \qquad 0.611\,260 \qquad 0.950\,484$$

the relevant one is

$$s \approx 0.611\,260 \text{ (ac)}.$$

Define the spreads of the sectors

$$r \equiv s \left(\overleftrightarrow{C A_0 A_2} \right) = s \left(\overleftrightarrow{C A_2 A_0} \right)$$
$$r_1 \equiv s \left(\overleftrightarrow{V A_0 A_2} \right) = s \left(\overleftrightarrow{V A_2 A_0} \right)$$
$$s_1 \equiv s \left(\overleftrightarrow{A_0 V A_2} \right).$$

Use the Isosceles triangle theorem (page 122) with $\overline{A_0 A_2 C}$ to get

$$s = S_2(r) = 4r(1-r)$$

so that

$$r = \frac{1 \pm \sqrt{1-s}}{2}.$$

This gives the possibilities

$$r \approx 0.188\,25 \qquad r \approx 0.811\,75$$

and the Triangle spread rules show that the relevant one is

$$r \approx 0.811\,75 \text{ (ac)}.$$

Use the Spread law in $\overline{A_0 A_2 C}$ to see that

$$Q(A_0, C) = Q(A_2, C) = \frac{rQ(A_0, A_2)}{s}$$

$$\approx \frac{0.811\,745}{0.611\,260} \times 2 \approx 2.655\,9.$$

Then use Pythagoras' theorem in $\overline{A_0 C V}$ to obtain

$$Q(A_0, V) \approx 2.655\,9 + 1 = 3.655\,9.$$

Apply the Isosceles triangle theorem to $\overline{A_0 A_2 V}$ to get

$$4Q(A_0, V)(1 - r_1) = Q(A_0, A_2) = 2$$

so that

$$r_1 \approx 0.863\,24$$

and

$$s_1 = S_2(r_1) = 4r_1(1 - r_1) \approx 0.472\,24.$$

The triangle $\overline{A_0 A_2 V}$ thus has approximate quadrances $2, 3.655\,9$ and $3.655\,9$, and respective approximate spreads $0.472\,2, 0.863\,2$ and $0.863\,2$. ∎

Exercise 22.4 Show that the spread S between the planes $V A_0 A_2$ and $V A_2 A_4$ is approximately $0.224\,4$. ◇

Physics applications

Some applications to physics are given, including maximizing the trajectory of a projectile, a derivation of Snell's law, and a rational formulation of Lorentzian addition of velocities in Einstein's special theory of relativity. An example of algebraic dynamics over a finite field is discussed. Some basic calculus will be assumed here.

23.1   Projectile motion

The motion of a projectile is a parabola, and if the projectile begins at the origin with velocity $\vec{v} \equiv [a, b]$ as in Figure 23.1, then its position at time t is given by

$$\left[at, bt - \frac{gt^2}{2}\right]$$

where g is the acceleration due to gravity.

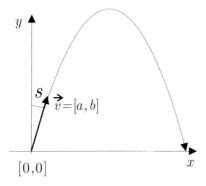

Figure 23.1: Projectile motion

Problem 14 Given that the initial speed $v \equiv \sqrt{a^2 + b^2}$ is fixed, what spread s from the vertical results in the projectile traveling the farthest horizontally before it comes to ground again at a point $[x, 0]$ for some x?

Solution. The projectile comes to ground at time t, where

$$bt - \frac{gt^2}{2} = 0$$

so that either $t = 0$ or $t = 2b/g$. Using rational trigonometry, quadrance is preferred over distance, so the question is what value of $A \equiv a^2$ and $B \equiv b^2$, subject to the condition $A + B = v^2 \equiv V$, results in the horizontal quadrance

$$x^2 = (at)^2 = \frac{4AB}{g^2}$$

being maximized? This is then the problem of maximizing the product AB of two numbers A and B given their sum V. The maximum occurs when $A = B = V/2$, giving a maximum horizontal quadrance of

$$x^2 = \frac{V^2}{g^2}.$$

So the projectile should be fired at a spread of $s = 1/2$ from the vertical. ∎

Problem 15 Suppose that the projectile is fired from the origin on a hill represented by the line l through the origin making a spread of r with the vertical as in Figure 23.2. Given that the initial speed v is fixed, what spread s from the vertical results in a maximal horizontal displacement after landing?

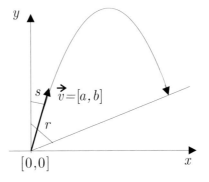

Figure 23.2: Projectile fired on a hill

Solution. The hill is determined by the equation $x^2 = r\left(x^2 + y^2\right)$ and so the projectile intercepts the hill when

$$(at)^2 = r\left((at)^2 + \left(bt - gt^2/2\right)^2\right).$$

This yields that $t = 0$, or t satisfies the quadratic equation

$$\left(t - \frac{2b}{g}\right)^2 = \frac{4a^2\left(1 - r\right)}{g^2 r}.$$

Thus

$$t = \frac{2b}{g} \pm \frac{2a}{g}\sqrt{\frac{1-r}{r}}.$$

To maximize the horizontal displacement, you need to maximize at, or equivalently

$$f\left(a, b\right) \equiv ab \pm a^2 c$$

by choosing a and b subject to the constraint

$$g\left(a, b\right) \equiv a^2 + b^2 = V \qquad (23.1)$$

and where c is the constant

$$c \equiv \sqrt{\frac{1-r}{r}}.$$

This can now be done by converting it to a one-dimensional calculus problem, but it is also interesting to apply the method of Lagrange. At a relative maximum the gradients

$$\nabla f = \left(b \pm 2ac, a\right) \qquad \nabla g = \left(2a, 2b\right)$$

should be proportional, implying that

$$\left(b \pm 2ac\right)b - a^2 = 0.$$

Rearrange and square to eliminate the ambiguity of the sign

$$4a^2 b^2 c^2 = \left(a^2 - b^2\right)^2$$

and substitute using (23.1) to get

$$4a^2\left(V - a^2\right)c^2 = \left(2a^2 - V\right)^2.$$

This quadratic equation in a^2 can be written

$$\left(a^2 - \frac{V}{2}\right)^2 = \frac{V^2 c^2}{4\left(1 + c^2\right)} = \frac{V^2\left(1 - r\right)}{4}.$$

Thus

$$a^2 = \frac{V}{2}\left(1 \pm \sqrt{1 - r}\right)$$

and the spread s between the initial direction and the vertical is

$$s = \frac{a^2}{V} = \frac{1 \pm \sqrt{1-r}}{2}.$$

But this is equivalent to

$$r = 4s\left(1 - s\right) = S_2\left(s\right)$$

so that the projectile's initial direction should bisect the vertex formed by the hill and the vertical. Note that there are two solutions, one downhill and the other uphill. ∎

23.2 Algebraic dynamics

Recently mathematicians have begun investigating dynamics in finite fields. Here is a particularly simple case modelled on the usual projectile motion under constant negative acceleration due to gravity. Whether such an example has any possible physical significance is unclear, but it seems interesting from a mathematical perspective.

Example 23.1 Suppose that in $\mathbb{F}_{11}$ a particle starts at time $t = 0$ with position $p_0 \equiv [0, 0]$, velocity $v_0 \equiv [1, 3]$ and has constant acceleration $a_t \equiv [0, -1]$ for times $t = 0, 1, 2, 3, \cdots$. Suppose that subsequent positions and velocities are determined for future times by the equations

$$p_{t+1} \equiv p_t + v_t$$
$$v_{t+1} \equiv v_t + a_t.$$

This results in the following positions and velocities, which then repeat.

Time	0	1	2	3	4	5
Position	$[0, 0]$	$[1, 3]$	$[2, 5]$	$[3, 6]$	$[4, 6]$	$[5, 5]$
Velocity	$[1, 3]$	$[1, 2]$	$[1, 1]$	$[1, 0]$	$[1, 10]$	$[1, 9]$

Time	6	7	8	9	10	11
Position	$[6, 3]$	$[7, 0]$	$[8, 7]$	$[9, 2]$	$[10, 7]$	$[0, 0]$
Velocity	$[1, 8]$	$[1, 7]$	$[1, 6]$	$[1, 5]$	$[1, 4]$	$[1, 3]$

The position at time t is $\left[t, 5t^2 - 2t\right]$. The trajectory contains exactly those points lying on the curve with equation $x^2 + 4x + 2y = 0$, which turns out to be a parabola (black circles) in the sense of Chapter 15. The directrix is the line $l \equiv \langle 0 : 1 : 3 \rangle$ (gray boxes) and the focus is $F \equiv [9, 7]$ (open box) as shown in Figure 23.3. Notice, perhaps surprisingly, that the vertex of this parabola is the point $[9, 2]$.

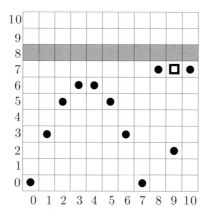

Figure 23.3: Trajectory in $\mathbb{F}_{11}$ $\diamond$

23.3 Snell's law

Problem 16 Suppose a particle travels from the point $A \equiv [0, a]$ to the point $B \equiv [c, -b]$, where $a, b > 0$, via some variable point $D \equiv [x, 0]$ on the horizontal axis as in Figure 23.4. If the particle has speed v_1 in the region $y \geq 0$, and speed v_2 in the region $y < 0$, what choice of D minimizes the total time taken?

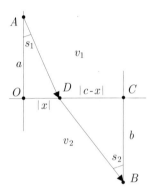

Figure 23.4: Snell's Law

Solution. The basic formula relating distance d, time t and speed v is

$$v = d/t. \tag{23.2}$$

This is not a formula involving universal geometry, as distance is involved. Nevertheless, let's proceed some way in the classical framework before switching over to rational trigonometry. With $|O, D| = |x|$ and $|D, C| = |c - x|$, the times t_1 and t_2 taken to travel from A to D (in a straight line) and from D to B respectively are

$$t_1 = \frac{|A, D|}{v_1} = \frac{\sqrt{a^2 + x^2}}{v_1}$$

$$t_2 = \frac{|D, B|}{v_2} = \frac{\sqrt{(c - x)^2 + b^2}}{v_2}.$$

The total time t taken is then

$$t = \frac{\sqrt{a^2 + x^2}}{v_1} + \frac{\sqrt{(c - x)^2 + b^2}}{v_2}.$$

This is a function of x, since a, b, v_1 and v_2 are constants. You could now use calculus to find the value of x at which this function attains a maximum or minimum.

To do so, the derivative of $\sqrt{x}$ is required. Instead, let's reconsider the problem from the viewpoint of rational trigonometry.

Since $Q \equiv d^2$ is a rational concept, it makes sense to square (23.2), obtaining

$$V = Q/T$$

where $V \equiv v^2$ and $T \equiv t^2$. Since $Q(A, D) = a^2 + x^2$ and $Q(D, B) = (c - x)^2 + b^2$, the squared times T_1 and T_2 taken to travel from A to D and from D to B respectively are

$$T_1 \quad = \quad \frac{a^2 + x^2}{V_1} \tag{23.3}$$

$$T_2 \quad = \quad \frac{(c - x)^2 + b^2}{V_2}. \tag{23.4}$$

Now $t = t_1 + t_2$, so Exercise 5.8 shows that $\{T, T_1, T_2\}$ is a quad triple. All three quantities depend on a variable x and the aim is to choose x so as to minimize T. The following argument deals with this general situation.

Suppose that $\{T, T_1, T_2\}$ is a quad triple, so that

$$(T_1 + T_2 - T)^2 = 4T_1 T_2 \tag{23.5}$$

and that all three quantities T, T_1 and T_2 depend on a variable x. Take differentials to obtain

$$2(T_1 + T_2 - T)\left(\frac{dT_1}{dx} + \frac{dT_2}{dx} - \frac{dT}{dx}\right) = 4\frac{d(T_1 T_2)}{dx}. \tag{23.6}$$

To maximize or minimize T, set

$$\frac{dT}{dx} = 0.$$

Square (23.6) to get

$$(T_1 + T_2 - T)^2 \left(\frac{dT_1}{dx} + \frac{dT_2}{dx}\right)^2 = 4\left(T_2\frac{dT_1}{dx} + T_1\frac{dT_2}{dx}\right)^2.$$

Now substitute (23.5) so that

$$T_1 T_2 \left(\frac{dT_1}{dx} + \frac{dT_2}{dx}\right)^2 = \left(T_2\frac{dT_1}{dx} + T_1\frac{dT_2}{dx}\right)^2.$$

Upon expansion, rearrangement and cancellation of an extraneous factor $T_1 - T_2$, this becomes the following general formula for a maximum or minimum

$$T_2\left(\frac{dT_1}{dx}\right)^2 = T_1\left(\frac{dT_2}{dx}\right)^2. \tag{23.7}$$

Now to return to the case at hand, apply (23.7) to (23.3) and (23.4) where

$$\frac{dT_1}{dx} = \frac{2x}{V_1}$$
$$\frac{dT_2}{dx} = \frac{2(x-c)}{V_2}.$$

You get

$$\frac{\left((c-x)^2 + b^2\right)}{V_2} \times \frac{4x^2}{V_1^2} = \frac{(a^2 + x^2)}{V_1} \times \frac{4(c-x)^2}{V_2^2}$$

or

$$\frac{V_2}{V_1} = \frac{(c-x)^2}{(c-x)^2 + b^2} \times \frac{(a^2 + x^2)}{x^2}.$$

But the spreads s_1 and s_2 made by the lines AD and DB respectively with the vertical are

$$s_1 = \frac{x^2}{a^2 + x^2}$$

and

$$s_2 = \frac{(c-x)^2}{(c-x)^2 + b^2}.$$

This yields *Snell's Law—The time taken is minimized when*

$$\frac{V_2}{V_1} = \frac{s_2}{s_1}. \quad \blacksquare$$

The rational solution presented here avoids differentiation of the square root function and uses only derivatives of linear and quadratic functions.

This analysis also suggests a view of physics in which not only the square of distance, but also the squares of speed and time play a larger role. Such ideas were introduced in Einstein's theory of relativity in 1905. In fact Einstein showed that neither the square of distance nor the square of time was ultimately of significance, but in suitable units only the *difference* between them. The square of mass also figures prominently.

In retrospect one can speculate that if rational trigonometry had been developed prior to the twentieth century, then the value of Einstein's revolutionary ideas would have been recognized more readily, and indeed they might have been anticipated earlier. Universal geometry and relativity theory naturally have common aspects.

Perhaps there is the potential to take this further, as current formulations of special (and general) relativity rely on square root functions, and from the point of view of universal geometry this is not optimal. The next section shows how to eliminate this dependence in one special situation.

23.4   Lorentzian addition of velocities

If a train travels along a track with speed v_1 and a bullet is fired from the train in the same direction with speed v_2 with respect to the train, then in Newtonian mechanics the speed v of the bullet with respect to the ground is the sum of the two speeds

$$v = v_1 + v_2. \qquad (23.8)$$

Thus the respective squares V, V_1 and V_2 of the speeds v, v_1 and v_2 form a quad triple, in other words

$$(V_1 + V_2 - V)^2 = 4V_1V_2. \qquad (23.9)$$

In Einstein's special theory of relativity, (23.8) needs to be modified to

$$v = \frac{v_1 + v_2}{1 + v_1 v_2} \qquad (23.10)$$

where units have been chosen so that the speed of light is $c = 1$. Square both sides of (23.10) and rearrange to get

$$v^2 \left(1 + 2v_1 v_2 + v_1^2 v_2^2\right) = v_1^2 + 2v_1 v_2 + v_2^2$$

or

$$v^2 - v_1^2 - v_2^2 + v^2 v_1^2 v_2^2 = 2v_1 v_2 \left(1 - v^2\right).$$

Then square both sides again to get

$$(V_1 + V_2 - V - VV_1V_2)^2 = 4V_1V_2 (1 - V)^2. \qquad (23.11)$$

Note that for small values of V, V_1 and V_2 this is approximated by (23.9). Furthermore (23.11) can be rewritten as the symmetric expression

$$(V + V_1 + V_2 - VV_1V_2)^2 = 4 (VV_1 + VV_2 + V_1V_2 - 2VV_1V_2)$$

which is a form quite close to the Triple twist formula (page 93).

Surveying

In this chapter classical problems in surveying are solved using rational trigonometry, such as finding heights of objects from a variety of measurements, and Regiomontanus' problem of determining the maximum spread subtended by a window. Some of the examples are parallel to ones from [Shepherd], allowing a comparison between rational and classical methods. As an application of one of the formulas obtained, the important spherical analogue of Pythagoras' theorem is derived.

24.1 Height of object with vertical face

Problem 17 An observer at A measures the vertical spread s to the point B directly above C. The quadrance $Q(A,C) \equiv P$ is known. What is the vertical quadrance $Q \equiv Q(B,C)$?

Solution. The Complementary spreads theorem (page 79) shows that the spread at B is $1 - s$, so the Spread law gives

$$Q = \frac{sP}{1-s}. \quad \blacksquare$$

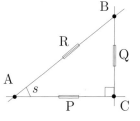

Example 24.1 Suppose the quadrance from A to C is 100 and the spread at A is measured with a theodolite to be $s \equiv 0.587$. Then

$$Q = \left(\frac{0.587}{0.413}\right) \times 100 = 142.131. \quad \diamond$$

24.2 Height of object with inaccessible base

Problem 18 The points A_1, A_2 and C are horizontal and in a line, and the point A_3 is vertically above C, as in either of the diagrams in Figure 24.1. The spreads s_1 and s_2 in $\overline{A_1 A_2 A_3}$ are measured, and the quadrance $Q_3 \equiv Q(A_1, A_2)$ is known. What is the vertical quadrance $Q \equiv Q(A_3, C)$?

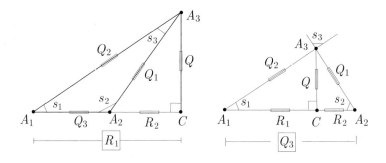

Figure 24.1: Height from two spread readings

Solution. Let $s_3 \equiv s(A_3 A_1, A_3 A_2)$. The Triple spread formula as a quadratic equation in s_3 is

$$(s_3 - (s_1 + s_2 - 2s_1 s_2))^2 = 4s_1 s_2 (1 - s_1)(1 - s_2).$$

For each of the two solutions the triangle $\overline{A_1 A_2 A_3}$ may be solved using the Spread law for the quadrance Q_1, since Q_3 is known. Then the right triangle $\overline{A_2 A_3 C}$ with right vertex C may be solved, using s_2 and Q_1, to obtain Q. ∎

Example 24.2 Suppose that $Q_3 \equiv 25$ and that $s_1 \equiv s\left(\overleftrightarrow{A_2 A_1 A_3}\right) \equiv 0.2352$ (ac) and $s_2 \equiv s\left(\overleftrightarrow{A_1 A_2 A_3}\right) \equiv 0.3897$ (ob) as in the first of the diagrams in Figure 24.1. The Triple spread formula becomes $(s_3 - 0.4416)^2 = 0.1711$. Use the Triangle spread rules, and the fact that $s_1 + s_2 \leq 1$, to get

$$s_3 = r_l(s_1, s_2) \text{ (ac)} = 0.4416 - \sqrt{0.171\,1} \text{ (ac)} \approx 0.0280 \text{ (ac)}.$$

Then apply the Spread law in $\overline{A_1 A_2 A_3}$ to get

$$0.0280/25 \approx 0.2352/Q_1$$

from which $Q_1 \approx 211.5$. Then in the right triangle $\overline{A_2 A_3 C}$

$$Q = s_2 Q_1 \approx 0.3897 \times 211.5 \approx 82.4. \quad \diamond$$

24.3   Height of a raised object

Problem 19 The points A_1, A_2 and C are horizontal and in a line. There are two points D and A_3 vertically above the point C as in Figure 24.2. The spreads s_1 and s_2 in triangle $\overline{A_1 A_2 A_3}$ are measured, as is the spread $r \equiv s(A_2C, A_2D)$. The quadrance Q_3 between A_1 and A_2 is known. What is the vertical quadrance $R \equiv Q(A_3, D)$?

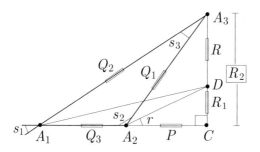

Figure 24.2: Height of a raised object

Solution.   Define the quadrances $R_1 \equiv Q(C, D)$, $R_2 \equiv Q(C, A_3)$ and $P \equiv Q(A_2, C)$. Use the Triple spread formula and the Triangle spread rules in $\overline{A_1 A_2 A_3}$ to find s_3. Then the Spread law in $\overline{A_1 A_2 A_3}$ gives

$$Q_1 = \frac{s_1 Q_3}{s_3}.$$

In the right triangle $\overline{A_2 A_3 C}$

$$R_2 = s_2 Q_1 = \frac{s_1 s_2 Q_3}{s_3} \tag{24.1}$$

and

$$P = (1 - s_2) Q_1.$$

Then in the right triangle $\overline{A_2 D C}$

$$R_1 = \frac{rP}{1 - r} = \frac{(1 - s_2) r Q_1}{1 - r}$$

so that also

$$R_1 = \frac{s_1 (1 - s_2) r Q_3}{s_3 (1 - r)}. \tag{24.2}$$

Now $\{R, R_1, R_2\}$ is a quad triple so solve

$$(R - R_1 - R_2)^2 = 4 R_1 R_2$$

with the Collinear quadrance rules (page 215) to obtain R. ∎

24.4 Regiomontanus' problem

Regiomontanus, whose name was Johann Müller, lived from 1436 to 1476, and published mathematical and astronomical books. In his most famous work *On Triangles of Every Kind*, he mentions the following extremal problem.

Problem 20 (Regiomontanus' problem) In Figure 24.3, what value of the quadrance P will maximize the spread s subtended by the window $\overline{BD}$? The positions of the points B, D and C on the vertical line are known and fixed, so the quadrances Q, Q_1 and Q_2 can be taken as given.

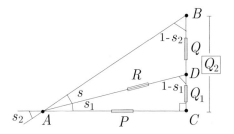

Figure 24.3: Regiomontanus' problem

Solution. Pythagoras' theorem gives $R = P + Q_1$, while from the Spread ratio theorem
$$s_2 = \frac{Q_2}{P + Q_2}.$$
From the Spread law in $\overline{ABD}$
$$\frac{s}{Q} = \frac{1 - s_2}{R}.$$
Combine these equations to get
$$s = \frac{QP}{(P + Q_1)(P + Q_2)}$$
$$= \frac{Q}{Q_1 + Q_2 + P + (Q_1 Q_2 / P)}.$$
Now choose P so that this expression is maximized, or equivalently so that
$$P + \frac{Q_1 Q_2}{P}$$
is minimized. With the product of two summands constant, the sum is minimum when the summands are equal, so that $P^2 = Q_1 Q_2$. Thus P must be the *geometric mean* of Q_1 and Q_2. ∎

24.5 Height from three spreads

Problem 21 A triangle $\overline{A_1A_2A_3}$ is horizontal, the point B is directly above A_3, and D is a third point lying on A_1A_2, as in Figure 24.4. The vertical spreads

$$r_1 \equiv s\left(A_1A_3, A_1B\right) \qquad r_2 \equiv s\left(A_2A_3, A_2B\right) \qquad r_3 \equiv s\left(DA_3, DB\right)$$

are known, as are the quadrances $P_1 \equiv Q\left(A_1, D\right)$ and $P_2 \equiv Q\left(A_2, D\right)$. Find the vertical quadrance $H \equiv Q\left(A_3, B\right)$.

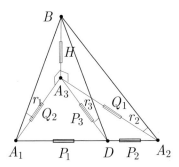

Figure 24.4: Height from three spreads

Solution. Suppose the quadrances of $\overline{A_1A_2A_3}$ are Q_1, Q_2 and Q_3 as usual. Let $P_3 \equiv Q\left(A_3, D\right)$. From the right triangle $\overline{A_1A_3B}$

$$r_1 = \frac{H}{H + Q_2}$$

so that

$$Q_2 = \frac{(1 - r_1)\, H}{r_1}.$$

Similarly from the right triangles $\overline{A_2A_3B}$ and $\overline{DA_3B}$

$$Q_1 = (1 - r_2)\, H/r_2 \qquad \text{and} \qquad P_3 = (1 - r_3)\, H/r_3.$$

Now in the triangle $\overline{A_1A_2A_3}$ use Stewart's theorem (page 136) to get

$$P_2\left(P_3 + P_1 - Q_2\right)^2 = P_1\left(P_3 + P_2 - Q_1\right)^2.$$

Substitute for Q_2, Q_1 and P_3, to get for H the quadratic equation

$$P_2\left(H\left(\frac{1}{r_3} - \frac{1}{r_1}\right) + P_1\right)^2 = P_1\left(H\left(\frac{1}{r_3} - \frac{1}{r_2}\right) + P_2\right)^2. \quad \blacksquare$$

24.6   Vertical and horizontal spreads

Problem 22 The points A_1, A_2 and A_3 form a horizontal triangle with quadrances Q_1, Q_2 and Q_3, and spreads s_1, s_2 and s_3 as usual. The point B is directly above the point A_3. What is the relationship between the vertical spreads $r_1 \equiv s(A_1 A_3, A_1 B)$ and $r_2 \equiv s(A_2 A_3, A_2 B)$?

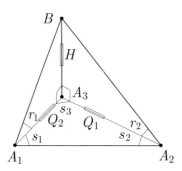

Figure 24.5: Vertical and horizontal spreads

Solution.   Suppose that $H \equiv Q(A_3, B)$ as in Figure 24.5. From the right triangle $\overline{A_1 A_3 B}$

$$\frac{H}{Q_2} = \frac{r_1}{1 - r_1}$$

and similarly from the right triangle $\overline{A_2 A_3 B}$

$$\frac{H}{Q_1} = \frac{r_2}{1 - r_2}.$$

Use the Spread law in the triangle $\overline{A_1 A_2 A_3}$ and the previous equations to get

$$\frac{s_1}{s_2} = \frac{Q_1}{Q_2} = \frac{r_1}{(1 - r_1)} \frac{(1 - r_2)}{r_2}.$$

This can also be written as either

$$\frac{s_1 (1 - r_1)}{r_1} = \frac{s_2 (1 - r_2)}{r_2}$$

or

$$\frac{s_1}{r_1} - \frac{s_2}{r_2} = s_1 - s_2. \ \blacksquare$$

24.7 Spreads over a right triangle

Problem 23 (Spreads over a right triangle) Suppose that the points A_1, A_2 and A_3 form a horizontal right triangle with right vertex at A_3, and that B is directly above the point A_3 as in Figure 24.6. What is the relationship between the spreads $s \equiv s(BA_1, BA_2)$, $r_1 \equiv s(A_1A_3, A_1B)$ and $r_2 \equiv s(A_2A_3, A_2B)$?

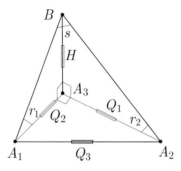

Figure 24.6: Spreads over a right triangle

Solution. Let the quadrances of $\overline{A_1A_2A_3}$ be Q_1, Q_2 and Q_3, and let $H \equiv Q(A_3, B)$. By Pythagoras' theorem

$$Q(A_1, A_2) = Q_3 = Q_1 + Q_2$$
$$Q(A_1, B) = Q_2 + H$$
$$Q(A_2, B) = Q_1 + H.$$

From the Cross law in $\overline{A_1A_2B}$

$$((Q_1 + H) + (Q_2 + H) - (Q_1 + Q_2))^2 = 4(Q_1 + H)(Q_2 + H)(1 - s).$$

Thus ultimately independent of the triangle $\overline{A_1A_2A_3}$,

$$1 - s = \left(\frac{H}{Q_1 + H}\right)\left(\frac{H}{Q_2 + H}\right) = r_1r_2. \quad \blacksquare \tag{24.3}$$

Exercise 24.1 (Harder) Suppose $\overline{A_1A_2A_3}$ is an equilateral triangle, and that B is directly above the circumcenter C of $\overline{A_1A_2A_3}$. Show that if

$$q \equiv s(BA_1, BA_2) = s(BA_2, BA_3) = s(BA_1, BA_3)$$

and S is the spread between any two of the planes A_1A_2B, A_2A_3B and A_1A_3B, then

$$(1 - Sq)^2 = 4(1 - S)(1 - q). \quad \diamond$$

24.8   Spherical analogue of Pythagoras' theorem

From (24.3) follows a remarkable and important formula. Suppose that the points A_1, A_2 and A_3 form a horizontal right triangle with right vertex at A_3, and that O is directly above the point A_3. Define the spreads $q_1 \equiv s\,(OA_1, OA_3)$, $q_2 \equiv s\,(OA_2, OA_3)$ and $q \equiv s\,(OA_1, OA_2)$ as in Figure 24.7. Then q_1 and q_2 are complementary to the spreads r_1 and r_2 in Figure 24.6.

The use of the small letter q here and in the previous exercise anticipates projective trigonometry, where the quadrance between two 'projective points' is defined to be the spread between the associated lines through the origin.

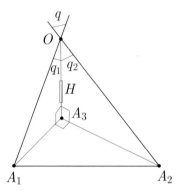

Figure 24.7: Spherical Pythagoras' theorem

Using (24.3),

$$q = 1 - r_1 r_2$$
$$= 1 - (1 - q_1)\,(1 - q_2)\,.$$

So

$$q = q_1 + q_2 - q_1 q_2.$$

This is the *spherical or (elliptic) analogue of Pythagoras' theorem*. Its pivotal role in projective trigonometry will be explained more fully in a subsequent volume. Note that if q_1 and q_2 are small then this is approximated by the usual planar form of Pythagoras' theorem.

Resection and Hansen's problem

The problems of Snellius-Pothenot and Hansen are among the most famous of surveying problems, and are also of importance in navigation. The Snellius-Pothenot, or resection, problem has a number of solutions, and the one presented here uses Euler's Four point relation. Hansen's problem is illustrated with a specific example, and an exercise shows its connection with a somewhat notorious problem of elementary Euclidean geometry.

25.1 Snellius-Pothenot problem

The problem of resection was originally stated and solved by Snellius (1617) and then by Pothenot (1692).

Problem 24
The quadrances Q_1, Q_2 and Q_3 of $\overline{A_1 A_2 A_3}$ are known. The spreads $r_1 \equiv s(BA_2, BA_3)$, $r_2 \equiv s(BA_1, BA_3)$ and $r_3 \equiv s(BA_1, BA_2)$ are measured. Find $P_1 \equiv Q(B, A_1)$, $P_2 \equiv Q(B, A_2)$ and $P_3 \equiv Q(B, A_3)$.

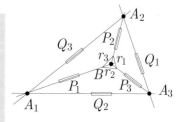

The problem cannot be solved if B lies on the circumcircle c of $\overline{A_1 A_2 A_3}$, since in that case the Subtended spread theorem (page 178) shows that any point on c yields the same values for r_1, r_2 and r_3. Here is a procedure to find P_1 and P_2, which works provided B is not on c, using the Four point relation (page 191).

Solution. Take the circumcircle c_3 of $\overline{A_1 A_2 B}$ and let H, called **Collin's point**, be the intersection of c_3 with $A_3 B$ which is distinct from B.

Define the quadrances $R_1 \equiv Q(H, A_1)$, $R_2 \equiv Q(H, A_2)$ and $R_3 \equiv Q(H, A_3)$. By the Subtended spread theorem, the spreads $s(A_1 H, A_1 A_2)$, $s(A_2 H, A_2 A_1)$ and $s(HA_1, HA_2)$ are respectively r_1, r_2 and r_3. Let $v_1 \equiv s(HA_1, HA_3)$ and $v_2 \equiv s(HA_2, HA_3)$. This is shown in Figure 25.1.

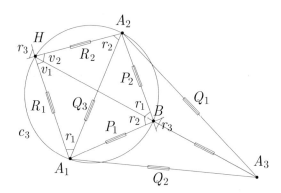

Figure 25.1: Snellius-Pothenot problem

Use the Spread law in $\overline{A_1 A_2 H}$ to get

$$R_1 = r_2 Q_3 / r_3 \qquad \text{and} \qquad R_2 = r_1 Q_3 / r_3. \tag{25.1}$$

The Four point relation applied to the triangle $\overline{A_1 A_2 A_3}$ with the additional point H is

$$E(Q_1, Q_2, Q_3, R_1, R_2, R_3) = 0.$$

By Exercise 17.5, this is the quadratic equation in R_3 given by

$$\left(R_3 - R_1 - R_2 + Q_3 - Q_1 - Q_2 + \frac{(Q_1 - Q_2)(R_2 - R_1)}{Q_3} \right)^2$$
$$= \frac{A(Q_1, Q_2, Q_3) A(R_1, R_2, R_3)}{4 Q_3^2}$$

where A is Archimedes' function. After substituting for the values of R_1 and R_2 from (25.1), this becomes the equation

$$(R_3 - C)^2 = D$$

where

$$C = \frac{(Q_1 + Q_2 + Q_3)(r_1 + r_2 + r_3) - 2(Q_1 r_1 + Q_2 r_2 + Q_3 r_3)}{2 r_3}$$

and

$$D = \frac{r_1 r_2 A(Q_1, Q_2, Q_3)}{r_3}.$$

For either of the two solutions to this equation, the Cross law in $\overline{A_1 A_3 H}$ gives

$$v_1 = 1 - \frac{(R_1 + R_3 - Q_2)^2}{4 R_1 R_3}$$

while the Cross law in $\overline{A_2 A_3 H}$ gives

$$v_2 = 1 - \frac{(R_2 + R_3 - Q_1)^2}{4 R_2 R_3}.$$

Then the Spread laws in $\overline{A_1 B H}$ and $\overline{A_2 B H}$ give the required values

$$P_1 = \frac{v_1 R_1}{r_2} = \frac{v_1 Q_3}{r_3}$$

$$P_2 = \frac{v_2 R_2}{r_1} = \frac{v_2 Q_3}{r_3}. \quad \blacksquare$$

Example 25.1 Suppose that the triangle $\overline{A_1 A_2 A_3}$ has points

$$A_1 \equiv [1, 1] \qquad A_2 \equiv [5, 2] \qquad A_3 \equiv [3, -1]$$

with quadrances

$$Q_1 = 13 \qquad Q_2 = 8 \qquad Q_3 = 17.$$

If B is taken to be the point $[4, 5]$ then

$$r_1 = 81/370 \qquad r_2 = 196/925 \qquad r_3 = 169/250.$$

The three values r_1, r_2 and r_3 will be taken as measurements, and the location of B otherwise considered unknown. Then from (25.1)

$$R_1 = r_2 Q_3/r_3 \qquad \text{and} \qquad R_2 = r_1 Q_3/r_3$$

gives

$$R_1 = 33320/6253 \qquad \text{and} \qquad R_2 = 34425/6253.$$

Now use the Four point relation

$$E(Q_1, Q_2, Q_3, R_1, R_2, R_3) = 0$$

to get the quadratic equation

$$\left(R_3 - \frac{46\,216}{6\,253} \right)^2 = \left(\frac{2\,520}{481} \right)^2$$

with solutions

i) $R_3 = 13456/6253$ \qquad or \qquad ii) $R_3 = 78976/6253.$

i) If $R_3 = 13456/6253$ then

$$v_1 = 1 - \frac{(R_1 + R_3 - Q_2)^2}{4R_1 R_3} = \frac{169}{170}$$

$$v_2 = 1 - \frac{(R_2 + R_3 - Q_1)^2}{4R_2 R_3} = \frac{169}{425}$$

so that

$$P_1 = \frac{v_1 R_1}{r_2} = \frac{v_1 Q_3}{r_3} = 25$$

$$P_2 = \frac{v_2 R_2}{r_1} = \frac{v_2 Q_3}{r_3} = 10.$$

ii) If $R_3 = 78976/6253$ then

$$v_1 = 1 - \frac{(R_1 + R_3 - Q_2)^2}{4R_1 R_3} = \frac{33\,124}{52\,445}$$

$$v_2 = 1 - \frac{(R_2 + R_3 - Q_1)^2}{4R_2 R_3} = \frac{474\,721}{524\,450}$$

so that

$$P_1 = \frac{v_1 R_1}{r_2} = \frac{v_1 Q_3}{r_3} = \frac{9\,800}{617}$$

$$P_2 = \frac{v_2 R_2}{r_1} = \frac{v_2 Q_3}{r_3} = \frac{14\,045}{617}.$$

The first of these cases correctly yields the quadrances to the initial point $B \equiv [4,5]$. ◇

The two solutions obtained in the previous Example correspond to the two points B and B' that make the same spreads r_1, r_2 and r_3 with the reference triangle $\overline{A_1 A_2 A_3}$. The relation between these two points may be described by the following known result (see [Wells, page 258]).

Let B be a point not on the lines $A_1 A_2$, $A_2 A_3$ and $A_1 A_3$, and let B_3, B_1 and B_2 be the reflections of B in the lines $A_1 A_2$, $A_2 A_3$ and $A_3 A_1$ respectively. Let c_1, c_2 and c_3 be the respective circumcircles of the triangles $\overline{A_2 A_3 B_1}$, $\overline{A_1 A_3 B_2}$ and $\overline{A_1 A_2 B_3}$. Then c_1, c_2 and c_3 intersect in a unique point B'.

The map that sends B to B' in the above result is not a bijection. If B is any point on the circumcircle of $\overline{A_1 A_2 A_3}$, then it turns out that B' is always the orthocenter of $\overline{A_1 A_2 A_3}$.

Exercise 25.1 Use the Triangle spread rules to identify the correct choice of R_3 in the previous Example. ◇

Exercise 25.2 Find another solution to the resection problem, not using the Four point relation. ◇

25.2   Hansen's problem

Problem 25 (Hansen's problem) Two known points A and B with known quadrance $Q \equiv Q(A, B)$ are sighted from two variable points C and D. The four spreads $s(DA, DB)$, $s(DB, DC)$, $s(CA, CB)$ and $s(CA, CD)$ are measured from the points C and D. The positions of C and D are to be determined, in the sense that the quadrances $Q(A, C)$, $Q(B, C)$, $Q(A, D)$ and $Q(B, D)$ are to be found.

This problem was solved by Hansen (1795-1884), a German astronomer, but according to [Dorrie] also by others before him. The treatment presented here will be illustrated by a particular example. The general case follows the same lines. Assume the quadrance between the fixed points A and B is $Q(A, B) \equiv 26$.

Suppose that the following spreads are known

$$s\left(\overleftrightarrow{ADB}\right) = 361/425 \text{ (ac)} \qquad s\left(\overrightarrow{BDC}\right) = 169/250 \text{ (ac)}$$

$$s\left(\overleftrightarrow{BCA}\right) = 441/697 \text{ (ac)} \qquad s\left(\overleftrightarrow{ACD}\right) = 121/410 \text{ (ac)}.$$

This information is shown to scale in Figure 25.2, along with the intersection E of AC and BD.

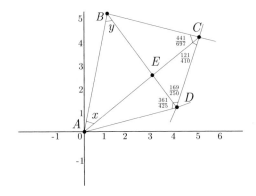

Figure 25.2: Hansen's problem I

Solution. Apply the Triangle spread rules to the three sectors with base D. Note that this new application *inverts the type*. Since

$$361/425 + 169/250 = 6483/4250 \geq 1$$

and both spreads are acute,

$$s\left(\overleftrightarrow{ADC}\right) = r_b\left(\frac{361}{425}, \frac{169}{250}\right) \text{ (ob)}$$

$$= \frac{361}{425} + \frac{169}{250} - 2 \times \frac{361}{425} \times \frac{169}{250}$$

$$+2\sqrt{\frac{361}{425} \times \frac{169}{250} \times \frac{64}{425} \times \frac{81}{250}} \text{ (ob)} = \frac{121}{170} \text{ (ob)}.$$

Similarly apply the Triangle spread rules to the sectors with base C. Since

$$441/697 + 121/410 = 6467/6970 \le 1$$

and both spreads are acute,

$$s\left(\overleftrightarrow{BCD}\right) = r_b\left(\frac{441}{697}, \frac{121}{410}\right) \text{ (ac)}$$

$$= \frac{441}{697} + \frac{121}{410} - 2 \times \frac{441}{697} \times \frac{121}{410}$$

$$+2\sqrt{\frac{441}{697} \times \frac{121}{410} \times \frac{256}{697} \times \frac{289}{410}} \text{ (ac)} = \frac{169}{170} \text{ (ac)}.$$

Now apply the Triangle spread rules to $\overline{CDE}$. In this case, no inversion of type takes place. Since

$$169/250 + 121/410 = 4977/5125 \le 1$$

and both spreads are acute,

$$s\left(\overleftrightarrow{DEC}\right) = r_b\left(\frac{169}{250}, \frac{121}{410}\right) \text{ (ob)}$$

$$= \frac{169}{250} + \frac{121}{410} - 2 \times \frac{169}{250} \times \frac{121}{410}$$

$$+2\sqrt{\frac{169}{250} \times \frac{121}{410} \times \frac{81}{250} \times \frac{289}{410}} \text{ (ob)} = \frac{1024}{1025} \text{ (ob)}.$$

The spreads $s\left(\overleftrightarrow{DAC}\right)$ and $s\left(\overleftrightarrow{DBC}\right)$ may now be determined using the same procedure, but an alternative is to use the Two spread triples theorem (page 98) and the function

$$P(a, b, c, d) \equiv \frac{(a-b)^2 - (c-d)^2}{2(a+b-c-d-2ab+2cd)}.$$

Then

$$s\left(\overleftrightarrow{DAC}\right) = P\left(\frac{1024}{1025}, \frac{361}{425}, \frac{121}{170}, \frac{121}{410}\right) = \frac{121}{697}$$

and

$$s\left(\overleftrightarrow{DBC}\right) = P\left(\frac{1024}{1025}, \frac{441}{697}, \frac{169}{250}, \frac{169}{170}\right) = \frac{169}{425}.$$

This information is now summarized in Figure 25.3, with the unknown spreads x and y to be determined.

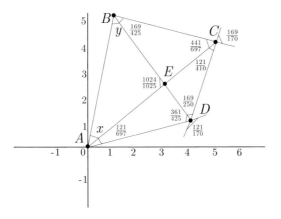

Figure 25.3: Hansen's problem II

The Alternate spreads theorem, extended to a quadrilateral as in Exercise 11.9, gives the formula

$$\frac{169}{425} \times \frac{121}{410} \times \frac{361}{425} \times x = \frac{441}{697} \times \frac{169}{250} \times \frac{121}{697} \times y$$

so that

$$a \equiv \frac{x}{y} = \frac{11\,025}{14\,801}.$$

Now in the notation of the Spread from ratio theorem (page 91), with $s = 1024/1025$,

$$a\,(1 - s) = 441/606841 = (21/779)^2$$

so set

$$r \equiv 21/779.$$

Then

$$y = s/\,(a + 1 \pm 2r)$$

and

$$x = ya.$$

Substitute to get the possibilities

$$[x, y] = \left[\frac{441}{1066}, \frac{361}{650}\right]$$

or

$$[x, y] = \left[\frac{112\,896}{256\,537}, \frac{92\,416}{156\,425}\right].$$

The first of these corresponds to the picture above. The Spread law in $\overline{ABD}$ gives

$$\frac{361/425}{26} = \frac{361/650}{Q\,(A, D)}.$$

Thus $Q(A, D) = 17$. The Spread law in $\overline{ABC}$ gives

$$\frac{441/697}{26} = \frac{441/1066}{Q(B, C)}$$

so that $Q(B, C) = 17$. The Spread law in $\overline{ADC}$ gives

$$\frac{121/410}{17} = \frac{121/170}{Q(A, C)}$$

so that $Q(A, C) = 41$. The Spread law in $\overline{BCD}$ gives

$$\frac{169/250}{17} = \frac{169/170}{Q(B, D)}$$

so that $Q(B, D) = 25$. This establishes the four required quantities. ∎

The example was chosen with $A \equiv [0, 0]$, $B \equiv [1, 5]$, $C \equiv [5, 4]$ and $D \equiv [4, 1]$, and the validity of each of these computations may thereby be checked.

Exercise 25.3 (Rational version of a notorious problem) The triangle $\overline{A_1 A_2 A_3}$ represented to scale in Figure 25.4 is isosceles with $Q(A_1, A_3) = Q(A_2, A_3) \equiv 58$ and $Q(A_1, A_2) \equiv 36$. Also known are the spreads

$$s\left(\overleftrightarrow{A_1 A_2 B_2}\right) \equiv 49/170 \text{ (ac)} \qquad s\left(\overleftrightarrow{A_2 A_1 B_1}\right) \equiv 64/185 \text{ (ac)}$$

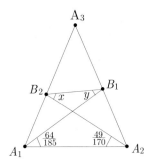

Figure 25.4: A notorious problem

Use the analysis of this section to determine the spreads

$$x = s\left(\overleftrightarrow{A_2 B_2 B_1}\right) \qquad y = s\left(\overleftrightarrow{A_1 B_1 B_2}\right).$$

[The answer is

$$x = \frac{9\,834\,496}{25\,778\,545} \text{ (ac)}$$

$$y = \frac{28\,654\,609}{112\,212\,490} \text{ (ac)}.] \quad \diamond$$

26

Platonic solids

Rational trigonometry can be used to understand aspects of the five *Platonic solids*: the (regular) tetrahedron, cube, octahedron, icosahedron and dodecahedron. A more complete investigation involves projective trigonometry, the rational analogue of spherical trigonometry which will be explained in a future volume.

This chapter computes the *face spread S* of each Platonic solid, namely the spread between adjacent faces, as well as some related results. Curiously, the face spreads turn out to be rational numbers in all five cases.

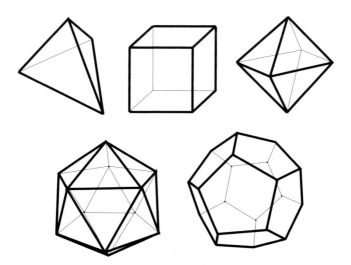

Figure 26.1: The five Platonic solids

26.1 Tetrahedron

The *tetrahedron* has four points, six sides and four faces, each an equilateral triangle. To determine the face spread, suppose that each side of a tetrahedron $\overline{ABCD}$ has quadrance Q, with M the midpoint of the side $\overline{AB}$ as in Figure 26.2. Then by Pythagoras' theorem $Q(C, M) = Q(D, M) = 3Q/4$.

The isosceles triangle $\overline{CMD}$ therefore has quadrances $3Q/4, 3Q/4$ and Q, so the Isosceles triangle theorem (page 122) shows that

$$s \equiv s\,(MC, MD) = \frac{Q}{3Q/4}\left(1 - \frac{Q}{3Q}\right) = \frac{8}{9}.$$

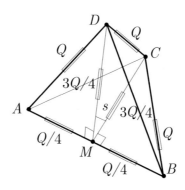

Figure 26.2: Tetrahedron

This is equal to the face spread $S \equiv S\,(ABC, ABD)$, as can be seen by applying the Perpendicular spreads theorem (page 79) to the plane DCM. The 'three-dimensional sector' formed by these faces towards the interior of the tetrahedron is in a natural sense acute.

Exercise 26.1 Show that the quadrance from one point of the tetrahedron to the centroid of the opposite face is $2Q/3$. Show that the quadrance from one point of the tetrahedron to the center P of the tetrahedron is $3Q/8$. ◇

Exercise 26.2 Show that the face spread $S = 8/9$ is the same as the spread $s\,(PA, PB)$, where P is the center of the tetrahedron. ◇

Exercise 26.3 By comparing the spread $s = 8/9$ with the appropriate zero of $S_5\,(s)$, show that it is possible to arrange five solid tetrahedrons sharing a common side. Show that it is not possible to arrange six solid tetrahedrons sharing a common side. ◇

26.2 Cube

The *cube* has eight points, twelve sides and six faces, each a square. Clearly the spread made by adjacent faces is $S = 1$.

Let's consider the problem of determining the possible spreads made by two lines from the center of a cube to two points of the cube.

Suppose that a cube has each side of quadrance Q, and center P with points labelled as in Figure 26.3.

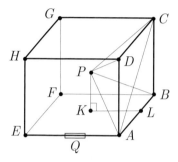

Figure 26.3: Cube

Since $Q(P, K)$, $Q(K, L)$ and $Q(A, L)$ are all equal to $Q/4$, use Pythagoras' theorem to get

$$Q(P, L) = Q/4 + Q/4 = Q/2$$
$$Q(P, A) = Q(P, L) + Q(A, L) = 3Q/4$$
$$Q(A, C) = Q(A, B) + Q(B, C) = 2Q.$$

The Isosceles triangle theorem applied to $\overline{APC}$, with quadrances $3Q/4$, $3Q/4$ and $2Q$, shows that

$$s(AP, AC) = 1 - \frac{2Q}{4(3Q/4)} = \frac{1}{3}$$
$$s(PA, PC) = \frac{2Q}{3Q/4}\left(1 - \frac{2Q}{4(3Q/4)}\right)$$
$$= \frac{8}{3} \times \frac{1}{3}$$
$$= \frac{8}{9}.$$

Note that since $\overline{ACFH}$ is a tetrahedron, this latter formula recovers the result of Exercise 26.2.

26.3 Octahedron

The *octahedron* has six points, twelve sides and eight faces, each an equilateral triangle. To determine the face spread S, suppose that the common quadrance of a side is Q, and let M be the midpoint of the side $\overline{BE}$ as in Figure 26.4, so that CM and AM are both perpendicular to BE, and $Q(A,M) = Q(M,C) = 3Q/4$.

Then the isosceles triangle $\overline{ACM}$ has quadrances $3Q/4, 3Q/4$ and $2Q$, so using the Isosceles triangle theorem

$$S \equiv s(MA, MC) = \frac{2Q}{3Q/4}\left(1 - \frac{2Q}{3Q}\right) = \frac{8}{9}.$$

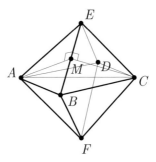

Figure 26.4: Octahedron

While the spread between adjacent faces of the tetrahedron and octahedron thus agree, the former is acute, while the latter is obtuse.

To see the equality directly, observe that the six midpoints of the sides of a tetrahedron form an octahedron. This octahedron can also be obtained by slicing off at each vertex of the tetrahedron a smaller corner tetrahedron as in Figure 26.5. The corner tetrahedron so sliced off shares adjacent faces with the central octahedron, so the face spreads are the same.

Figure 26.5: Slicing corners off a tetrahedron

26.4 Icosahedron

The *icosahedron* has twelve points, thirty sides and twenty faces, each an equilateral triangle. To determine the face spread S, suppose that V is a point of the icosahedron with adjacent points A, B, C, D and E forming a regular pentagon as in Figure 26.6. Suppose that the common quadrance of a side is Q, and that M is the midpoint of the side $\overline{VE}$, so that DM and MA are perpendicular to VE, and that $Q(D, M) = Q(M, A) = 3Q/4$.

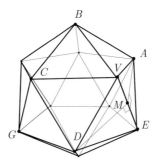

Figure 26.6: Icosahedron

Recall from Exercise 14.3 that $Q(A, D) = \beta Q / \alpha$ where

$$\alpha \equiv \left(5 - \sqrt{5}\right)/8 \approx 0.345\,491\ldots \qquad \text{and} \qquad \beta \equiv \left(5 + \sqrt{5}\right)/8 \approx 0.904\,508\ldots.$$

Apply the Isosceles triangle theorem to $\overline{ADM}$ with sides $3Q/4, 3Q/4$ and $\beta Q/\alpha$ and some pleasant simplification to get

$$
\begin{aligned}
S \quad \equiv \quad s(MD, MA) &= \frac{\beta Q/\alpha}{3Q/4}\left(1 - \frac{\beta Q/\alpha}{3Q}\right) \\
&= \frac{4\beta}{3\alpha}\left(1 - \frac{\beta}{3\alpha}\right) = \frac{4}{9}.
\end{aligned}
$$

Exercise 26.4 Using the same diagram, show that

$$s(MD, MG) = \frac{10 - 2\sqrt{5}}{15}$$

and

$$s(MA, MG) = \frac{10 + 2\sqrt{5}}{15}.$$

Hence deduce that

$$Q(A, G) = \left(\frac{5 + \sqrt{5}}{2}\right)Q. \quad \diamond$$

26.5 Dodecahedron

The *dodecahedron* has twenty points, thirty sides and twelve faces, each a regular pentagon. To determine the face spread S, suppose that each side of the dodecahedron has quadrance Q. Three sides meet at every point.

If the point V has adjacent points A, B and C then $\overline{ABC}$ is an equilateral triangle with quadrances $\beta Q/\alpha$, since this is the quadrance of a diagonal side of a regular pentagon of quadrance Q, as in Exercise 14.3. Furthermore the spread $r \equiv s(VA, VB)$ is equal to β, since this is the spread between adjacent lines of a regular pentagon. This is shown in Figure 26.7.

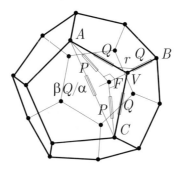

Figure 26.7: Dodecahedron

Now suppose that F is the foot of the altitude from A to BV, and so by symmetry also the foot of the altitude from C to BV. Then using the right triangle $\overline{AFV}$, the quadrance $P \equiv Q(A, F) = Q(C, F)$ is

$$P = rQ(A, V) = \beta Q.$$

In the isosceles triangle $\overline{AFC}$ the quadrances are then $\beta Q, \beta Q$ and $\beta Q/\alpha$. Use the Isosceles triangle theorem and some pleasant simplification to obtain the face spread

$$
\begin{aligned}
S &\equiv s(FA, FC) = \frac{\beta Q/\alpha}{\beta Q}\left(1 - \frac{\beta Q/\alpha}{4\beta Q}\right) \\
&= \frac{4\alpha - 1}{4\alpha^2} = \frac{4}{5}.
\end{aligned}
$$

To summarize: the face spreads of the regular tetrahedron, cube, octahedron, icosahedron and dodecahedron are respectively

$$8/9 \quad 1 \quad 8/9 \quad 4/9 \quad 4/5 \ .$$

Rational spherical coordinates

One of the important traditional uses of angles and the transcendental trigonometric functions $\cos\theta$ and $\sin\theta$ is to establish polar coordinates in the plane, and spherical and cylindrical coordinates in three-dimensional space. This simplifies problems with rotational symmetry in advanced calculus, mechanics and engineering.

This chapter shows how to employ rational analogues to accomplish the same tasks, with examples chosen from some famous problems in the subject. The rational approach employs conventions that generalize well to higher dimensions.

27.1   Polar spread and quadrance

For a point $A \equiv [x, y]$ in Cartesian coordinates, introduce the **polar spread** s and the **quadrance** Q by

$$
\begin{aligned}
s &\equiv x^2 / (x^2 + y^2) \\
Q &\equiv x^2 + y^2.
\end{aligned}
$$

Then $[s, Q]$ are the **rational polar coordinates** of the point $A \equiv [x, y]$. The spread s is defined between OA and the y *axis*. This convention

- corresponds to the usual practice in surveying and navigation

- integrates more smoothly with higher dimensional generalizations

- is natural for human beings, for whom *up* is more interesting than *right*.

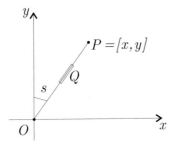

Figure 27.1: Rational polar coordinates

The rational polar coordinates s and Q determine x and y up to sign, so determine A uniquely in the first quadrant. This quadrant is better described by the respective signs of x and y, so call it also the $(++)$-**quadrant**.

To specify a general point A, the rational coordinates s and Q need to be augmented with two additional bits of information—the signs of x and y respectively. Now

$$
\begin{aligned}
x^2 &= sQ \\
y^2 &= (1-s)\,Q.
\end{aligned}
\tag{27.1}
$$

Take differentials of these two relations to obtain

$$
\begin{aligned}
2x\,dx &= Q\,ds + s\,dQ \\
2y\,dy &= -Q\,ds + (1-s)\,dQ.
\end{aligned}
$$

Thus in the $(++)$-quadrant

$$
\begin{aligned}
4xy\,dx\,dy &= \begin{vmatrix} Q & s \\ -Q & 1-s \end{vmatrix} ds\,dQ \\
&= \begin{vmatrix} Q & s \\ 0 & 1 \end{vmatrix} ds\,dQ = Q\,ds\,dQ.
\end{aligned}
\tag{27.2}
$$

For future reference, note that the determinant is evaluated by adding the first row to the second to get a diagonal matrix. In the $(++)$-quadrant, use (27.1) to obtain

$$
xy = \sqrt{s\,(1-s)}\,Q
$$

so the element of area is

$$
dx\,dy = \frac{1}{4\sqrt{s\,(1-s)}}\,ds\,dQ.
\tag{27.3}
$$

Example 27.1 The area a of the central circle of quadrance K is, by symmetry,

$$a = 4 \int_0^K \int_0^1 \frac{1}{4\sqrt{s(1-s)}}\, ds\, dQ = K \int_0^1 \frac{1}{\sqrt{s(1-s)}}\, ds.$$

This is not an integral which can be evaluated explicitly using basic calculus, motivating the definition of the number

$$\pi = \int_0^1 \frac{1}{\sqrt{s(1-s)}}\, ds. \qquad (27.4)$$

So the area of the central circle of quadrance K is πK. $\diamond$

Exercise 27.1 Use the substitutions $s \equiv r^2$ and $s \equiv 1/t$ to show that

$$\pi = 2 \int_0^1 \frac{dr}{\sqrt{1-r^2}} = \int_1^\infty \frac{dt}{t\sqrt{t-1}}.$$

Then use the substitutions $r \equiv 2u/\left(1+u^2\right)$ and $v \equiv 1/u$ to show that

$$\pi = 4 \int_0^1 \frac{du}{1+u^2} = 4 \int_1^\infty \frac{dv}{1+v^2}. \quad \diamond$$

Example 27.2 A lemniscate of Bernoulli has Cartesian equation

$$\left(x^2 + y^2\right)^2 = x^2 - y^2 \qquad (27.5)$$

and polar equation

$$r^2 = \cos 2\theta.$$

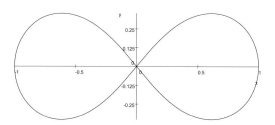

Figure 27.2: Lemniscate of Bernoulli

Replace x^2 and y^2 in (27.5) using (27.1) to get

$$
\begin{aligned}
Q^2 &= sQ - (1-s)\, Q \\
&= (2s-1)\, Q.
\end{aligned}
$$

So either of
$$Q = 2s - 1 \qquad \text{or} \qquad s = (Q+1)/2$$
is a **rational polar equation** of the lemniscate. Rational polar equations of some other classical curves are described in Appendix 1. For the lemniscate the polar spread varies in the range $1/2 \le s \le 1$, so the area is

$$
\begin{aligned}
a &= 4 \int_{1/2}^{1} \int_{0}^{2s-1} \frac{1}{4\sqrt{s(1-s)}} \, dQ \, ds \\
&= \int_{1/2}^{1} \frac{2s-1}{\sqrt{s(1-s)}} \, ds = \int_{0}^{1/4} \frac{1}{\sqrt{u}} \, du = 1. \; \diamond
\end{aligned}
$$

Example 27.3 The integral $I = \int_{0}^{\infty} e^{-x^2} dx$ is difficult to evaluate using only the calculus of one variable. Using rational polar coordinates, the idea is as follows, where the integral is over the $(++)$-quadrant.

$$
\begin{aligned}
I^2 &= \int_{0}^{\infty} e^{-x^2} dx \int_{0}^{\infty} e^{-y^2} dy \\
&= \int_{0}^{\infty} \int_{0}^{\infty} e^{-(x^2+y^2)} \, dx \, dy \\
&= \int_{0}^{\infty} \int_{0}^{1} \frac{e^{-Q}}{4\sqrt{s(1-s)}} \, ds \, dQ \\
&= \int_{0}^{\infty} e^{-Q} \, dQ \int_{0}^{1} \frac{1}{4\sqrt{s(1-s)}} \, ds \\
&= \left[-e^{-Q} \right]_{Q=0}^{\infty} \times \pi/4 \\
&= \pi/4
\end{aligned}
$$

so that $I = \sqrt{\pi}/2$. $\diamond$

The rotationally invariant measure $d\mu$ on the circle of quadrance $Q = r^2$ is, since $dQ = 2r \, dr$, determined by the equation

$$dx \, dy = d\mu \, dr = \frac{d\mu \, dQ}{2r}.$$

Compare this with (27.3) to see that

$$d\mu = \frac{r}{2\sqrt{s(1-s)}} \, ds.$$

It follows that the quarter of the central circle of radius r in the $(++)$-quadrant has measure $\pi r/2$, and the full circle has measure $2\pi r$.

27.2 Evaluating $\pi^2/16$

The unit quarter circle has area $\pi/4$, so a squared area of
$$\pi^2/16 \approx 0.616\,850\,275\,068\ldots.$$
To evaluate this constant, we follow ideas of Archimedes. Approximate a quarter circle successively by first one, then two, then four isosceles triangles, and so on, each time subdividing each triangle into two by a vertex bisector, as shown in Figure 27.3.

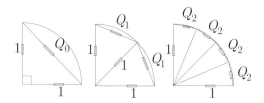

Figure 27.3: Approximations to a quarter circle

By the Quadrea spread theorem (page 82), the quadrea of an isosceles triangle with $Q_1 = Q_2 \equiv 1$ and spread $s_3 \equiv s$ is $\mathcal{A} = 4s$. After n divisions there are 2^n congruent isosceles triangles, each with spread s_n at the common point, and hence each with quadrea $4s_n$. This gives for the resulting $(2^n + 2)$-gon a total quadrea of $\mathcal{A}_n = (2^n)^2 \times 4s_n$, and so a squared area of $a_n^2 = \mathcal{A}_n/16 = 2^{2n-2}s_n$. Now since
$$s_{n+1} = \frac{1 - \sqrt{1 - s_n}}{2}$$
it follows that
$$
\begin{aligned}
a_{n+1}^2 &= 2^{2n}s_{n+1} = 2^{2n-1}\left(1 - \sqrt{1 - s_n}\right) \\
&= 2^{2n-1}\left(1 - 2^{-n+1}\sqrt{2^{2n-2} - a_n^2}\right) \\
&= 2^{2n-1} - 2^n\sqrt{2^{2n-2} - a_n^2}.
\end{aligned}
$$
Surprisingly, this recurrence relation yields a pleasant form for the general term a_n^2, as indicated by the following computations.
$$
\begin{aligned}
a_0^2 &= 2^{-2} = 0.25 \\
a_1^2 &= 2^{-1} - 2^0\sqrt{2^{-2} - 2^{-2}} = 2^{-1} = 0.5 \\
a_2^2 &= 2^1 - 2^1\sqrt{2^0 - 2^{-1}} = 2 - \sqrt{2} \approx 0.585\,786 \\
a_3^2 &= 2^3 - 2^2\sqrt{2^2 - 2 + \sqrt{2}} = 8 - 4\sqrt{2 + \sqrt{2}} \approx 0.608\,964 \\
a_4^2 &= 2^5 - 2^3\sqrt{2^4 - \left(8 - 4\sqrt{2 + \sqrt{2}}\right)} = 32 - 16\sqrt{2 + \sqrt{2 + \sqrt{2}}} \approx 0.614\,871
\end{aligned}
$$

Exercise 27.2 Show that this pattern continues, giving a closed expression for a_n^2. ◇

27.3 Beta function

Following Euler, for decimal numbers $p > 0$ and $q > 0$ define the **Beta function**, or **Beta integral**,

$$B(p,q) \equiv \int_0^1 s^{p-1}(1-s)^{q-1}\,ds.$$

There is a standard expression for the Beta function in terms of the **Gamma function** defined for $t > 0$ by

$$\Gamma(t) \equiv \int_0^\infty e^{-u}u^{t-1}\,du = 2\int_0^\infty e^{-x^2}x^{2t-1}\,dx.$$

Integration by parts and direct calculation shows that

$$\begin{aligned}
\Gamma(t+1) &= t\,\Gamma(t) \\
\Gamma(1) &- 1.
\end{aligned}$$

This implies that

$$\Gamma(n) = (n-1)!$$

for any positive integer $n \geq 1$.

Use rational polar coordinates to rewrite the following integral over the $(++)$-quadrant

$$\begin{aligned}
\Gamma(p)\,\Gamma(q) &= 4\int_0^\infty e^{-x^2}x^{2p-1}\,dx\int_0^\infty e^{-y^2}y^{2q-1}\,dy \\
&= \int_0^\infty \int_0^\infty e^{-(x^2+y^2)}x^{2(p-1)}y^{2(q-1)}\,4xy\,dx\,dy \\
&= \int_0^\infty \int_0^1 e^{-Q}(sQ)^{p-1}((1-s)Q)^{q-1}\,Q\,ds\,dQ \\
&= \int_0^\infty e^{-Q}Q^{p+q-1}\,dQ\int_0^1 s^{p-1}(1-s)^{q-1}\,ds \\
&= \Gamma(p+q)\,B(p,q)
\end{aligned}$$

where (27.2) was used to go from the second to the third line. Thus

$$B(p,q) = \frac{\Gamma(p)\,\Gamma(q)}{\Gamma(p+q)}. \tag{27.6}$$

Values of the Beta function are particularly useful in calculations involving rational polar or spherical coordinates. Note that in particular

$$B(1/2, 1/2) = \pi = (\Gamma(1/2))^2$$

so that, recovering the computation of Example 27.3,

$$\Gamma(1/2) = 2\int_0^\infty e^{-x^2}\,dx = \sqrt{\pi}.$$

27.4 Rational spherical coordinates

Represent a point in three-dimensional space by $A \equiv [x, y, z]$, and define the **rational spherical coordinates** $[s, q, R]$ of A by

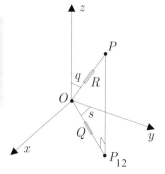

$$
\begin{aligned}
s &\equiv x^2 / \left(x^2 + y^2\right) \\
q &\equiv \left(x^2 + y^2\right) / \left(x^2 + y^2 + z^2\right) \\
R &\equiv x^2 + y^2 + z^2.
\end{aligned}
$$

Geometrically
if $A_{12} = [x, y, 0]$ is the perpendicular projection of
A onto the $x - y$ plane, then s is the polar spread between
OA_{12} and the y axis, while the **second polar spread**
q is the spread between OA and the z axis. Then R is the
three-dimensional quadrance, and $Q \equiv x^2 + y^2 = qR$.

Then

$$
x^2 = sqR \qquad y^2 = (1-s)\,qR \qquad z^2 = (1-q)\,R \qquad (27.7)
$$

so that x, y and z are determined, up to sign, by $[s, q, R]$. Take differentials to obtain

$$
\begin{aligned}
2x\,dx &= qR\,ds + sR\,dq + sq\,dR \\
2y\,dy &= -qR\,ds + (1-s)\,R\,dq + (1-s)\,q\,dR \\
2z\,dz &= 0\,ds - R\,dq + (1-q)\,dR.
\end{aligned}
$$

Thus in the $(+ + +)$-octant, where the signs of x, y and z are all positive,

$$
\begin{aligned}
8xyz\,dx\,dy\,dz &=
\begin{vmatrix}
qR & sR & sq \\
-qR & (1-s)\,R & (1-s)\,q \\
0 & -R & 1-q
\end{vmatrix} ds\,dq\,dR \\[2mm]
&=
\begin{vmatrix}
qR & sR & sq \\
0 & R & q \\
0 & 0 & 1
\end{vmatrix} ds\,dq\,dR = qR^2\,ds\,dq\,dR
\end{aligned}
$$

where the determinant is evaluated by adding the first row to the second, and then the second row to the third, to obtain a diagonal matrix.

In the $(+ + +)$-octant, combine the equations of (27.7) to obtain

$$
xyz = R^{3/2} q \sqrt{s\,(1-s)\,(1-q)}
$$

so the element of volume is

$$
dx\,dy\,dz = \frac{\sqrt{R}}{8\sqrt{s\,(1-s)\,(1-q)}}\,ds\,dq\,dR. \qquad (27.8)
$$

Example 27.4 The volume v of the central sphere of quadrance $K \equiv k^2$ ($k \geq 0$) is eight times the volume in the $(+++)$-octant. It is thus

$$v = 8 \int_0^K \int_0^1 \int_0^1 \frac{\sqrt{R}}{8\sqrt{s(1-s)(1-q)}} \, ds \, dq \, dR$$

$$= \int_0^1 \frac{ds}{\sqrt{s(1-s)}} \int_0^1 \frac{dq}{\sqrt{1-q}} \int_0^K \sqrt{R} \, dR$$

$$= \pi \left[-2\sqrt{1-q} \right]_{q=0}^1 \left[\frac{2R^{\frac{3}{2}}}{3} \right]_{R=0}^K = \frac{4\pi K^{\frac{3}{2}}}{3} = \frac{4\pi k^3}{3}.$$

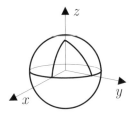

Figure 27.4: Volume of a sphere ◇

Example 27.5 An 'ice cream cone' lies above the cone $z^2 = x^2 + y^2$, and inside the projective sphere $x^2 + y^2 + z^2 = z$ centered at $[0, 0, 1/2]$ with quadrance $1/4$. Write the cone as $q = 1/2$ and the sphere as $R = 1 - q$, so that the volume v is

$$v = 4 \int_0^1 \int_0^{1/2} \int_0^{1-q} \frac{\sqrt{R}}{8\sqrt{s(1-s)(1-q)}} \, dR \, dq \, ds$$

$$= \frac{\pi}{2} \int_0^{1/2} \frac{1}{\sqrt{1-q}} \left[\frac{2R^{3/2}}{3} \right]_{R=0}^{1-q} dq$$

$$= \frac{\pi}{3} \int_0^{1/2} (1-q) \, dq = \frac{\pi}{3} \left[q - \frac{q^2}{2} \right]_{q=0}^{1/2} = \frac{\pi}{8}.$$

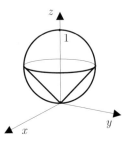

Figure 27.5: Volume of an ice cream cone ◇

Example 27.6 To find the volume v of the spherical cap inside the sphere $x^2 + y^2 + z^2 = K \equiv k^2$ ($k \geq 0$) and lying above the plane $z = d \geq 0$, where $d \leq k$, use **rational cylindrical coordinates** $[s, Q, z]$

$$
\begin{aligned}
v &= 4 \int_0^1 \int_0^{K-d^2} \int_d^{\sqrt{K-Q}} \frac{1}{4\sqrt{s(1-s)}} \, dz \, dQ \, ds \\
&= \pi \int_0^{K-d^2} \left(\sqrt{K-Q} - d \right) dQ = \pi \left[-2(K-Q)^{3/2}/3 - Qd \right]_{Q=0}^{K-d^2} \\
&= \frac{\pi}{3} \left(d^3 - 3dk^2 + 2k^3 \right) = \frac{\pi}{3} (k-d)^2 (2k+d).
\end{aligned}
$$

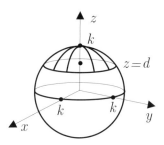

Figure 27.6: Volume of spherical cap ◇

Example 27.7 The volume of the spherical ring remaining when a cylinder with axis the z-axis is removed from the central sphere of quadrance $K \equiv k^2$ ($k \geq 0$), leaving a solid bounded by the planes $z = d$ and $z = -d$, where $d \leq k$, is

$$
\begin{aligned}
v &= 8 \int_0^1 \int_{K-d^2}^K \int_0^{\sqrt{K-Q}} \frac{1}{4\sqrt{s(1-s)}} \, dz \, dQ \, ds = 2\pi \int_{K-d^2}^K \sqrt{K-Q} \, dQ \\
&= 2\pi \left[-2(K-Q)^{3/2}/3 \right]_{Q=K-d^2}^K = \frac{4\pi}{3} d^3.
\end{aligned}
$$

Curiously, this is independent of the quadrance K of the sphere.

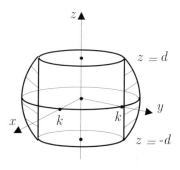

Figure 27.7: Volume of spherical ring ◇

Example 27.8 To find the volume v above the paraboloid $z = x^2 + y^2$ and below the plane $z = r \geq 0$

$$v = 4 \int_0^1 \int_0^r \int_R^r \frac{1}{4\sqrt{s(1-s)}}\, dz\, dR\, ds = \pi \int_0^r (r-R)\, dR = \frac{\pi r^2}{2}.$$

As discovered by Archimedes, this is one half of the volume of the cylinder of height r and radius $\sqrt{r}$.   ◇

Example 27.9 The moment M_{xy} of the upper hemisphere of the unit sphere of density 1 and mass $M \equiv 2\pi/3$ with respect to the xy−plane is

$$M_{xy} = 4 \int_0^1 \int_0^1 \int_0^1 \frac{z\sqrt{R}}{8\sqrt{s(1-s)(1-q)}}\, ds\, dq\, dR$$

where $z = \sqrt{(1-q)}\, R$. Thus

$$M_{xy} = \frac{\pi}{2} \times 1 \times \int_0^1 R\, dR = \frac{\pi}{4}$$

and the centroid has z coordinate $\bar{z} \equiv M_{xy}/M = 3/8$, so is $[0, 0, 3/8]$.

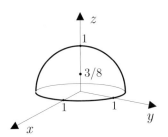

Figure 27.8: Center of mass of upper hemisphere   ◇

Example 27.10 The moment of inertia of the solid unit ball around the z axis is

$$\begin{aligned}
I_z &= 8 \int_0^1 \int_0^1 \int_0^1 \frac{qR\sqrt{R}}{8\sqrt{s(1-s)(1-q)}}\, ds\, dq\, dR \\
&= \pi \int_0^1 R^{3/2} dR \int_0^1 \frac{q}{\sqrt{1-q}}\, dq \\
&= \pi \times \frac{2}{5} \times B\left(2, \frac{1}{2}\right) = \pi \times \frac{2}{5} \times \frac{4}{3} = \frac{8\pi}{15}
\end{aligned}$$

since from (27.6)

$$B\left(2, \frac{1}{2}\right) = \frac{\Gamma(2)\,\Gamma\left(\frac{1}{2}\right)}{\Gamma\left(\frac{5}{2}\right)} = \frac{\Gamma\left(\frac{1}{2}\right)}{\frac{3}{2} \times \Gamma\left(\frac{3}{2}\right)} = \frac{\Gamma\left(\frac{1}{2}\right)}{\frac{3}{2} \times \frac{1}{2} \times \Gamma\left(\frac{1}{2}\right)} = \frac{4}{3}.$$ ◇

Example 27.11 The volume v of the hyperbolic cap shown in Figure 27.9, above the top sheet of the hyperboloid $z^2 - x^2 - y^2 = K \equiv k^2$ $(k \geq 0)$ and below the plane $z = d \geq 0$, where $d \geq k$, is

$$
v = 4 \int_0^1 \int_0^{d^2-K} \int_{\sqrt{Q+K}}^d \frac{1}{4\sqrt{s(1-s)}} \, dz \, dQ \, ds = \pi \int_0^{d^2-K} \left(d - \sqrt{Q+K} \right) dQ
$$

$$
= \pi \left[Qd - 2(Q+K)^{3/2}/3 \right]_{Q=0}^{d^2-K} = \frac{\pi}{3} (k-d)^2 (2k+d).
$$

This is the same formula as the volume of a spherical cap in Example 27.6!

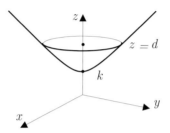

Figure 27.9: Volume of hyperbolic cap ◇

Example 27.12 The volume of the hyperbolic ring shown in Figure 27.10 inside a cylinder with axis the z-axis and outside the hyperboloid of one sheet $x^2 + y^2 - z^2 = K \equiv k^2$ $(k \geq 0)$ bounded by the planes $z = d$ and $z = -d$ is

$$
v = 8 \int_0^1 \int_K^{d^2+K} \int_0^{\sqrt{Q-K}} \frac{1}{4\sqrt{s(1-s)}} \, dz \, dQ \, ds = 2\pi \int_K^{d^2+K} \sqrt{Q-K} \, dQ
$$

$$
= 2\pi \left[2(Q-K)^{3/2}/3 \right]_{Q=K}^{d^2+K} = \frac{4\pi}{3} d^3.
$$

Curiously, this is independent of K, and is the same as the volume of the spherical ring in Example 27.7!

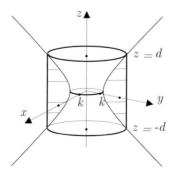

Figure 27.10: Volume of hyperbolic ring ◇

27.5   Surface measure on a sphere

For a fixed value K of R, the polar spreads s and q parametrize that part of the surface of the sphere of quadrance K contained in the $(+++)$-octant. To describe the full sphere these two spreads must be augmented by three additional bits of information, namely the signs of x, y and z.

The rotationally invariant surface measure $d\nu$ on the sphere $R \equiv r^2$ is, since $dR = 2r\,dr$, determined by

$$dx\,dy\,dz = d\nu\,dr = d\nu\,dR\,/2r.$$

Compare this with (27.8) to get

$$\frac{\sqrt{R}}{8\sqrt{s\,(1-s)\,(1-q)}}\,ds\,dq\,dR = \frac{1}{2\sqrt{R}}\,d\nu\,dR.$$

Thus

$$d\nu = \frac{R\,ds\,dq}{4\sqrt{s\,(1-s)\,(1-q)}}.$$

Example 27.13 The total surface area a of the sphere of quadrance $K \equiv k^2$ is

$$
\begin{aligned}
a &= 8\int_0^1\int_0^1 \frac{K}{4\sqrt{s\,(1-s)\,(1-q)}}\,ds\,dq \\
&= 2K\int_0^1 \frac{ds}{\sqrt{s\,(1-s)}}\int_0^1 \frac{dq}{\sqrt{1-q}} \\
&= 2K \times \pi \times 2 = 4\pi K = 4\pi k^2. \quad \diamond
\end{aligned}
$$

Example 27.14 The surface area a of the spherical cap of the sphere $x^2 + y^2 + z^2 = K \equiv k^2$ $(k \geq 0)$ lying above the plane $z = d \geq 0$, where $d \leq k$, as shown in Figure 27.6, is

$$
\begin{aligned}
a &= 4\int_0^{(K-d^2)/K}\int_0^1 \frac{K}{4\sqrt{s\,(1-s)\,(1-q)}}\,ds\,dq \\
&= \pi K \left[-2\,(1-q)^{1/2}\right]_{q=0}^{(K-d^2)/K} \\
&= 2\pi k^2 \left(1 - \frac{d}{k}\right).
\end{aligned}
$$

The linear dependence of this expression on d is one of the most remarkable properties of a sphere, and is responsible for the fact that an egg slicer subdivides a sphere into strips of constant surface area. This fact is also important for harmonic analysis on a sphere, and for the representation theory of the rotation group. $\diamond$

27.6 Four dimensional rational spherical coordinates

For a point $A \equiv [x, y, z, w]$ in four dimensional space define

$$
\begin{aligned}
s &\equiv x^2 / (x^2 + y^2) \\
q &\equiv (x^2 + y^2) / (x^2 + y^2 + z^2) \\
r &\equiv (x^2 + y^2 + z^2) / (x^2 + y^2 + z^2 + w^2) \\
T &\equiv x^2 + y^2 + z^2 + w^2.
\end{aligned}
$$

Then T is the four-dimensional quadrance, and r is the **third polar spread** between OA and the new (fourth) w−axis. Then

$$
\begin{aligned}
x^2 &= sqrT \\
y^2 &= (1 - s)\, qrT \\
z^2 &= (1 - q)\, rT \\
w^2 &= (1 - r)\, T.
\end{aligned}
\tag{27.9}
$$

Take differentials and follow the established pattern to get

$$
16\, xyzw\, dx\, dy\, dz\, dw \;=\; \begin{vmatrix} qrT & srT & sqT & sqr \\ -qrT & (1-s)\,rT & (1-s)\,qT & (1-s)\,qr \\ 0 & -rT & (1-q)\,T & (1-q)\,r \\ 0 & 0 & -T & 1-r \end{vmatrix} ds\, dq\, dr\, dT
$$

$$
= \begin{vmatrix} qrT & srT & sqT & sqr \\ 0 & rT & qT & qr \\ 0 & 0 & T & r \\ 0 & 0 & 0 & 1 \end{vmatrix} ds\, dq\, dr\, dT
$$

$$
= qr^2 T^3\, ds\, dq\, dr\, dT.
$$

In the $(++++)$-octant, (27.9) yields

$$
xyzw = s^{1/2} q\, r^{3/2} T^2 \sqrt{(1-s)(1-q)(1-r)}
$$

so the element of content (four dimensional version of volume) is

$$
dx\, dy\, dz\, dw = \frac{\sqrt{r}\, T}{16\sqrt{s\,(1-s)(1-q)(1-r)}}\, ds\, dq\, dr\, dT.
$$

Example 27.15 The central sphere of quadrance $K \equiv k^2$ has content

$$
\begin{aligned}
c &= 16 \int_0^K \int_0^1 \int_0^1 \int_0^1 \frac{\sqrt{r}\, T}{16\sqrt{s\,(1-s)(1-q)(1-r)}}\, ds\, dq\, dr\, dT \\
&= \int_0^1 \frac{ds}{\sqrt{s\,(1-s)}} \int_0^1 \frac{dq}{\sqrt{1-q}} \int_0^1 \frac{\sqrt{r}\, dq}{\sqrt{1-r}} \int_0^K T\, dT \\
&= \pi \times 2 \times B\left(\frac{3}{2}, \frac{1}{2}\right) \times \frac{K^2}{2}.
\end{aligned}
$$

But
$$B\left(\frac{3}{2},\frac{1}{2}\right) = \frac{\Gamma\left(\frac{3}{2}\right)\Gamma\left(\frac{1}{2}\right)}{\Gamma\left(2\right)} = \frac{\frac{1}{2}\Gamma\left(\frac{1}{2}\right)\Gamma\left(\frac{1}{2}\right)}{1} = \frac{\pi}{2}$$

so that
$$c = \frac{\pi^2 K^2}{2} = \frac{\pi^2 k^4}{2}. \quad \diamond$$

If $d\nu$ denotes spherical surface measure on the unit 3-sphere determined by

$$dx\,dy\,dz\,dw = d\nu\,dT\,/2$$

then (since $T = 1$)

$$d\nu = \frac{\sqrt{r}}{8\sqrt{s\left(1-s\right)\left(1-q\right)\left(1-r\right)}}\,ds\,dq\,dr.$$

Exercise 27.3 Use this to show that the surface volume of the unit 3-sphere is $2\pi^2$. $\diamond$

It should now be clear how to extend rational spherical coordinates to higher dimensions. In n-dimensional space, rational spherical coordinates involve $(n-1)$ polar spreads, and one quadrance. The basic relations are algebraic, and so do not require an understanding and visualization of projections.

27.7 Conclusion

Congratulations on having made it this far—hopefully without too much cheating!

This book is only a beginning, and much remains to be done. Hundreds of classical results of Euclidean geometry may be generalized to the universal setting. A coherent and precise framework for three-dimensional geometry should be created. The number theoretical and combinatorial implications of metrical geometry over finite fields requires investigation, as do the spread polynomials along with other related special functions. Researchers should ponder the opportunities in regarding algebraic geometry as an essentially metrical theory. Many additional applications should be developed and tested, both in applied and pure mathematics. Physicists might enjoy speculating about the implications for their subject.

Rational analogues of spherical and hyperbolic geometries will be described in a future book, along with the remarkable synthesis of Euclidean and non-Euclidean geometries called *chromogeometry*.

But perhaps the most exciting possibility of all is to re-evaluate the mathematics taught (and not taught) in schools and colleges, and to think about ways of presenting to young people this simpler and more logical approach to trigonometry and geometry.

Appendix A

Rational polar equations of curves

Recall that the relationships between the Cartesian coordinates $[x, y]$ and the rational polar coordinates $[s, Q]$ of spread and quadrance are given by

$$s = x^2 / (x^2 + y^2) \qquad Q = x^2 + y^2$$
$$x^2 = sQ \qquad y^2 = (1 - s) Q.$$

In this Appendix, some well known curves are listed, together with the usual Cartesian and polar forms, as well as new rational polar forms involving s and Q. As in the case of both Cartesian and polar coordinates, rational polar coordinates will have the most pleasant form only when the position of the curve is suitably chosen. For example, both the Cartesian and polar equations of the ellipse become more complicated if the ellipse is rotated and/or translated.

With rational polar coordinates it often becomes convenient to express s as a function of Q, not the other way around as the usual polar situation might suggest. Surprisingly, many diverse curves seem to have rational polar equations of a somewhat similar form, typically a quadratic equation in s. This occurs particularly frequently when the equation of the curve is even. This phenomenon should be explained.

It is important to note that the rational polar forms of these curves have an enormous advantage over the usual polar forms for pure mathematics—they allow extensions of these curves to general fields. In the examples below, we adopt the notational convention that $A \equiv a^2$ and $B \equiv b^2$. The Cartesian and polar forms for these classical curves are taken from *A catalog of special plane curves* [Lawrence] and *A book of curves* [Lockwood].

The derivations of the rational polar equations are left to the reader; they are often interesting. Of course there are many additional curves to investigate.

Line The *line* has Cartesian equation $y = ax$ and polar equation $\tan \theta = a$. Using rational polar coordinates its equation is

$$s = \frac{1}{1 + A}.$$

Ellipse The *ellipse* has Cartesian equation

$$\frac{x^2}{a^2} + \frac{y^2}{b^2} = 1$$

and polar equation

$$r = \frac{ab}{\sqrt{b^2 \cos^2 \theta + a^2 \sin^2 \theta}}.$$

Using rational polar coordinates its equation is

$$s = \frac{A(Q - B)}{Q(A - B)}.$$

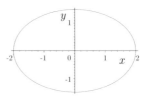

Figure A.1: Ellipse

Hyperbola The *hyperbola* has Cartesian equation

$$\frac{x^2}{a^2} - \frac{y^2}{b^2} = 1$$

and polar equation

$$r = \frac{ab}{\sqrt{b^2 \cos^2 \theta - a^2 \sin^2 \theta}}.$$

Using rational polar coordinates its equation is

$$s = \frac{A(Q + B)}{Q(A + B)}.$$

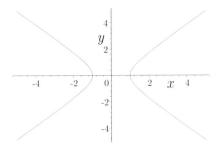

Figure A.2: Hyperbola

Parabola The *parabola* has Cartesian equation

$$y^2 = 4ax$$

and polar equation

$$\frac{2a}{r} = 1 - \cos\theta.$$

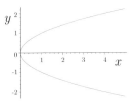

Figure A.3: Parabola

Using rational polar coordinates its equation is

$$(1-s)^2 Q = 16As$$

or

$$\left(s - \frac{Q+8A}{Q}\right)^2 = \frac{16A(Q+4A)}{Q^2}.$$

Cardioid The *cardioid* has polar equations of the form

$$r = 2a(1 + \cos\theta)$$
$$r = 2a(1 - \cos\theta)$$

with the following respective graphs.

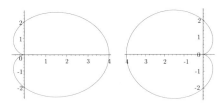

Figure A.4: Two cardioids

Both cases are covered by the rational polar equation

$$\left(s - \frac{Q + 4A}{4A}\right)^2 = \frac{Q}{A}.$$

This results in the 'symmetric cardioid' shown in Figure A.5.

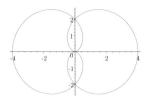

Figure A.5: Symmetric cardioid

Limacon The *limacon* is a generalization of the cardioid, and has polar equation

$$r = 2a\cos\theta + b.$$

Using rational polar coordinates its equation is

$$\left(s - \frac{Q + B}{4A}\right)^2 = \frac{BQ}{4A^2}.$$

If $B = 4A$ then this reduces to a cardioid. If $B = A$ then this is the *trisectrix* with rational polar equation

$$\left(s + \frac{(Q+A)}{4A}\right)^2 = \frac{Q}{4A}.$$

Figure A.6 shows a graph of a trisectrix.

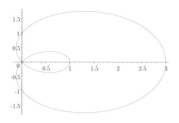

Figure A.6: Trisectrix

Astroid The *astroid* has Cartesian equation

$$x^{\frac{2}{3}} + y^{\frac{2}{3}} = a^{\frac{2}{3}}$$

or

$$\left(x^2 + y^2 - a^2\right)^3 + 27a^2x^2y^2 = 0.$$

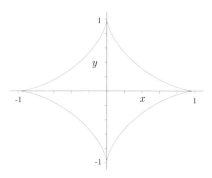

Figure A.7: Astroid

Using rational polar coordinates its equation is

$$\left(s - \frac{1}{2}\right)^2 = \frac{1}{4} - \frac{(A-Q)^3}{27AQ^2}.$$

Eight curve The *eight curve*, or *lemniscate of Gerono*, has Cartesian equation

$$x^4 = a^2 \left(x^2 - y^2 \right)$$

and polar equation

$$r^2 = a^2 \sec^4 \theta \cos 2\theta.$$

Using rational polar coordinates its equation is

$$\left(s - \frac{A}{Q} \right)^2 = \frac{(A - Q)\, A}{Q^2}.$$

Bullet nose The *bullet nose* has Cartesian equation

$$\frac{a^2}{x^2} - \frac{b^2}{y^2} = 1$$

and polar equation

$$r^2 \sin^2 \theta \cos^2 \theta = a^2 \sin^2 \theta - b^2 \cos^2 \theta.$$

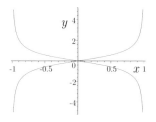

Figure A.8: Bullet nose

Using rational polar coordinates its equation is

$$\left(s - \frac{A + B + Q}{2Q} \right)^2 = \frac{(A + B + Q)^2 - 4AQ}{Q^2}.$$

Deltoid The *deltoid* has the Cartesian equation

$$\left(x^2 + y^2 \right)^2 - 8ax \left(x^2 - 3y^2 \right) + 18a^2 \left(x^2 + y^2 \right) = 27a^4.$$

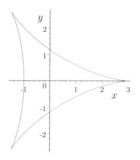

Figure A.9: Deltoid

Using rational polar coordinates its equation is

$$s\left(3-4s\right)^2 = \frac{\left(Q^2+18AQ-27A^2\right)^2}{64Q^3A}.$$

The three-fold symmetry of the curve is reflected in the appearance of the third spread polynomial $S_3\left(s\right) = s\left(3-4s\right)^2$.

Hippopede The *hippopede*, or *horse fetter*, (Proclus, 75 BC) has Cartesian equation

$$\left(x^2+y^2\right)^2+4b^2\left(b^2-a^2\right)\left(x^2+y^2\right) = 4b^4x^2$$

and polar equation

$$r^2 = 4b^2\left(a^2-b^2\sin^2\theta\right).$$

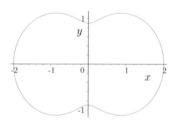

Figure A.10: Horse fetter

Using rational polar coordinates its equation is

$$s = \frac{Q}{4B} - A + B.$$

Lemniscate of Bernoulli The *lemniscate of Bernoulli* has Cartesian equation

$$\left(x^2 + y^2\right)^2 = 2\left(x^2 - y^2\right)$$

and polar equation

$$r^2 = 2\cos 2\theta.$$

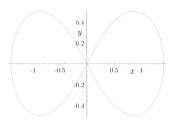

Figure A.11: Lemniscate of Bernoulli

Using rational polar coordinates its equation is

$$s = \frac{Q+2}{4}.$$

Folium of Descartes The *folium of Descartes*, has Cartesian equation

$$x^3 + y^3 + 3xy = 0.$$

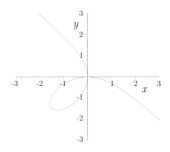

Figure A.12: Folium of Descartes

This curve has a more complicated rational polar equation; it is

$$(2s-1)^2 \left(s^2 - s + 1\right)^2 Q^2 - 18s\left(1-s\right)\left(1 - 3s + 3s^2\right)Q + 81s^2\left(1-s\right)^2 = 0.$$

Appendix B

Ellipson

The **ellipson** consists of all points $[x, y, z]$ inside, or on, the unit cube $0 \leq x, y, z \leq 1$ satisfying the Triple spread formula

$$(x + y + z)^2 = 2\left(x^2 + y^2 + z^2\right) + 4xyz.$$

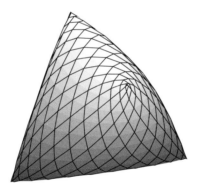

Figure B.1: The ellipson

This surface resembles an inflated tetrahedron, and indeed intersects the unit cube at precisely a tetrahedron, with points $[0, 0, 0], [1, 1, 0], [1, 0, 1]$ and $[0, 1, 1]$, and volume $1/3$. Its cross sections in any of the coordinate plane directions is otherwise always an ellipse, tangent to the unit square.

For example, the cross sections corresponding to $z = 0.1, 0.2, 0.4$ and 0.8 are shown in the $x - y$ plane in Figure B.2.

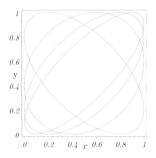

Figure B.2: Elliptical cross sections

On the other hand, a cross section parallel to a face of the tetrahedron, such as the plane $x + y + z = 2$, yields the interesting curve shown in Figure B.3.

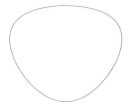

Figure B.3: Oblique cross section

In suitable coordinates, such a curve has an equation of the form

$$3b^2 a \sqrt{6} - 6a^2 - a^3 \sqrt{6} - 6b^2 + 5/6 = 0.$$

In rational polar coordinates this becomes

$$s (3 - 4s)^2 = \frac{(36Q - 5)^2}{(6Q)^3}$$

which bears some similarity to the equation defining the deltoid. The three-fold symmetry is reflected by the fact that the left hand side is $S_3(s)$.

Exercise B.1 (Harder, requires calculus) Show that the ellipson has volume

$$\pi^2/16 \approx 0.616\,850\,275 \cdots . \quad \diamond$$

Theorems with pages and Important Functions

Important Functions

$$A(a, b, c) = (a + b + c)^2 - 2\left(a^2 + b^2 + c^2\right).$$

$$S(a, b, c) = (a + b + c)^2 - 2\left(a^2 + b^2 + c^2\right) - 4abc.$$

$$Q(a, b, c, d) = \left((a + b + c + d)^2 - 2\left(a^2 + b^2 + c^2 + d^2\right)\right)^2 - 64abcd.$$

$$R(a, b, c, d) = \left(\begin{array}{c} (a + b + c + d)^2 - 2\left(a^2 + b^2 + c^2 + d^2\right) \\ -4\left(abc + abd + acd + bcd\right) + 8abcd \end{array}\right)^2$$
$$- 64abcd\left(1 - a\right)\left(1 - b\right)\left(1 - c\right)\left(1 - d\right).$$

$$E(Q_1, Q_2, Q_3, P_1, P_2, P_3)$$
$$= 2\left(\begin{array}{c} 4P_1 P_2 P_3 + (P_2 + P_1 - Q_3)(P_2 + P_3 - Q_1)(P_1 + P_3 - Q_2) \\ -P_1(P_2 + P_3 - Q_1)^2 - P_2(P_1 + P_3 - Q_2)^2 - P_3(P_2 + P_1 - Q_3)^2 \end{array}\right).$$

Bibliography

[Coxeter] H. S. M. Coxeter, *Introduction to Geometry* (2nd ed.), John Wiley and Sons, New York, 1989.

[Coxeter-Greitzer] H. S. M. Coxeter and S. L. Greitzer, *Geometry Revisited*, Random House, New York, 1967.

[Dorrie] H. Dorrie, *100 Great Problems of Elementary Mathematics: Their history and solution*, translated by D. Antin, Dover, New York, 1965.

[Euclid] Euclid, *The Elements (in three volumes)*, Dover, New York, 1956.

[Gutierrez] A. Gutierrez, 'Eyeball theorems', in *The Changing Shape of Geometry*, Editor Chris Pritchard, Cambridge University Press, Cambridge, 2003.

[Hilbert] D. Hilbert, *Foundations of Geometry*, Revised by P. Bernays, Open Court, LaSalle, Illinois, 1971.

[Lawrence] J. D. Lawrence, *A Catalog of Special Plane Curves*, Dover, New York, 1972.

[Lockwood] E. H. Lockwood, *A Book of Curves*, Cambridge University Press, London, 1961.

[Maor] E. Maor, *Trigonometric Delights*, Princeton University Press, Princeton, 1998.

[Robbins] D. A. Robbins, 'Areas of Polygons Inscribed in a Circle', *The American Mathematical Monthly* Volume 102 Number 6 (1995) 523–530.

[Shepherd] F. A. Shepherd, *Surveying Problems and Solutions*, Edward Arnold, London, 1968.

[Shklarsky-Chentzov-Yaglom] D. O. Shklarsky, N. N. Chentzov and I. M. Yaglom, *The USSR Olympiad Problem Book*, W. H. Freeman and Company, San Francisco, 1962.

[Snapper-Troyer]   E. Snapper and R. J. Troyer, *Metric Affine Geometry*,
                          Academic Press, New York, 1971.

[Weisstein]   E. W. Weisstein, *CRC Concise Encyclopedia of
                          Mathematics*, Chapman and Hall, Boca Raton, 1999.

[Wells]   D. Wells, *The Penguin Dictionary of Curious and
                          Interesting Geometry*, Penguin, London, 1991.

[Wildberger]   N. J. Wildberger, 'Real Fish, Real Numbers, Real Jobs',
                          Mathematical Intelligencer Volume 21 Number 2 (1999)
                          4–7.

[Zeilberger]   D. Zeilberger (with S. B. Ekhad), 'Plane Geometry: An
                          elementary school textbook (ca. 2050)', *Mathematical
                          Intelligencer* Volume 21 Number 3 (1999) 64-70.

Index